Hormone Action in Plant Development – A Critical Appraisal

Hormone Action in Plant Development – A Critical Appraisal

G. V. Hoad BSc, PhD, CBiol, FIBiol

J. R. Lenton BSc, PhD

M. B. Jackson BSc, MSc, DPhil

R. K. Atkin BA, PhD, CBiol, MIBiol

Butterworths
London Boston Durban Singapore Sydney Toronto Wellington

First published, 1987

© **Butterworth & Co. (Publishers) Ltd, 1987**

British Library Cataloguing in Publication Data

Hormone action in plant development: a critical appraisal
   1. Plants – Development   2. Plant hormones
   I. Hoad, G. V.
   581.3   QK731

   ISBN 0-408-00796-6

Library of Congress Cataloging in Publication Data

Hormone action in plant development.

   "Papers presented at the Tenth Long Ashton Symposium in September 1986 . . . organized jointly by Long Ashton Research Station and the British Plant Growth Regulator Group"–Pref.
   Bibliography: p.
   Includes index.
   1. Plant hormones–Congresses.   2. Plants–Development–Congresses.   3. Growth (Plants)–Congresses.
I. Hoad, G. V. (Gordon Victor)   II. Long Ashton Symposium (10th : 1986)   III. Long Ashton Research Station.
IV. British Plant Growth Regulator Group.
QK731.H645   1987   581.3   87-15094

   ISBN 0-408-00796-6

Photoset by Butterworths Litho Preparation Department
Printed and bound by Robert Hartnoll Ltd, Bodmin, Cornwall

PREFACE

This volume contains papers presented at the Tenth Long Ashton Symposium in September 1986, which was convened to assess the evidence for and against the view that plant hormones are endogenous regulators of plant development. The meeting also aimed to focus on and assess promising strategies for future research. The importance of bringing different approaches to bear on the problem of plant hormone action was recognised from the outset in planning the Symposium which was organised jointly by Long Ashton Research Station and the British Plant Growth Regulator Group.

Early studies of plant hormones derived from attempts to understand plant development in terms of responses to the environment. This led to the concept which dominated our thinking for many years, namely that without hormones there would be no plant growth. Certainly the view that the concentration of hormones in tissues controls growth has been challenged by those who maintain that tissue sensitivity to hormones is more important than hormone concentration *per se*. Others find these arguments ill-conceived in terms of understanding the role of hormones in plant development. Thus the Symposium and these proceedings are timely as the subject might be considered by some to be at a cross-roads.

Our current knowledge of the biosynthesis, metabolism and transport of plant hormones has benefited from increasingly sophisticated analytical procedures. However, progress on primary hormone action, including the characterisation of receptors and the possible involvement of secondary messengers, has been disappointingly slow. Advances in immunological techniques should permit the eventual subcellular localisation of hormones, their metabolising enzymes and primary receptors, and hence the determination of hormone concentration at the active site. We shall still need to incorporate such information at the molecular level into a credible conceptual framework to explain the role of hormones in plant development. In attempting to achieve this objective, speakers were asked to examine hormone action from the molecular level to that of the whole plant and to be deliberately speculative. This led to lively discussions after each session (not recorded in this volume).

The Symposium was opened with the Douglas Wills Lecture, given by Professor Carl Leopold. In many respects, progress in research on animal hormones seems greater than in the plant sciences and there may well be merit in following progress in animal hormone research as suggested by Professor Leopold. The organisers are grateful to him for setting the scene so effectively for the Symposium papers that followed.

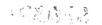

The Symposium comprised four sessions. The introductory session considered the coordinating role of hormones in plant growth and development, and focussed on hormone action at the molecular level, including their binding to receptors and their control of gene expression. The next two sessions embraced contributions on the experimental manipulation of development by genetic (notably by biochemical mutants), chemical (for example, with gibberellin/biosynthesis inhibitors) and environmental (including drought stress) means. All these approaches consolidated the central importance of hormones in plant growth. In the final session, three speakers suggested some promising avenues for future research into the physiology (Dr D. J. Osborne), biochemistry (Dr J. L. Stoddart) and molecular biology (Professor T. C. Hall) of plant hormones.

We hope that delegates to the Symposium (over 230 from 25 countries) found the deliberately wide-ranging discussion of hormone action in plant development a thoroughly thought-provoking and critical appraisal of the subject and that the published proceedings will be equally stimulating to a wider audience.

We are grateful to many of our colleagues, both at Long Ashton and on the Programme Sub-committee of the British Plant Growth Regulator Group, for unstinting help at all stages of the organisation of the Symposium, especially Mrs Joan Llewellyn and Miss Helen Clarke for their essential secretarial skills. We also thank staff of the 'Secretary Machine', Bristol for assistance in the production of the camera-ready copy.

G. V. Hoad
J. R. Lenton
M. B. Jackson
R. K. Atkin
Long Ashton Research Station
University of Bristol

March 1987

CONTENTS

viii

ABBO, Mr. S., - Plant Genetics Dept., The Weitzmann Institute of Science, Rehovot,
76100, ISRAEL
ABBOTT, Dr. A.J., - Long Ashton Research Station, University of Bristol, Long Ashton,
Bristol, Avon, BS18 9AF, UK
ADAM, Miss J.S., - Long Ashton Research Station, University of Bristol, Long Ashton,
Bristol, Avon, BS18 9AF, UK
ADEBONE, Professor A.C., - Faculty of Science, University of Ife, Ife-Ife, Nigeria.
AINSWORTH, Dr. C., - Dept. of Botany, University of Bristol, Avon, BS8 1UG, UK
ALLEN, Dr. J., - Ciba-Geigy Ltd., Werk Stein, 4332 Stein/Aargau, SWITZERLAND
ALLPORT, Miss J.F., - Dept. of Agriculture and Horticulture, Reading University,
Earley Gate, Reading, RG6 2AT, UK
ANDERSON, Mr. H.M., - Long Ashton Research Station, University of Bristol, Long
Ashton, Bristol, Avon, BS18 9AF, UK
APPLEFORD, Mr. N.E.J., - Long Ashton Research Station, University of Bristol, Long
Ashton, Bristol, Avon, BS18 9AF, UK
ASTLE, Dr. M.C., - Jealott's Hill Research Station, Bracknell, Berks. RG12 6EY, UK
ATKIN, Dr. R.K., - Long Ashton Research Station, University of Bristol, Long Ashton,
Bristol, Avon, BS18 9AF, UK
AYISIRE, Mr. B.E., - Dept. of Botany, University of Bristol, Bristol, Avon, BS8 1UG,
UK
BABIANO, Miss J., - Dpto. Fisiologia Vegetal, Facultad Biologia, Universidad de
Salamanca, Salamanca, SPAIN
BAILEY, Dr. J.A., - Long Ashton Research Station, University of Bristol, Long Ashton,
Bristol, Avon, BS18 9AF, UK
BARLOW, Dr. P.W., - Long Ashton Research Station, University of Bristol, Long Ashton,
Bristol, Avon, BS18 9AF, UK
BARRATT, Dr. P., - Long Ashton Research Station, University of Bristol, Long Ashton,
Bristol, Avon, BS18 9AF, UK
BATTEY, Dr. N.H., - Institute of Horticultural Research, East Malling Research
Station, Maidstone, Kent, ME19 6BJ, UK
BAULCOMBE, Dr. D.C., - Plant Breeding Institute, Trumpington, Cambridge, CB2 2LQ, UK
BAYLIS, Dr. A.D., - ICI Plant Protection Division, Jealotts Hill Research Station,
Bracknell, Berks. UK
BAZAID, Mr. S.A., - Dept. of Botany, University of Bristol, Bristol, Avon, BS8 1UG,
UK
BEALE, Dr. R.H., - School of Chemistry, University of Bristol, Bristol, Avon, BS8
1TS, UK
BELCHER, Mrs. A.R., - Long Ashton Research Station, University of Bristol, Long
Ashton, Bristol, Avon, BS18 9AF, UK
BIDDINGTON, Dr. N.L., - National Vegetable Research Station, Wellesbourne, Warwick,
CV35 9EF, UK
BLACK, Professor M., - Dept. of Biology, King's College, Campden Hill Road, London,
W8 7AH, UK
BLACKMAN, Dr. P.G., - Shell Research Ltd., Sittingbourne Research Centre,
Sittingbourne, Kent, ME9 8AG, UK
BLAKESLEY, Dr. D., - Twyford Plant Labs., Baltonsborough, Glastonbury, Somerset, BA6
8QG, UK
BOOTHER, Ms. G., - School of Chemistry, University of Bristol, Bristol, Avon, BS8
1TS, UK
BOSSELAERS, Mr. J., - Janssen Pharmaceutica NV, Turnmoutseweg 30, B-2340 Beerse,
BELGIUM
BROCKLEHURST, Dr. P.A., Shell Research Ltd., Sittingbourne Research Centre,
Sittingbourne, Kent, ME9 8AG, UK
BROOMES, Ms. V., - Dept. of Botany, University of Sheffield, Sheffield, S10 2TN UK
BROWN, Dr. B.H., - Dept. of Botany and Microbiology, University College of Wales,
Aberystwyth, Dyfed, SY23 3DA, UK
BROWNING, Dr. G., - Institute of Horticultural Research, East Malling Research
Station, Maidstone, Kent, ME19 6BJ, UK

BURDEN, Dr. R.S., - Long Ashton Research Station, University of Bristol, Long Ashton, Bristol, Avon, BS18 9AF, UK

BUTCHER, Dr. D.N., - Long Ashton Research Station, University of Bristol, Long Ashton, Bristol, Avon, BS18 9AF, UK

CALDWELL, Dr. C.D., - Dept. of Plant Science, Nova Scotia Agricultural College, P.O. Box 550, Truro, Nova Scotia, B2N 5E3, CANADA

CAMPEN, Mr. R., - Leicester Polytechnic, School of Life Sciences, Scraptoft Campus, Leicester, LE7 9SU, UK

CHAPMAN, Dr. J.M., - Dept. of Biology, King's College, Campden Hill Road, London, W8 7AM, UK

CHAWLA, Dr. H.S., - Institut für Resistenz Genetik, D 8059 Bockhorn, Gruenbach, WEST GERMANY

CHILD, Mr. R.D., - Long Ashton Research Station, University of Bristol, Long Ashton, Bristol, Avon, BS18 9AF, UK

CLARK, Ms J.A., - Long Ashton Research Station, University of Bristol, Long Ashton, Bristol, Avon, BS18 9AF, UK

CLARKE, Dr. N., - Long Ashton Research Station, University of Bristol, Long Ashton, Bristol, Avon, BS18 9AF, UK

COGAN, Ms. D., - Butterworth Scientific Ltd., PO Box 63, Westbury House, Bury St., Guildford, Surrey, GU2 5BH, UK

COOKE, Mr. D.T., - Long Ashton Research Station, University of Bristol, Long Ashton, Bristol, Avon, BS18 9AF, UK

COUVREUR, Miss F., - Station Experimentale ITCF - Boigneville, 91720. Maisse, FRANCE

DAVIES, Dr. W.J.,- Dept. of Biological Sciences, University of Lancaster, Bailrigg, Lancaster, LA1 4YQ, UK

DEVESON, Mr. M., - Dept. of Agricultural Botany, Plant Science Labs., Reading University, Whiteknights Park, Reading, Berks. RG6 2AS, UK

DIGBY, Dr. J., - Dept. of Biology, University of York, Heslington, York. Y01 5DD, UK

DUNN, Miss R.J., - Long Ashton Research Station, University of Bristol, Long Ashton, Bristol, Avon, BS18 9AF, UK

DUPON, Dr. M., - Dept. Biologie, Universitaire Instelling Antwerpen, Universiteitsplain-1, B-2610 Antwerpen (Wilrijk), BELGIUM

EL-SAWI, Mr. Z., - Dept. of Botany and Microbiology, University College of Wales, Aberystwyth, Dyfed, SY23 3DA, UK

ERNSTSEN, Mr. A., - Dept. of Forest Genetics & Plant Physiology, The Swedish University of Agricultural Sciences, S-901 83 Umea, SWEDEN

FELIPPE, Professor G.M., - c/o Prof. J. E. Dale, Botany Dept., University of Edinburgh, King's Buildings, Edinburgh, EH9 3JH, UK

FIDO, Dr. R.J., - Long Ashton Research Station, University of Bristol, Long Ashton, Bristol, Avon, BS18 9AF, UK

FIRN, Dr. R.D., - Dept. of Biology, University of York, Heslington, York, Y01 5DD, UK

FLEGMANN, Dr. A.W., - School of Biological Sciences, University of Bath, Claverton Down, Bath, Avon, BA2 7AY, UK

FLEMING, Mr. A.J., - Botany School, Downing Site, University of Cambridge, Cambridge, UK

FLORE, Professor J.A., - Dept. of Horticulture, Michigan State University, East Lansing, Michigan, U.S.A.

FRANSSEN, Dr. J.M., - Bulb Research Centre, P. O. Box 85, 2160 AB Lisse, NETHERLANDS

FRITSCH, Dr. H., - BASF AG., Agricultural Research Centre, D-6703 Limburgerhof, WEST GERMANY

GADEYNE, Dr. J., - Dept. Biologie, Universitaire Instelling Antwerpen, Universiteitsplain-1, B-2610 Antwerpen (Wilrijk), BELGIUM

GAHAN, Professor P.B., Dept. of Biology, King's College London, Campden Hill Road, London, W8 7AH, UK

GALE, Dr. M.D., - Plant Breeding Institute, Trumpington, Cambridge, CB2 2LQ, UK

GALLANT, Mr. S.C., - Dept. of Botany and Microbiology, University College, Gower St., London, WC1E 6BT, UK

GARROD, Dr. J.F., - Schering Agriculture, Chesterfield Park Research Station, Saffron Walden, Essex, CB10 1XL, UK

GASKIN, Dr. P., - School of Chemistry, University of Bristol, Bristol, Avon, BS8 1TS, UK

GENDLE, Mr. P., - Long Ashton Research Station, University of Bristol, Long Ashton, Bristol, Avon, BS18 9AF, UK

GILBERT, Dr. D.A., - Dept. Biochemistry, University of Witwatersrand, 1 Jan Smuts Ave., Johannesburg, SOUTH AFRICA

GILBERT, Mr. I.R., - P.E.S Plant Physiology, School of Agriculture, Sutton Bonington, Loughborough, Leics. LE12 5RD, UK

GORDON, Dr. M.E., - Dept. of Botany, Victoria University of Wellington, Private Bag, Wellington, NEW ZEALAND

GOREN, Professor R., - Faculty of Agriculture, P.O. Box 12, Rehovot, 76-100 ISRAEL

GRAEBE, Professor J.E., - Pflanzenphysiologisches Institut, Untere Karspuele 2, D-3400 Goettingen, WEST GERMANY

GRANTZ, Dr. D.A., - Dept. of Agricultural Botany, Hebrew University, Faculty of Agriculture, Rehovot, ISRAEL

GRAYLING, Mr. A., - Botany School, Downing Street, University of Cambridge, Cambridge, UK

GREEN, Miss J., - Long Ashton Research Station, University of Bristol, Long Ashton, Bristol, Avon, BS18 9AF, UK

GRESSHOFF, Dr. P.M., - Botany Dept. - Genetics Research Group, Australian National University Canberra, ACT, 2061, AUSTRALIA

GRIERSON, Dr. D., - School of Agriculture, University of Nottingham, Sutton Bonington, Loughborough, Leics, LE12 5RD, UK

GRIEVE, Miss T.M., - School of Life Sciences, Scraptoft Campus, Leicester Polytechnic, Leicester, LE7 9SU, UK

GROCHOWSKA, Professor M.J., - Research Institute of Pomology and Floriculture, 18 Pomologiczna Str., 96-100 Skierniewice, POLAND

GROSSKOPF, Miss D., - Grenzhoeferweg 22, 6900 Heidelberg, WEST GERMANY

HALL, Professor T.C., - Dept. of Biology, College Station, Texas A and M University, Texas, USA

HALLBERG, Dr. M., - Swedish University of Agricultural Sciences, Dept. of Horticultural Science,Box 55, S-230 53 Alnarp, SWEDEN

HART, Dr. J.W., - Dept. of Plant Science, University of Aberdeen, Aberdeen, UK

HEDDEN, Dr. P. - Long Ashton Research Station, University of Bristol, Bristol, Avon, BS18 9AF, UK

HILL, Dr. T.A., - Wye College, University of London, Nr. Ashford, Kent, TN25 5AH, UK

HILTON, Dr. J.R., - Long Ashton Research Station, University of Bristol, Long Ashton, Bristol, Avon, BS18 9AF, UK

HOAD, Dr. G.V., - Long Ashton Research Station, University of Bristol, Bristol, Avon, BS18 9AF, UK

HOCKING, Dr. T., - The School of Applied Sciences, The Polytechnic, Wulfruna St., Wolverhampton, WV1 1SB, UK

HOOGENDOORN, Dr. J., - Cytogenetics Dept., Plant Breeding Institute, Cambridge, CB2 2LQ, UK

HOOLEY, Dr. R., - Long Ashton Research Station, University of Bristol, Long Ashton, Bristol, Avon, BS18 9AF, UK

HOPWOOD, W.J., - Shell Research Limited, Broad Oak Road, Sittingbourne, Kent, UK

HORGAN, Dr. R., - University College of Wales, Aberystwyth, Dyfed, SY23 3DD, UK

HUGHES, Dr. W.A., - Colworth House, Unilever Research Laboratory, Sharnbrook, Bedford, UK

HUGO, Ms S., - Wye College, University of London, Wye, Nr. Ashford, Kent, TA25 5AH, UK

HUTCHEON, Ms J.A., - Long Ashton Research Station, University of Bristol, Long Ashton, Bristol, Avon, BS18 9AF, UK

JACKSON, Dr. M.B.,- Long Ashton Research Station, University of Bristol, Bristol, Avon, BS18 9AF, UK

JAMES, Mr. D.C., - King's College London, Dept. of Biology, Half Moon Labs., 68 Half Moon Lane, London, SE24 9JF, UK

JOHANSEN, Miss L.G., - Norwegian Forest Research Institute, Nirsk-Bergen, N-5047 Faua, NORWAY

JONES, Dr. H.G., - Institute of Horticultural Research, East Malling Research Station, Maidstone, Kent, ME19 6BJ, UK

JONES, Dr. M.G., - Dept. of Biochemistry, University College of Wales, Aberystwyth, Dyfed, SY23 3DD, UK

JONES, Professor R.L., - Pflanzenphysiologisches Institut der Universitat Gottingen, Untere Karspule 2, 3400 Gottingen, WEST GERMANY

JORDAN, Dr. V.W.L., - Long Ashton Research Station, University of Bristol, Long Ashton, Bristol, Avon, BS18 9AF, UK

JUPE, Mr. S., - Dept. of Botany and Microbiology, University College of Wales, Aberystwyth, Dyfed, SY23 3DA, UK

KAMIYA, Dr. Y., - Institute of Physical and Chemical Research, Wako-shi, Saitama 351-01, JAPAN

KARI, Mr. J., - Kemira Oy, Espoo Research Centre, P.O. Box 44, SF-02271 Espoo, FINLAND

KARSSEN, Professor C.M., - Dept. of Plant Physiology, Arboretum Laan 4, 6703 BD Wageningen, THE NETHERLANDS

KINET, Dr. J., - Dept. of Botany, B22 University of Liege, Sart Tilman, B-4000 Liege, BELGIUM

KNEE, Dr. M., - Institute of Horticultural Research, East Malling Research Station, Maidstone, Kent, ME19 6BJ, UK

KONTTURI, Mr. M., - Finnish Agricultural Research Centre, Dept. of Plant Husbandry, SF31600, Jokioinan, FINLAND

KYLLINGSBAEK, Dr. A., - State Laboratory for Soil and Crop Research, Lottenborgvej 24, DK-2800 Lyngby, DENMARK

LAIDMAN, Dr. D.L., - Dept. of Biochemistry and Soil Science, University College of North Wales, Bangor, Gwynedd, LL57 2UW, UK

LANE, Miss A., - Dept. of Botany, University College of Wales, Aberystwyth, Dyfed, SY23 3DA, UK

LAZARUS, Dr. C.M., - Dept. of Botany, University of Bristol, Bristol, Avon, BS8 1TS, UK

LEITCH, Mrs. C., - Dept. of Botany, University of Bristol, Bristol, Avon, BS8 1UG, UK

LEJEUNE, Mr. P., - Dept. of Botany, B22 University of Liege, Sart Tilman, B-4000 Liege, BELGIUM

LENTON, Dr. J.R., - Long Ashton Research Station, University of Bristol, Long Ashton, Bristol, Avon, BS18 9AF, UK

LEOPOLD, Professor A. Carl, - Boyce Thompson Institute, Cornell University, Ithaca, New York 14853, USA

LEOPOLD, Mrs. L., - c/o Boyce Thompson Institute, Cornell University, Ithaca, New York 14853, USA

LINFORTH, Dr. R., - Dept. of Plant Physiology, School of Agriculture, University of Nottingham, Sutton Bonington, Loughborough, Leics, LE12 5RD, UK

LUCAS, Miss B., - Dept. of Botany, RHBNC, Egham Hill, Egham, Surrey, TW20 OEX, UK

LUIB, Dr. M., - BASF Aktiengesellschaft, Landw. Versuchsstation, Postfach 220, 6703 Limburgerhof, WEST GERMANY

LÜRSSEN, Dr. K., - Bayer AG, Pflanzenschutz Anwendungstechnik, Biologische, Forschung, D 5090 Leverkusen, WEST GERMANY

LYNDON, Dr. R.F., - Dept. of Botany, University of Edinburgh, Mayfield Road, Edinburgh, EH9 3JH, UK

MACDONALD, Dr. I.R., - Macaulay Instutute for Soil Research, Craigiebuckler, Aberdeen, AB9 2QJ, UK

MACMILLAN, Professor J., - School of Chemistry, University of Bristol, Bristol, Avon, BS8 1TS, UK

MAGUIRE, Professor J.D., - Washington State University, Pullman, Washington 99164, U.S.A.

MANNING, Mr. K., - Institute of Horticultural Research, Glasshouse Crops Research Institute, Worthing Road, Littlehampton, West Sussex, BN17 6LP, UK

MAPELLI, Dr. O., - CNR-IBV via Bassini 15, 20133 Milano, ITALY

MARTIN, Dr. H.V., - Institute of Plant Biology and Physiology, University of Lausanne, 1015 Lausanne, SWITZERLAND

MARTIN, Dr. L., - Dept. of Plant Physiology, Faculty of Biology, University of Salamanca, Salamanca, SPAIN

MARTIN, Mr. P., - Institut für Pflanzenernährung 330, Universität Hohenheim, Postfach
        700562, D-7000 Stuttgart 70, WEST GERMANY
MARTIN, Mr. T.J., - Bayer UK Ltd., Eastern Way, Bury St. Edmunds, Suffolk, IP32 7AH,
        UK
MAYNE, Dr. R., - Biochemistry Dept., ICI Plant Protection Division, Jealotts Hill,
        Bracknell, Berks. RG12 6EY, UK
McCREADY, Dr. C.C., - Dept. of Plant Sciences, University of Oxford, South Parks
        Road, Oxford, OX1 3RA, UK
McGILLIVRAY, Miss L.A., - Dept. of Horticulture, University of Bath, South Building,
        Claverton Down, Bath, Avon, BA2 7AY, UK
MEAKIN, Mr. P., - Dept. of Plant Physiology, School of Agriculture, Sutton Bonington,
        Loughborough, Leics. LE12 5RD, UK
MERTENS, Miss H., - Sprenger Instituut, Haagsteeg 6, 6708 PM., Wageningen,   THE
        NETHERLANDS
MERTENS, Dr. R., - Schering AG, Gollanczstrass 57 - 101, D 1000 Berlin 28,
        WEST GERMANY
METTRIE, Miss R., - RUCA, Dienst Algemene Biologie, Groenenborger Laan 171, 2020
        Antwerpen, THE NETHERLANDS
MILLAM, Mr. S., - School of Applied Sciences, The Polytechnic, Wolverhampton, WV1
        1LY, UK
MINGO-CASTEL, Professor A.M., - Catedratico Fisiologia Vegetal, E.T.S. Ingenieros
        Agronomos, Rovira Roure 177, Lerida, SPAIN
MORGAN, Dr. C.B., - Dept. of Applied Biology, Cambridge University, Pembroke Street,
        Cambridge, UK
MORITZ, Mr. T., - Dept. of Forest Genetics and Plant Physiology, The Swedish
        University of Agricultural Sciences, S-901 83 Umea, SWEDEN
MOSS, Dr. G., - CSIRO, Centre for Irrigation and Freshwater Research, Private Mail
        Bag, Griffith, New South Wales 2680, AUSTRALIA
NAPIER, Mr. J., - Dept. of Biology, King's College, Campden Hill Road, London, W8
        7AH, UK
NEILL, Dr. S.J., - Dept. of Botany & Microbiology, University College of Wales,
        Aberystwyth, Dyfed, SY23 3DA, UK
NICHOLLS, Dr. P.B., - Dept. of Plant Physiology, Waite Agricultural Research
        Institute, Glen Osmond, South Australia 5064, AUSTRALIA
NICHOLS, Dr. R., - Institute of Horticultural Research, Glasshouse Crops Research
        Institute, Worthing Road, Littlehampton, West Sussex, BN17 6LP, UK
NISSEN, Professor P., - Dept. of Microbiology and Plant Physiology, University of
        Bergen, Allegaten 70, N-5000 Bergen, NORWAY.
NOTTON, Dr. B.A., - Long Ashton Research Station, University of Bristol, Long Ashton,
        Bristol, Avon, BS18 9AF, UK
ODÉN, Dr. P.C., - Dept. of Forest Genetics & Plant Physiology, The Swedish University
        of Agricultural Sciences, S-901 83 Umeå, SWEDEN
OMER, Miss J., - Dept. of Biology, The Open University, Walton Hall, Milton Keynes,
        MK7 6AA, UK
OSBORNE, Dr. D.J., - Dept. of Plant Sciences, University of Oxford, Oxford, OX1 3RA,
        UK
PARRY, Mr. A.D., - Dept. of Botany & Microbiology, University College of Wales,
        Aberystwyth, Dyfed, SY23 3DA, UK
PATERSON, Mr. N.W., - Dept. of Biological Sciences, University of Dundee, Dundee, DD1
        4HN, UK
PATRICK, Dr. J.W., - Dept. of Biological Sciences, University of Newcastle, New South
        Wales, AUSTRALIA
PEARCE, Dr. D., - Dept. of Biology, University of Calgary, Calgary, Alberta, T2N 1N4,
        CANADA
PEARSON, Dr. J.A., - Dept. of Botany, University of Durham, South Road, Durham City,
        DH1 3LE, UK
PHINNEY, Professor B.O., - Dept. of Biology, University of California, Los Angeles
        90049 USA
PINFIELD, Dr. N.J., - Dept. of Botany, University of Bristol, Bristol, Avon, BS8 1UG,
        UK

PINTHUS, Professor M.J., - The Hebrew University, Faculty of Agriculture, Rehovot, 76
          - 100, ISRAEL
PORTER, Mr. A.J.R., - Dept. of Agricultural Botany, Plant Science Labs., University
          of Reading, Whiteknights, Reading, RG6 2AS, UK
PORTER, Dr. J.R., - Long Ashton Research Station, University of Bristol, Long Ashton,
          Bristol, Avon, BS18 9AF, UK
POWELL, Mr. B.A., - Ecology Lab., Dept. of Agricultural Botany, University of
          Reading, Whiteknights Park, Reading, Berks. RG6 2AS, UK
PRINSEN,   Dr. E., - Dept. Biologie, Universitaire Instelling Antwerpen,
          Universiteitsplain-1, B-2610 Antwerpen (Wilrijk), BELGIUM
PRITCHARD, Dr. M.K., - Dept. of Plant Science, University of Manitoba, Winnipeg,
          CANADA
PROSSER, Mr. I.M., - Long Ashton Research Station, University of Bristol, Long
          Ashton, Bristol, Avon, BS18 9AF, UK
QUARRIE, Dr. S.A., - Plant Breeding Institute, Trumpington, Cambridge, CB2 2LQ, UK
REILLY, Dr. M.L., - Agriculture Building, University College, Belfield, Dublin 4,
          IRELAND
ROBERTS, Dr. J.A., - School of Agriculture, University of Nottingham, Sutton
          Bonington, Loughborough, Leics., LE12 5RD, UK
RUBERY, Dr. P.H., - Dept. of Biochemistry, University of Cambridge, Cambridge, UK
RUDELSHEIM, Dr. P., - Dept. Biologie, Universitaire Instelling Antwerpen,
          Universiteitsplain-1, B-2610 Antwerpen (Wilrijk), BELGIUM
RYAN, Miss L.A., - School of Life Sciences, Scraptoft Campus, Leicester Polytechnic,
          Leicester, LE7 9SU, UK
SANDBERG, Dr. G., - Dept. of Forest Genetics and Plant Physiology, The Swedish
          University of Agricultural Sciences, S-901 83 Umea, SWEDEN
SCHMIDT, Dr. O., - BASF AG., Agricultural Research Centre, D-6703 Limburgerhof,
          WEST GERMANY
SCHULZ, Dr. G., - BASF Aktiengesellschaft, - c/o ZH/Tagungen, D-6700 Ludwigshafen,
          WEST GERMANY
SCHURR, Mr. U., - Lehrstuhl Pflanzenökologie der Universität Bayreuth, Postfach 8580
          Bayreuth, WEST GERMANY
SCHWABE, Professor W.W. - Dept. of Horticulture, Wye College, University of London,
          Ashford, Kent, TN25 5AH, UK
SCOTT, Dr. I., - Dept. of Botany & Microbiology, University College of Wales,
          Aberystwyth, Dyfed, SY23 3DA, UK
SELF, Mr. G.K., - Dept. of Botany, University of Edinburgh, The King's Buildings,
          Mayfield Road, Edinburgh, EH9 3JH, UK
SHERRIFF, Miss C., - Long Ashton Research Station, University of Bristol, Long
          Ashton, Bristol, Avon, BS18 9AF, UK
SLATER, Dr. A., - School of Life Sciences, Leicester Polytechnic, Scraptoft Campus,
          Leicester, LE7 9SU, UK
SMITH, Dr. P., - Dept. of Botany, University of Edinburgh, The King's Building,
          Mayfield Road, Edinburgh, EH9 3JH, UK
SMITH, Miss S.B., - Dept. of Botany, Plant Science Labs., University of Reading,
          Whiteknights, Reading, RG6 2AS, UK
SMITH, Miss S.J., - Long Ashton Research Station, University of Bristol, Long Ashton,
          Bristol, Avon, BS18 9AF, UK
SMITH, Dr. T.A., - Long Ashton Research Station, University of Bristol, Long Ashton,
          Bristol, Avon, BS18 9AF, UK
SMITH, Dr. V.A., - School of Chemistry, University of Bristol, Bristol, Avon, BS8
          1TS, UK
SNAITH, Dr. P., - Shell Research Ltd., Sittingbourne Research Centre, Sittingbourne,
          Kent, ME9 8AG, UK
SOEJIMA, Mr. J., - Fruit Tree Research Station, Min. of Agriculture Forest &
          Fisheries, Yatabe, Tsukuba, Ibaraki 305, JAPAN
SPONSEL, Dr. V.M., - School of Chemistry, University of Bristol, Bristol, Avon, BS8
          1TS, UK
SRINIVASAN, Mr. A., - Dept. of Applied Biology, Pembroke Street, University of
          Cambridge, Cambridge, CB2 3DX, UK

STARLING, Dr. R.J., - Dept. of Botany and Microbiology, University College of Wales, Aberystwyth, Dyfed, SY23 3DA, UK
STEAD, Dr. A.D., - Dept. of Botany, RHBNC, Egham Hill, Egham, Surrey, TW20 OEX, UK
STEVENS, Dr. M.A., - 4 Portugal Place, Cambridge, CB5 8AF, UK
STINCHCOMBE, Mr. G.R., - Long Ashton Research Station, University of Bristol, Long Ashton, Bristol, Avon, BS18 9AF, UK
STODDART, Dr. J.L., - Welsh Plant Breeding Station, Aberystwyth, Dyfed, SY23 3EB, UK
STUCHBURY, Dr. T., - Dept. of Agricultural Biochemistry, University of Aberdeen, 581 King Street, Aberdeen, AB9 1UD, UK
STUTCHBURY, Miss P.A., - Dept. of Botany, University of Bristol, Bristol, Avon, BS8 1UG, UK
SUBAGYO, Mr. T., - Bridges Hall, University of Reading, Whiteknights Road, Reading, RG6 2BG, UK
SUNDBERG, Mr. B., - Dept. of Forest Genetics and Plant Physiology, The Swedish University of Agricultural Sciences, S-901 83 Umea, SWEDEN
SUNLEY, Mr. R.L., - ICI Plant Protection Division, Jealotts Hill Research Station, Bracknell, Berks. RG12 6EY, UK
SWEETMAN, Mr. J.A., - Dept. of Botany and Microbiology, School of Biological Sciences, U.C.W., Aberystwyth, Dyfed, SY23 3DA, UK
TARR, Mr. A.R., - Dept. of Plant Physiology, School of Agriculture, Sutton Bonington, Loughborough, Leics. LE12 5RD, UK
TAYLOR, Miss A., - Dept. of Plant Science, University of Aberdeen, St. Machar Drive, Aberdeen, AB9 2UD, UK
TAYLOR, Ms G., - Dept. of Biological Science, University of Lancaster, Lancaster, LA1 4XP, UK
TAYLOR, Dr. I., - Dept. of Physiology and Environmental Science, University of Nottingham, School of Agriculture, Sutton Bonington, Nr. Loughborough, Leics. LE12 5RD, UK
TAYLOR, Miss J.E., - Dept. of Botany and Microbiology, University College of Wales, Aberystwyth, Dyfed, SY23 3DA, UK
TAYLOR, Miss S., - Dept. of Horticulture, TOB 2/Lab 3, University of Reading, Earley Gate, P.O. Box 236, Reading, RG6 2AT, UK
TELLADO, Dr. F.G. - Instituto de Productos Naturales Organicos del CSIC, Bartolome Carrasco 2, La Laguna, Tenerife, SPAIN
THOMAS, Dr. T.H., - Long Ashton Research Station, University of Bristol, Long Ashton, Bristol, Avon, BS18 9AF, UK
TREHARNE, Professor K.J., - Long Ashton Research Station, University of Bristol, Long Ashton, Bristol, Avon, BS18 9AF, UK
TREWAVAS, Dr. A.J., - Dept. of Botany, University of Edinburgh, Scotland, EH9 3JH, UK
TSANTILI, Miss E., - c/o Fruit Storage Dept., Institute of Horticultural Research, East Malling Research Station, Maidstone, Kent, ME19 6BJ, UK
TUCKER, Dr. G.A., - School of Agriculture, University of Nottingham, Sutton Bonington, Loughborough, Leics, LE12 5RD, UK
VALLE, Dr. T., - Dept. de Fisiologia Vegetal, Facultad de Biologia, Universidad de Salamanca, Salamanca, SPAIN
VAN LOON, Dr. L.C., - Dept. of Plant Physiology, Agricultural University, Arboretum Laan 4 6703 BD, Wageningen, THE NETHERLANDS
VANDEN DRIESSCHE, Professor T., - Department de Biologie Moleculaire, Universite Libre de Bruxelles, 67 Rue de Cheveaux, 1640 Rhode St. Genese, BELGIUM
VAUGHAN, Dr. D., - Macaulay Institute for Soil Research, Craigiebuckler, Aberdeen, AB9 2QJ, UK
VENIS, Dr. M.A., - Institute of Horticultural Research, East Malling Research Station, Maidstone, Kent, ME19 6BJ, UK
VILLALOBOS, Professor N., - Dept. of Plant Physiology, Faculty of Biology, University of Salamanca, Salamanca, SPAIN
VREUGDENHIL, Dr. D., - Dept. of Plant Physiology, Agricultural University, Arboretum Laan 4 6703 BD, Wageningen, THE NETHERLANDS
WALSMA, Mr. J., - School of Life Sciences, Scraptoft Campus, Leicester Polytechnic, Leicester, LE7 9SU, UK
WARD, Mr. D.A., - Long Ashton Research Station, University of Bristol, Long Ashton, Bristol, Avon, BS18 9AF, UK

WARREN WILSON, Professor J., - Dept. of Botany, Australian National University, GPO Box 4, Canberra, ACT 2601, AUSTRALIA

WARREN WILSON, Dr. P.M., - Dept. of Developmental Biology, R.S.B.S., Australian National University, GPO Box 4, ACT 2601, AUSTRALIA

WATERHOUSE, Mr. S., - BASF United Kingdom Ltd., Lady Lane, Hadleigh, Ipswich, IP7 6BQ, UK

WATTS, Dr. J.W., - John Innes Institute, Colney Lane, Norwich, NR4 7UH, UK

WEIR, Ms. J., - School of Chemistry, University of Bristol, Bristol, Avon, BS8 1TS, UK

WELANDER, Dr. T., - Swedish University of Agricultural Sciences, Dept. of Horticultural Science, Box 55, S-230 53 Alnarp, SWEDEN

WESTON, Dr. G., - School of Life Sciences, Leicester Polytechnic, Scraptoft, Leicester, LE7 9SU, UK

WEYERS, Dr. J.D.B., - Dept. of Biological Sciences, University of Dundee, Dundee, DD1 4HN, UK

WHENHAM, Dr. R.J., - Biochemistry Section, Institute of Horticultural Research (National Vegetable Research Station), Wellesbourne, Warwick, CV35 9EF, UK

WHITFORD, Mr. P.N., - Long Ashton Research Station, University of Bristol, Long Ashton, Bristol, Avon, BS18 9AF, UK

WILDON, Dr. D., - School of Biological Sciences, University of East Anglia, Norwich, NR4 7TJ, UK

WILLIAMS, Miss C.A., - Dept. of Agriculture and Horticulture, School of Agriculture, University of Nottingham, Sutton Bonington, Loughborough, Leics, LE12 5RD, UK

WILLIAMS, Mr. R.A.N., - Dept. of Botany and Microbiology, University College of Wales, Aberystwyth, Dyfed, SY23 3DA, UK

WILLIS, Dr. C.L., - School of Chemistry, University of Bristol, Bristol, Avon, BS8 1TS, UK

WILSON, Ms. S., - c/o Dept. of Biology, Biological Sciences Building, University of Calgary, Calgary, Alberta T2N 2N4, CANADA

WOODWARD, R., - Institute of Horticultural Research, East Malling Research Station, Maidstone, Kent, ME19 6BJ, UK

WOOLHOUSE, Professor H.W., - John Innes Institute, Colney Lane, Norwich, NR4 7UH, UK

XING, T., - Scraptoft Campus, School of Life Sciences, Leicester Polytechnic, Leicester, LE7 9SU, UK

YOUNG, Mr. S.F., - Long Ashton Research Station, University of Bristol, Long Ashton, Bristol, Avon, BS18 9AF, UK

YOUNGMAN, Dr. R.J., - SKW Trostberg AG, D-8223 Trostberg, WEST GERMANY

YOUSEFIAH, S., - c/o Plant Breeding Institute, Maris Lane, Trumpington, Cambridge, CB2 2LQ, UK

ZHANG, Mr. J., - c/o Dept. of Biological Sciences, University of Lancaster, Lancaster, LA1 4YQ, UK (Jiangsu Agricultural College, Yongzhou, Jiangsu, CHINA).

DOUGLAS WILLS INAUGURAL LECTURE

CONTEMPLATIONS ON HORMONES AS BIOLOGICAL REGULATORS

A. Carl Leopold

Boyce Thompson Institute, Cornell University, Ithaca NY 14853, USA

INTRODUCTION

As an observer and sometimes participant in the science of hormonal regulation in plants, I have long held the opinion that progress in the understanding of plant hormones was lagging behind what should have been expected from such a central sector of the science of plant growth and development. While animal physiologists have identified over 40 hormones, plus an even larger number of smaller regulators, along with isolation and characterization of the binding sites for some, and have identified second messengers for the majority of the hormones, we in the plant sciences, with our mere five known hormones, have no such bank of information to drawn on in understanding our plant organisms.

It seems an appropriate time to consider the comparative biology, so to speak, of plant and animal hormones, and to endeavour to improve our rate of progress in the plant field by improving our awareness of hormonal systems in other sectors of biology. With apologies for attempting such a review when I have no credentials or training in animal hormones, I shall attempt to abstract from the animal literature such characteristics as might be useful in finding new and perhaps more productive lines of research in the plant hormone field. It is my opinion that the need for such a review is sufficiently appealing that I will make the attempt, even with my limited knowledge and lack of appropriate background.

HORMONES AS CHEMICAL MESSENGERS

At the start, a word about whether plant hormones are truly hormones. I wish to evade the argument entirely, and I will do so by saying that hormones are what physiologists call hormones. For many years endocrinologists defined hormones as chemical entities which moved in the bloodstream. This nicely discriminated between hormones and neurotransmitters, which were secreted by neurons. It was later discovered, however that a substantial number of neurotransmitters travel in the bloodstream, and so the distinction was blurred. Current nomenclature substitutes the word neurohormones for the former neurotransmitters. Of course plant hormones cannot travel in a bloodstream, but in their chemical characteristics, their chemical messenger characteristics, and their receptor sites, they are closely analogous to the animal hormones -- especially to the more mobile neurohormones.

Of course hormones make a major contribution towards the systemic regulation of organisms, and with an evolutionary increase in size and complexity of organisms there would be an associated increasing array of hormones. In mammals, the highly complex system of multiple hormones would seem appropriate to the complexity of such organisms. The small number of plant hormones may be a reflection of lesser complexity required for immobile and less dynamic organisms, or it may reflect a more generalized and less specialized regulatory system.

Indirect support for the idea of less specialized plant hormones may be found in the fact that any one of the five plant hormones may serve to alter essentially any of the sectors of plant growth and development. A rough survey illustrating this point was made in 1972, as illustrated in Table I (Leopold, 1972).

The multiplicity of functions of hormones can be seen again in animal hormone effects; for example, thyroxin regulates an astounding array, ranging from

3

Table 1 The range of hormonal effects of the five known classes of plant hormones. For twelve different developmental process, the existence of known effects of each of the hormones on this process is indicated by an X. The absence of such a mark does not infer a lack of hormonal effects on that developmental process, but rather the absence of such report in the literature (from Leopold, 1972).

Developmental process:	Known regulatory activities of plant hormones:				
	Auxin	Gibberellin	Cytokinin	Abscisic Acid	Ethylene
Dormancy		x	x	x	x
Juvenility	x	x			
Growth Rate	x	x	x	x	x
Flower initiation	x	x	x	x	x
Sex determination	x	x	x		x
Fruit set	x	x	x		x
Fruit growth	x	x	x		x
Fruit ripening	x	x	x		x
Tuberization	x	x	x	x	x
Abscission	x	x	x	x	x
Rooting	x	x	x		x
Senescence	x	x	x	x	x

metamorphosis to learning ability, the development of teeth and of antlers, the absorption of glucose and water diuresis.

In marked contrast to the elaboration of a highly complex array of hormones, there appears to be only a limited number of second messengers involved in the intracellular transduction of hormonal signals. Second messengers will be considered in a later section, but at this point I will point out that the rather dazzling array of animal hormones has been evolved utilizing only three known types of second messengers, including cyclic nucleotides, protein kinases, and calcium. We know of no cases in which plants utilize cyclic nucleotides as second messengers, but they probably utilize the protein kinase and calcium messengers.

Hormones are clearly the most impressive carriers of information at the intercellular level. Their effectiveness may be attributed to (1) their mobility through the organism, (2) the potential for amplification of their signals, and (3) their capabilities for achieving even very complex regulatory actions through interactions.

A SURVEY OF HORMONES

A simple listing of the kinds of chemical entities utilized in animal and plant hormone systems (Tables 1 and 2) provides impressive evidence of some differences -- not only in terms of the contrasting numbers of animal and plant hormones, but also the contrasting types of chemical compounds utilized. Of the major categories of animal hormones -- the steroids and protein or peptide hormones -- there are no analogues among the plant hormones. The contrast between the large molecules of steroid and protein hormones and the small molecules of plant hormones may be a reflection of the ready availability of body fluids for hormone translocation in animals. In plants, lack of such facile bulk transport system may impose the requirement for small chemical messengers.

Steroid hormones are characteristically synthesized in ductless glands, from which they are transferred into the bloodstream. Protein, glycoprotein and peptide hormones are characteristically secreted from specialized cells -- usually

Table 2 A synopsis of common animal hormones.

SYNOPSIS OF COMMON ANIMAL HORMONES

Steroid:	estrogen	progesterone
	testosterone	dihydrotestosterone
	glucocorticoids	aldosterone
	cholecalciferol	
Protein:	insulin	glucagon
	growth hormone	placental lactogen
	prolactin	parathyroid hormone
	calcitonin	ACTH
	secretin	cholecystokinin
	gastrin	gastric inhibitor
	chalone inhibitor	
Glycoprotein:	FSH	LH
	chorionic gonadotropin	thyroid-stimulating hormone
Peptides:	vasopressin	melanocyte-stimulating hormone
	oxytocin	thyrotropin-releasing hormone
	somatostatin	gonadotrophin-releasing hormone
	angiotensin	
Amines:	thyroxin	triiodothyronine
	dopamine	epinephrine
	norepinephrin	melatonin
	serotonin	catechol amines
Fatty acids:	prostaglandins	leucotrienes

components of the nervous system. They, too, find their way into the blood stream and thus move through the animal organism. Some smaller animal hormones, such as the amines and fatty acids, are formed in a variety of body organs, and their translocation is characteristically much more localized. Some neurohumors, for example, may be transported only across a membrane, thus providing a much more limited type of messenger function.

We can be confident that the list of types of hormones will increase in the future. The polyamines and the newly discovered inhibitor of flowering (Jaffe and Bridle, in press) appear to be promising new candidates in the plant hormone area.

We can assume a rather simple set of features of all hormones, plant or animal; they include first, of course, the chemical messenger feature, then the linkage to a stereo-specific binding site on a membrane, the subsequent activation of one or more intracellular second messengers, and ultimately the alteration of some components of the genetic information (as through altered transcription, altered translation, or post-translational modifications). The alteration of available genetic information often provides only a part of the regulatory effects of hormones.

HORMONAL REGULATION

Mention has already been made of the amplifying capabilities of hormones in regulatory biology. In cases where the action of a hormone causes the activation of a specific enzyme, one can perceive the magnitude of the amplification potentials. As an example, the protein hormone, glucagon, gives rise, among other things, to a metabolism of glucose; Hardy (1981) calculates that one molecule of glucagon will result in the metabolism of 3 million molecules of glucose.

With the advent of an understanding of second messengers, the amplification characteristic becomes even more evident. Instead of a hormone turning on an enzyme, we can view the hormone as turning on a second messenger, and either in the cAMP system or the phosphoinositol system, a succession of enzymes is activated: enzymes such as adenyl cyclase form cAMP which then turns on further enzymes such as protein kinase or phosphorylase. Such sequences of enzymes turning on other enzymes in series must greatly expand the potential for amplification.

Hormone Receptors

The intuitive concept of hormone receptors is that each hormone will have a single, stereo-specific receptor, which can activate a specific response when the hormone is attached. In plant biology some of us have been surprised to find that more than one receptor can be found in a given tissue. In endocrinology, multiple receptors are common, with the associated phenomenon of pleiotropic responses -- or multiple effects from a single hormone. Many neurotransmitters have multiple receptors, in fact as many as five for a single hormone (Michell and Houslay, 1986). The steroid progresterone has likewise been found to have five different binding sites. It is probable that the different receptors serve to activate different cellular functions. Some are suspected to be involved with hormone metabolism, as especially in the case of protein hormones (Hadley, 1984).

For animal hormones other than the steroids there is a receptor located on the plasmalemma. The receptor for the protein hormones is ordinarily a glycoprotein, which presumably traverses the membrane, extending the hormone site out of the lipid region of the membrane. After protein hormones have formed a hormone-receptor complex, there results an activation of a second messenger, or intracellular agent.

In the case of steroid hormones if there is a plasmalemma receptor it may serve only as a carrier, bringing the hormone through the cytoplasm and into contact with the DNA where transformation occurs. There are also instances in which steroid hormones find receptors on the nuclear membrane. Ecdysone is known to bind directly onto the chromosome, resulting in the well-known phenomenon of chromosome "puffing".

Considerable attention has recently been turned to the manner of changing sensitivity to hormones as a means of modulating or regulating hormone responsiveness (Trewavas, 1982). The relationship between available binding sites and hormonal activity in animal systems is somewhat surprising. The abundance of binding sites greatly exceeds the abundance of hormone; in the case of glucagon, the hormonal effect is saturated when only one percent of the receptor sites is filled; the usual value for saturation is between one and five percent. In spite of this unbalance between hormones and receptors, the commonest means of lowering the sensitivity to a hormone is by reducing the numbers or availability of receptors -- a phenomenon called down-regulation. In this type of regulation, receptors are usually transferred into the cytoplasm by endocytosis, where they may be degraded by lysosomes (Hadley, 1984). A good example of down-regulation is insulin. The reverse, or the expansion of a tissue's sensitivity to a hormone by exposure to the hormone, termed up-regulation, can be illustrated by prolactin; treatment of cells with this hormone leads to a proliferation of receptor sites. In the case of the polypeptide growth factors, the affinity of the receptors may be lowered through a methylation action (Hirata and Axelrod, 1980).

Binding sites need not all be involved in hormone action, of course. The binding of hormones may provide a pool of hormones. In the case of the protein thyroid hormones, the binding of thyrotropin leads to the transformation of this inactive form into the active thyroxin; testosterone, too, is transformed into the more active dihydrotestosterone after binding to its receptor.

Not only may some hormones have more than one binding site, but the effect of the hormone may be directed by the receptor to which it binds. The binding sites for adrenaline or noradrenaline are of two sorts, alpha and beta; adrenalin binding to the alpha site results in arterial constriction, whereas binding to the beta site results in arterial dilation. Binding of insulin to the alpha site can result in an inhibition of insulin secretion, and binding to the beta site results in stimulated insulin secretion.

An impressive measure of the progress of endocrinology is the fact that some hormone receptors have not only been isolated, but characterized as to their amino acid sequences, and the probable site of hormonal attachment. Much of the splendid progress that has been made in locating and characterizing receptor sites in endocrinology has been due to the development of techniques utilizing the binding of radioactive hormones (Stumpf and Roth, 1966), in a manner quite similar to the technique developed by Hertel (Ray et al., 1977) for plant hormone receptors. The labeling technique has been greatly improved by the development of computer-assisted definition of specific binding sites (Clark and Hall, 1986). For the steroid hormones, isolation of the receptor sites was made possible through the utilization of hormone molecules with an unsaturated ketone which forms a covalent bond to the receptor upon radation with ultra-violet light (Gronemeyer, 1985).

Second Messengers

The discovery that hormones catalyze various enzymic processes within target cells through intracellular or second messenger carriers brought the Nobel Prize to E.W. Sutherland in 1971. The subsequent decade has gradually revealed other second messengers besides the cyclic AMP that Sutherland had found.

In animal systems, the commonest second messenger is, of course, cAMP, or in some instances cGMP (Fig. 1). It appears that protein hormones generally and some of the smaller hormones including some peptides and amines utilize cAMP as the second messenger. Steroid hormones and some amine and fatty acid hormones do not. Plants do not utilize cAMP, even through it's presence in plants has been verified.

The attachment of the hormone to the receptor results in the activation of adenyl cyclase, an enzyme located in the membrane which synthesizes cAMP from ATP. The cAMP moves through the cytoplasm and serves as an activator of any of several protein kinases, which in turn may activate specific enzymes in the cell through a phosphorylation step.

Another second messenger system, which probably does operate in plants, is the inositol trisphosphate system (Nishikuza, 1986). In this case, the attachment of a hormone to its receptor leads to the activation of a phospholipase C, which then preferentially hydrolyses phosphoinositol-4,5-bisphosphate (Fig. 2). The hydrolysis of this particular membrane component leads to the release into the cytoplasm of two second messengers: inositol triphosphate and diacylglycerol. The latter compound activates protein kinase C, and this central control point serves as a gate keeper regulating a wide array of processes through the selective phosphorylation of enzymes. An important feature of this regulatory system is that increased levels of cytoplasmic calcium are needed for the activity of protein kinase C to be realized. Inositol triphosphate serves to open calcium gates in membranes, and so the coordinated release of the two messengers from a membrane lipid brings about effective regulation of protein kinase C.

Yet another second messenger, cytoplasmic calcium, is a regulator of numerous hormonal signals throughout the biological world. The stimulation of calcium

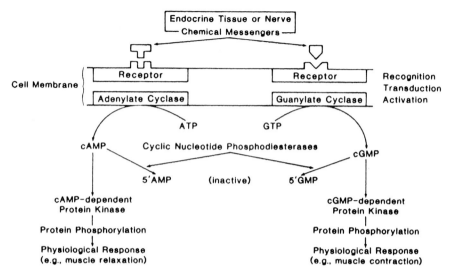

Fig. 1 Cyclic AMP and cyclic GMP as second messenger systems (from Hadley, 1984).

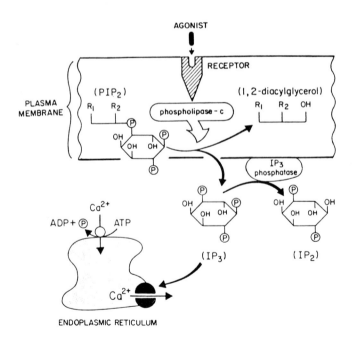

Fig. 2 Inositol trisphosphate as second messenger (from Joseph, 1984).

influx by inositol triphosphate has already been mentioned; increases can also result from a wide array of environmental signals such as light, cold, physical stimulation, as well as by hormonal actions. The cellular events that are modified by modest increases in cytoplasmic calcium are manifold; one of the major functions of calcium in animal hormone responses is the activation of protein kinase. For example, stimulation of a neuron and the resulting action of acetylcholine leads to the hydrolysis of phosphatidyl inositol triphosphate, calcium levels are consequently increased, and the calcium, together with calmodulin, activates the protein kinase. Calcium effects span a wide range of structural actions as for example the organization of tubulin into microtubules, membrane actions as for example the modification of membrane permeability, enzymic actions as for example the regulation of protein kinase, and kinetic actions as for example the regulation of cytokinesis and cell division. Many biological responses to light involve calcium mediated steps, ranging from vision in animals to phytochrome actions in plants (Cheung, 1980; Roux and Slocum, 1982).

Cytoplasmic calcium is enhanced by many hormones, including acetylcholine, secrotonin, insulin, pituitary hormones, and in general those hormones which activate the phosphatidyl-inositol system. When the cytoplasmic calcium level is expanded, whether by hormones or by environmental factors, a wide array of enzymic processes is activated (Joseph, 1984; Gronemeyer, 1985). The prominent role of calcium in hormonal regulatory processes seems to be as widespread in plants as it is in animals; exogenous applications of calcium can enhance effects of each of the five plant hormones (Leopold et al., 1974; Pooviah and Leopold, 1976). Evidence of calcium serving as a second messenger for auxin has been proposed by Hasenstein and Evans (1986). The possible effects of a hormone on cytoplasmic concentrations in the cells of higher plants have not yet been defined.

The entry of calcium is considered to be a passive response to the steep concentration gradient between the cytoplasm and either organelles or the extracellular medium. Calcium channels are opened after hormonal stimulation, or after various types of stress, light, physical or electrical stimulations. Restoration of the base level of calcium requires the activation of a sodium or potassium ATPase. Provision of the ATP needed for calcium stimulations can be provided as a consequence of the striking stimulatory effects of calcium on mitochondrial production of ATP (McCormack and Denton, 1986).

Mention of the regulatory actions of calcium in biology must include mention of the role of calmodulin -- a protein which serves as the most general binding site for calcium, and as the principal linkage of calcium to calcium-requiring enzymes (Cheung, 1980). Such linkages are involved in the regulation of such central enzymes as adenyl cyclase, phosphorylase, NAD kinase, phospholipase and phosphodiesterase. As in the case of calcium calmodulin may function in the regulations of most plant hormones (Elliott et al., 1983; Kelly, 1984). Calmodulin should not be itself considered as a second messenger; its concentration in the cytoplasm of target cells is not regulated by hormones.

Modulation of Hormones

The simplest model of hormonal regulatory functions would be that each hormone served to regulate an individual function, and that collectively, then, these functions could be integrated in the whole organism. Such a model of regulation runs into immediate problems: surely the number of processes that require regulation in a higher plant or animal far exceed the number of hormones or other regulators. In short, the very idea of individual hormones regulating individual processes cannot adequately describe biological regulation. The alternative, of course, is regulation through the interactions and collective modulations between hormonal systems. I use the word systems because it is clear that interactions may occur at various levels including the synthesis of hormones, hormone receptors, and second messengers, as well as at the level of ultimate hormone action.

In plant physiology we have employed such regulator names as "growth hormone", "cell division hormone", "dormancy hormone", and "ripening hormone"; in retrospect we can surely agree that these inferences of individual hormones regulating such complex developmental processes are simplistic and unrealistic. What can we learn about the means by which interacting hormones achieve complex regulatory effects?

Interactions

Among the animal hormones, interactions are the prevailing characteristic. We may think of insulin regulating glucose metabolism, but in doing so it is in turn dynamically controlled by somatostatin and glucagon. In part, these interactions involve controls of biosynthesis; for example glucagon stimulates insulin synthesis, and both insulin and somatostatin inhibit glucagon synthesis. Furthermore, insulin synthesis is stimulated by ACTH and TSH hormones and by several chemical signals from the gut through effects on the glucose levels. Furthermore hormone interactions may occur at the second messenger level, insulin stimulating phosphodiesterase and thus leading to a depletion of cAMP, an effect which is balanced by glucagon which stimulates adenly cyclase hence leading to an enhancement of cAMP levels. Some additional hormones which particplate in the regulation of glucose metabolism through cAMP are adrenalin, and some neurohumors. Some of the steroid hormones exert anti-insulin effects by favouring glycogen synthesis at the expense of glucose levels. From these examples we can see that even a fairly simple variable such as glucose metabolism is mediated by an elaborate hormonal system involving at least six hormones. Mammary secretion is dependent upon the integrated actions of eight hormones.

Interactions between hormones may also occur through modification of their respective binding sites. For example, insulin increases the affinity of the polypeptide IGF II for its binding site by ten-fold; phorbol esters decrease the affinity of several hormones for their binding sites. The phenomena of down-regulation and up-regulation have already been mentioned.

Among the features of animal hormone interactions is the curious feature of "permissive action"; this term refers to the requirement of certain processes for the presence of a given hormone, but without any apparent sensitivity to its concentration. An example is the requirement for the presence of the thyroid hormones for the action of insulin and several other hormones involved in heat production; the requirement is apparently not a quantitative one, and seems to have the characteristics of a synergistic effect.

Because one of the plant hormones is often autocatalytic in its effects, I was interested to find that some semblance of autocatalysis held for at least one animal' hormone: oxytocin. This peptide hormone stimulates the contraction of certain target cells in the reproductive system, including the muscles involved in parturition. When parturition has been initiated, oxytocin is released, which stimulates myometrial activity, causing more oxytocin release and an approximation of an autocatalytic sequence is established.

Inhibitions

The characteristic of auxin being able to inhibit at high concentrations the same functions that it promotes at lower concentrations makes the issue of inhibitions among animal hormones especially interesting. I am unable to find an instance of such a reversal of actions among animal hormones. However, there are effective chemical devices which inhibit the effectiveness of various hormones -- mainly through the actions of prostaglandins, a family of fatty acid compounds closely related to arachidonic acid. These small hormones have major suppressive effects on adenylate cyclase; the action of a hormone such as vasopressin, which involves the formation of cAMP as a second messenger, is markedly inhibited by prostaglandins. Curiously, some other hormones which utilize the same second messenger are synergized by prostaglandins.

A different type of hormonal inhibition is found in the chalones. These protein inhibitors (MW 12,000 to 26,000) provide reversible inhibitory effects on the binding of Epidermal Growth Factor (EGF) to its receptor (Wang and Hsu, 1986). Interferon is another natural hormone inhibitor. The effects of phorbol esters as inhibitors of hormone binding to receptors has already been mentioned.

From this casual examination of the important tissue of hormonal modulation, it seems clear that while individual animal hormones have specific functions, and these related to specific receptive cells with appropriate binding sites, the overall theme of regulation is one of complex interactions between hormones. These interactions may pertain to mutual regulation of hormonal concentrations, or they may relate to mutual interactions of a commonly regulated component of metabolism, or they may relate to effects on binding sites and second messengers. Their effects may be mutually synergistic, inhibitory, or their effects may depend upon the ratio between the interacting hormones. I have previously pointed out examples of each of these types of interactive effects between the plant hormones (Leopold and Noodén, 1984).

Hormone Actions

Plant physiologists have used the lag times for the effects of plant hormones as evidence about possible mechanisms (Warner and Leopold, 1969). The range of lag times in animal hormone responses is very much wider than that for plant hormones. Thyroxin and the thyroid hormones have a lag period of days; steroid hormones act within hours; the peptide hormones in minutes, and the amines in milliseconds. These times may be assumed to reflect the respective mechanisms of action, the steroid effect being principally on the nucleic acids, the peptides being principally on second messengers, and the amines affecting also second messengers but without any intercellular transport.

From a brief review of animal hormone effects, it seems logical to attribute hormone actions mainly to (a) effects on enzymic systems in receptor cells, or to (b) effects on the genetic information system (transcription, translation, or post-translational modification). The enzymic systems are regulated through the receptor/second messenger system, and the genetic systems are regulated through direct attachment of the hormone (or hormone plus receptor) to the nuclear material. The actual definition of mode of action of animal hormones has proved to be elusive, and the more closely one pursues the hormone action, the more complex the labyrinth of biochemistry that is revealed without allowing the researcher the reward of having found in fact the mechanism of action of any hormone.

SPECIAL HORMONAL ACTIONS

As plant physiologists, we should be alert as to possible novel types of regulations that occur in biological systems, and to the possibility of there being analogues within the plant world. I would like to draw your attention to two types of novel animal hormones that could have anlogies in plants.

We know that plants have a precise capability for measuring time, especially as it relates to photoperiodism, but also in shorter cyclic events. Animals, too, have this capability; they measure light/dark cycles by secretion from the pineal gland of the hormone melatonin. This is a small compound, derived from tryptophan and serotonin. It serves as a major component of the timing reactions related to ovulation, diurnal cycles, and possibly cycles of other duration as well.

We know that plants have effective capabilities of regulating salt levels, especially in species which are adapted to xerophytic conditions. In animals, the maintenance of a balance between sodium and potassium levels is established by the steroid, aldosterone. This hormone is synthesized from chloesterol under the stimulatory influences of peptide hormones: the angiotensins. Aldosterone provides powerful regulation of ion pumps, particularly of sodium and of potassium, and does this through the stimulation of DNA transcription leading to the synthesis of the protein components of the salt pumps.

EVOLUTIONARY CONSIDERATIONS

The chemical species which are employed as hormones in biology occur occasionally in organisms which have no hormonal use for them. For example, Roth et al. (1982) reported the occurrence of insulin in protozoa, fungi and E. coli. They found somatotrophin, ACTH and endorphin in protozoa. They suggested that hormones are selected from among compounds which are synthesized in biological systems, and that in evolutionary time some of these compounds have been adapted gradually to become components of regulatory systems.

A striking example of the biological commonality of hormones was the report of the plant hormone, abscisic acid, being isolated from mammalian brain cells (Lapage-Dequiry et al., 1986). Of course animal hormones, especially the amines and ecdysone are of fairly common occurrence in plants (Bulard and Leopold, 1958; Bowers et al., 1966; Jaffe, 1970). It is interesting that in the case of acetylcholine occurring in plants, all of the enzymes necessary for the esterification and hydrolysis of the molecule are present (Jaffe, 1970) without there being a known function.

A further surprise was that stereo-specific receptors for hormones have been found in tissues which show no regulatory responses to the hormones; for example, receptor sites for insulin have been found in mammalian brain tissues (Kolata, 1982).

As for hormone receptor sites, there seems no particular commonality among these proteins, and it does not seem likely that they arose from a common source. Occasionally there are strong similarities, such as the nearly identical receptor proteins for insulin and somatomedin, such that the two hormones show competitive interactions. A similar competition of sites occurs between oxytocin and vasopressin.

The gradual transformation of naturally occurring compounds into hormones probably began with small compound such as the neurohormones and the plant hormones. As animals increased in complexity and increased in needs for regulatory systems, the peptide and protein hormones might have been the next logical development. The utilization of endocrine hormones such as the steroids might have been a more recent evolutionary development (Turner and Bagnara, 1971).

The physiological use to which individual hormones have been put shows considerable variation. For example, insulin is principally a regulator of glucose metabolism in mammals, but it serves as a regulator of amino acid metabolsim in fishes; again, prolactin serves to regulate lactation in mammals, but it is a growth hormone in amphibians and a regulator of salt balance in fishes (Savin, 1969).

CONTEMPLATIONS

I hope that this comparison of plant and animal hormone systems may be useful and that it may bring into focus some possibilities for hormonal controls that we in the plant sciences have not been used to thinking about.

Similarities between the plant hormones and the smaller animal hormones include the basic actions involving membrane receptor attachments, and probably the utilization of second messengers. Similarities in terms of the complexity of hormonal control of metabolic or developmental processes are of interest, mainly in terms of the utilization of multiple hormonal influences and inter-hormonal modulations. Regulation of sensitivity to hormones is much clearer in animal systems, where down-regulation of receptor sites plays an important role, but changes in receptor affinity of binding and antagonistic effects by other hormones are also relevant.

Similarities appear once again in terms of the very wide range of mechanisms employed in hormonal regulation, not simply through the regulation of genetic transcription, but regulation of a wide range of events in the membranes and in the cytoplasm itself.

From an examination of the overall hormone field, can we make any suggestions of particularly attractive areas for research? Among the obvious attractive research objectives in plant hormone biochemistry would be the establishment of the identity of second messengers for the plant hormones. Such an effort would best be done using either tissue culture techniques or at least isolated homogeneous tissues. The possibility of establishing calcium as a second messenger is an obvious choice. A similarly attractive second messenger possibility would be the phosphoinositol system. Another attractive line of pursuit would be a search for up-regulation or down-regulation of hormonal responsiveness through changes in the abundance of receptor sites. With the increasing evidence of regulation through hormonal interactions, I feel that important potentials lie in the area of studies of interacting plant hormones.

Surely the splendid complexity of hormonal regulation must stir profound admiration in biologists, and sometimes beautiful and sometimes frustrating research results in regulatory biology must exemplify the words of W.Y. Cheung (1980):

"A living cell is the epitome of ingenious design."

REFERENCES

Bowers, W.S., Fales, H.M., Thompson, S.J., and Uebel, E.C. (1966). Juvenile hormone: identification of active compound from Balsam fir. Science **154**, 1020-1021.

Bulard, C. and Leopold, A.C. (1958). 5-Hydroxytryptamine chez les plantes superioures. Comptes Rendus Geod Sciences **247**, 1382-1384.

Cheung, W.Y. (1980). Calmodulin plays a pivotal role in cellular regulation. Science **207**, 19-27.

Clark, C.R. and Hall, M.D. (1986). Hormone receptor autoradiography: recent developments. Trends in Biochemical Sciences **11**, 195-199.

Elliott, D.C., Batchelor, S.M., Cassar, R.A., and Marinos, N.G. (1983). Calmodulin-binding drugs affect responses to cytokinin, auxin and gibberellic acid. Plant Physiology **72**, 219-224.

Gronemeyer, H. (1985). Photoaffinity labelling of steroid hormone binding sites. Trends in Biochemical Sciences **10**, 264-267.

Hadley, M.E. (1984) "Endocrinology". p 547, Prentice-Hall, Englewood Cliffs.

Hardy, R.N. (1981). "Endocrine Physiology", p 174. University Park Press, Baltimore.

Hasenstein, K.H. and Evans, M.L. (1986). Calcium dependence of rapid auxin action in maize roots. Plant Physiology **81**, 439-443.

Hirata, F. and Axelrod, J. (1980). Phospholipid methylation and biological signal transmission'. Science **209**, 1082-1090.

Jaffe, M.J. (1970). Evidence for the regulation of phytochrome-mediated processes in bean roots by the neurohumor, acetylcholine. Plant Physiology **46**, 769-777.

Jaffe, M.J. and Bridle, K. A new strategy for the identification of native plant photoperiodically regulated flowering substances. In "Manipulation of Flowering" (J.G. Atherton ed.). Butterworth, London (in press).

Joseph, S.K. (1984). Inositol trisphosphate: an intracellular messenger produced by Ca^{2+} mobilizing hormones. Trends in Biochemical Sciences 9, 420-421.

Kelly, G.J. (1984). Calcium, calmodulin and the action of plant hormones. Trends in Biochemical Sciences 9, 4-5.

Kolata, G. (1982). New theory of hormones proposed. Science 215, 1383-1384.

Lapage-Dequiry, M.T., Bidard, J.N., Rouier, E., Bulard, C. and Lazdunsliu, M. (1986). Presence of abscisic acid, a phytohormone, in the mammalian brain. Proceedings of the National Academy of Sciences (USA) 83, 1155-1158.

Leopold, A.C. (1972). Ethylene as a plant hormone. In "Hormonal Regulation in Plant Growth and Development", (H. Kaldewey and Y. Vardar eds.), pp 245-262. Verlag Chemie, Weinheim.

Leopold, A.C. and Noodén, L.D. (1984). Hormonal regulatory systems in plants. In "Hormonal Regulation of Development II. The Functions of Hormones from the Level of the Cell to the Whole Plant", Encyclopaedia of Plant Physiology New Series Vol 10 (T.K. Scott ed.), pp 4-22. Springer-Verlag, Berlin.

Leopold, A.C., Poovaiah, B.W., dela Fuente, R.K. and Williams, R.J. (1974). Regulation of growth with inorganic solutes. In "Plant Growth Substances 1973" (Y. Masuda, ed.), pp 780-788. Hirokawa Publ. Co., Tokyo.

McCormack, J.G. and Denton, R.M. (1986). Ca^{++} as a second messenger within mitochondria. Trends in Biochemical Sciences 11, 258-262.

Michell, B. and Houslay, M. (1986). Pleiotropic responses: regulation by programmable messengers on by multiple receptors? Trends in Biochemical Sciences 11, 239-241.

Nishikuza, Y. (1986). Studies and perspectives of protein kinase C. Science 233, 305-312.

Poovaiah, B.W. and Leopold, A.C. (1976). Effects of inorganic solutes on the binding of auxin. Plant Physiology 58, 783-785.

Ray, P.M., Dohrmann, V. and Hertel, R. (1977). Characterization of naphthaleneacetic acid binding to receptor sites on cellular membranes of maize coleoptile tissue. Plant Physiology 59, 357-364.

Roth, J., LeRoith, D., Shiloach, J., Rosenzweig, J.L., Lesniak, M.A., and Havrankova, J. (1982). The evolutionary origin of hormones. New England Journal of Medicine 306, 523-527.

Roux, S.J. and Slocum, R.D. (1982). Role of calcium in mediating functions important for growth and development in plants. In "Calcium and Cell Function" Vol 3 (W.Y. Cheung, ed.), pp 409-453. Academic Press, New York.

Stumpf, W.E. and Roth, L.J. (1966). High resolution radiography with dry mounted freeze-dried frozen sections. Journal of Histochemistry and Cytochemistry 14, 274-257.

Savin, C.T. (1969). "The Hormones". Little Brown, Boston.

Trewavas, A.J. (1982). Growth substance sensitivity: the limiting factor in plant development. Physiologia Plantarium 55, 60-72.

Turner, C.D. and Bagnara, J.T. (1971). "General Endocrinology". W.B. Saunders, Philadelphia.

Wang, J.L. and Hsu, Y.M. (1986). Negative regulation of cell growth. Trends in Biochemical Sciences 11, 24-26.

Warner, H.L. and Leopold, A.C. (1969). Timing of plant hormone responses in etiolated pea seedlings. Biochemical and Biophysical Research Communications 44, 989-994.

SECTION I

CONCEPTUAL FRAMEWORK - FROM THE WHOLE PLANT TO THE MOLECULAR

SENSITIVITY AND SENSORY ADAPTATION IN GROWTH SUBSTANCE RESPONSES

A. Trewavas

Botany Department, University of Edinburgh, King's Buildings, Mayfield Road, Edinburgh EH9 3JH, Scotland

It is a commonly-held view that growth substances act pivotally in plant growth and development. The effects of exogenously-added growth substances and biosynthesis mutants represent the main experimental support for such a notion. The thesis of this article is that instead, growth substances are sensitive controllers of development only under certain discrete circumstances. These conditions, which are characteristically poor for growth, are characterised by specific imbalance(s) (starvation) for particular resources; they lead to phenotypic and developmental plasticity. In poor growth conditions the competition for resources between the growing tissues or between polarities of growth or specific metabolic processes is intensified; those which incorporate the extra stimulus of a growth substance survive the competitive conditions more effectively. As a result the balance of developmental processes is altered and growing tissues may become thinner or thicker, the result of coupling of one or other growth polarities to a growth substance. In well-nourished plants specific tissues acquire the capability to synthesise growth substances and sensitivity to specific growth substances ontogenetically. But in these well-nourished conditions the contribution of the growth substance to growth or other acts of development is essential but insensitive and therefore not controlling. It may be possible to associate specific growth substances with specific resource starvation. Thus auxin and gibberellin may be associated with carbohydrate and amino acid and starvation in etiolated and green plants respectively, cytokinin with nitrogen starvation, abscisic acid with water and ethylene with ATP (O_2) starvation.

REASONS FOR HAVING GROWTH SUBSTANCES

A broad array of chemicals and treatments can be used to modify many (and probably all) aspects of plant development (Trewavas, 1986a). For example, the promotion of adventitious root formation or breakage of seed dormancy may be accelerated by acids, growth substances, respiratory inhibitors, SH group reagents, electron donors such as nitrate, hydrophobic chemicals like ethanol or chloroform, sucrose, minerals, gases of varying types and environmental treatments such as temperature variation, wounding, osmotic shocks of varying kinds and so on.

Certain critical deductions can be made from these observations.

1. The nature of the response is built into the system and does not require an unusual specific inducing chemical.

2. When cells are predisposed to a particular developmental pathway, metabolic perturbation at a variety of places can induce or accelerate developmental progress.

3. There is no one obligatory molecular sequence underlying developmental progress. A particular physiological state can be achieved from a number of

different molecular directions. Induction of developmental by exogenous molecules cannot be equated with endogenous control.

What then is the function of mobile molecules like growth substances in development? These observations indicate it to be more subtle than the all-embracing control frequently espoused.

The critical feature to growth substances control is surely the requirement for a discriminating protein receptor. Thus it becomes easy to render some tissues or processes sensitive to a functioning growth substance system. On experiencing poor environmental conditions a co-ordinated set of limited metabolic and tissue changes can be elicited when needed. Only specific parts or metabolic reactions of the organism respond, even though all cells experience the change in circulating ions, growth substances and other molecules resulting from the environmental perturbation. In this context it seems significant that specific growth substances are often associated with promotive actions on specific tissues or groups of tissues, e.g. cytokinins with leaves, gibberellins with stems, and with inhibitory effects on others, e.g. cytokinins with stems, auxin with roots.

There are two ways in which this functional change can happen. Firstly, an active way. The co-ordinated growth substance system simply isn't operating and is switched on as a result of specific environmental perturbation. This is the hormonal model and is usually thought to operate via a change in growth substance concentration. Secondly and alternatively, the system is always functioning but it is not a sensitive control under normal well-nourished conditions. Environmental perturbations eliciting the response do so by stripping away other masking processes, leaving the growth substance-coupled reactions as a greater contributor, a more sensitive control of specific developmental processes. I believe the evidence favours the latter because even in well-nourished plants the biosynthesis of growth substances and responsiveness of tissues can be experimentally detected.

THE NECESSITY FOR OBTAINING SENSITIVE CONTROLS

'Control' is the sum total of metabolic and extracellular changes which contribute to any act of development. In turn, 'control strength' (or 'sensitivity to control') measures the individual contribution to overall control of any one process or chemical. Theoretically, control strength can be measured by making tiny changes in the contributing component (or altering the flux of a contributing process) and measuring the effect on the whole. Carried out over the complete spectrum of contributing chemicals and processes this would represent a sensitivity analysis.

An individual 'sensitivity to control' is not a constant property but depends on the state of the whole metabolic network. As the character of the network changes, as overall metabolic fluxes increase or decrease, individual control strengths may vary from strong (sensitive controls) to weak (insensitive controls, essential factors) or vice-versa (Trewavas, 1986a). Under any metabolic conditions, complete removal or gross elevation of a weakly-controlling component may considerably modify the overall process. Modification in itself is not an adequate justification for assuming a component to contribute strongly to overall control. This can only be assessed within the limits set by normal short term variation in the component. Thus the developmental modifications instituted by biosynthesis mutants or exogenously-added growth substance do not permit assessments to be made of the strength of controls unless they accurately mimic endogenous variation.

Fig. 1 shows a dose-response curve (ethylene versus seed germination) drawn perhaps unusually as concentration against effect. The data are calculated from Schonbeck and Egley (1981a). I have divided the curve into 2 regions, a sensitive region (S) and an insensitive region (I). In the sensitive region (covering some 20% of the total biological response) the unit of biological response/increment of ethylene change is up to 6 fold higher than in the insensitive region. The dose-response curve spans 3 orders of magnitude although only two orders are shown here. It could be any one of a number of growth substance dose response curves which in general are very broad (Nissen, 1985; Trewavas, 1981).

The data in Fig. 1 do not strike me as indicating a true control of germination by ethylene. However, removal of ethylene (by absorption or chemical competition) certainly impairs germination in seeds incorporating ethylene (Ketring, 1977) and dormant seeds synthesise ethylene, which is also present in many soils as a result of synthesis by fungi and bacteria. Ethylene can then be regarded as an essential factor in appropriate seeds but it is not a controlling factor under many of the germination circumstances investigated. This distinction is a very important one since it forms the basis of much of the criticism of the hormonal model. Being an essential factor and being coupled to certain early growth events in germination, removal of ethylene leads to impairment or even complete inhibition of germination. Thus these ethylene-coupled growth events are always part of the germination process regardless of circumstances; but they do not act to control the process with any sensitivity under these conditions. A biosynthesis mutant would not discriminate a sensitive control from an essential factor.

Why is this particular (and other) growth substance dose response so insensitive? I suspect it is because the rest of the metabolism of the embryo cells is not in step with the specific metabolic changes induced by ethylene under the circumstances examined. If you like, the analogy is a key which doesn't properly fit the lock; with a lot of effort it can be turned. If the key fits properly then little effort is required to turn and unlock. On our dose-response curve, the analogous latter situation would be when most of the biological respone (80-100%) is in the sensitive region. In addition we might expect the dose response to start perhaps at a lower ethylene concentration; since there is less resistance to turning the key. We expect control systems to work with reasonable sensitivity; if they don't, it's unlikely they are true controls.

The distinction between an essential factor and a controlling factor can be shown with an example from photosynthesis. Chlorophyll functions critically in photosynthesis and bleached or etiolated plants do not photosynthesise. However, much work in the earlier part of this century failed to establish any meaningful variation between assimilation rates and chlorophyll contents of appropriately examined leaves under many conditions (Stiles, 1950). The equivalent situation is very common between growth substance levels and development. We understand why in photosynthesis. Many molecules and processes contribute to the control of assimilation rates and control shifts continually between different elements of the system as conditions change. Under normal photosynthesising conditions, chlorophyll is an essential factor but an insensitive control. In contrast, chlorophyll content can be made a sensitive element in photosynthetic control if the process is carried out in a low light. Under these conditions the rate of capture of light energy more significantly constrains overall photosynthetic flux; it forms a greater contribution to the total metabolic control of the overall assimilation process. Variation in chlorophyll content would have a significant influence on assimilation rates.

Using this analogy we can see that changing the metabolic conditions or metabolic environment in which a growth substance response is examined may turn it from being an insensitive, but essential factor, to a sensitively-contributing component of development. There will probably be one metabolic configuration produced by a specific environmental perturbation in which growth substance-coupled reactions contribute to growth or development with greatest sensitivity. Sensibly, these are the environmental conditions which the growth substance systems evolved to help mitigate. So far as I can see they are conditions of poor growth; that is when resources arrive in unbalanced proportions for optimal growth. In these circumstances the competition for resources between various growing tissues or processes is heightened.

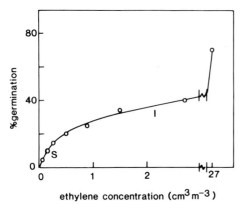

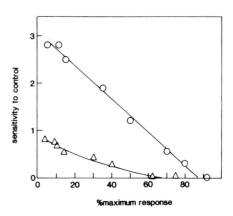

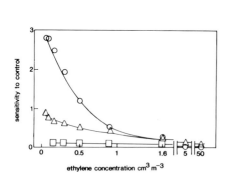

Fig. 1 Variation of seed germination (as % total) plotted against ethylene concentration. Data calculated from Schonbeck and Egley (1980).

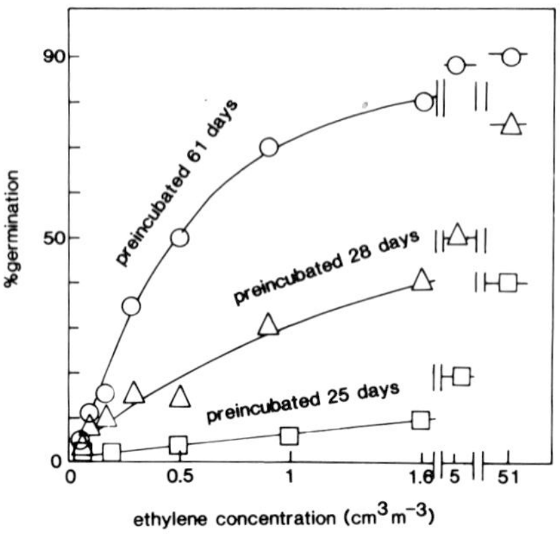

Fig. 2a Variation of Amaranthus seed germination with ethylene concentration on seed preincubated for 25, 28 and 61 days at 35°. Data calculated from Schonbeck and Egley (1981a).

Fig. 2b Variation of 'sensitivity to control' of germination with ethylene concentration. Symbols the same as Fig. 2a. 'Sensitivity to control' (arbitrary units) is calculated as germination response/unit ethylene change.

Fig. 2c Sensitivity to control of 61 day and 28 day preincubated seeds plotted against % maximum germination. Symbols the same as Fig. 2a.

To return to Fig. 1, ethylene does not control germination per se but may be a sensitive control of germination under a discrete set of circumstances. Dose-response curves enable us to define those circumstances. We have to look for conditions which initiate response at the lowest concentration and which give the steepest biological response against effector concentration.

MISLEADING USE OF THE TERM LIMITING FACTORS

Growth substances are often described as limiting factors. The term is misleadingly used in two ways. Firstly, it is used if an exogenously-applied chemical has an effect. With so many chemicals promoting developmental processes the term (to me) has little meaning. Secondly, growth substances are called limiting to imply a dominant position in a control hierarchy. How else could a hormone function unless it always over-rode everything else or so it is thought? This use of the term limiting fits a common simple (simplistic) model that supposes complex physiological processes to be regulated by one or two specific chemicals; an idea we can trace through concepts like phyllocaline, rhizocaline and later florigen.

A more correct use of the term limiting is to apply it to the asymptote to the curve in Fig. 1 running through the origin. At least here there is some possibility that ethylene limits germination. In complex metabolic networks however this 'limiting' situation never seems to be reached. That is why, for example, many substances can be used to break seed dormancy just as a variety of sugars (and probably many other chemicals) can be used to promote dwarf pea growth as well as gibberellin (Broughton and McComb, 1971). Complex networks are only stably regulated at many places. The way to examine their control is a sensitivity analysis (Trewavas, 1986b).

CONDITIONS INVOKING MAXIMUM GROWTH SUBSTANCE SENSITIVITY.   SOME CASE HISTORIES.

1 Seed Germination and Ethylene

Fig. 2a shows three dose response curves of Amaranthus seed germination versus ethylene with three germination pretreatment times at 35° (Schonbeck and Egley, 1981a). The two lower curves are good examples of insensitive control spanning many orders of magnitude and are included because they are like many dose-response curves in the literature (Nissen, 1985). The upper curve (a 61 day pretreatment at high temperature) is very different because it is clearly a much more sensitive response to ethylene. To emphasise this difference I have plotted the slope of the 3 curves at various ethylene concentrations in Fig. 2b. The slope measures the 'sensitivity to control'; in other words the responsiveness of the system to a change in ethylene concentration. Note that reasonable 'sensitivity to control' operates only over an order of magnitude change in ethylene and that differences between the three pretreatments are really only distinguishable in this part of the response. Initially the 61 day pretreatment is 4 times more 'sensitive to control' than the 28 day pretreatment and 20-30 fold higher than the 25 day pretreatment. Yet note again from Fig. 2a that substantial seed germination is induced in all three pretreated seed batches by the higher concentrations of ethylene. Indeed the dose-response curves of the 25 and 8 day pretreatments are almost certainly unfinished and probably span 4 orders of magnitude if not more. Fig. 2c shows a plot of sensitivity to control against the % maximum response induced. The straight line of the 61 day pretreatment contrasts strongly with the shallow curve of the 28 day sample.

Fig. 3a and b show data (Schonbeck and Egley, 1981a,b) again on Amaranthus seed germination/ethylene but with the data plotted as probits against log ethylene concentration. The advantage of this 'probit' procedure is that it linearises an S-shaped curve. Changes in sensitivity are thus easily seen as a simple change in the slope of a line and lines are also easier to fit accurately to data. Probits

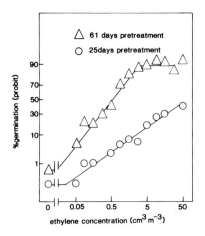

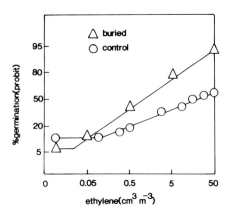

Fig. 3a Variation of % Amaranthus seed
germination calculated as probits and
plotted on probability paper against
logarithm ethylene concentration with
seed preincubation of 61 or 25 days at
35°. These should be compared with
'sensitivity to control' data shown in
Fig. 2b. Data calculated from
Schonbeck and Egley (1981a).

Fig. 3b Variation in probit of %
Amaranthus seed germination against
logarithm ethylene concentration on
seed buried for 5 months compared to
zero time controls. Data calculated
from Schonbeck and Egley (1981a).

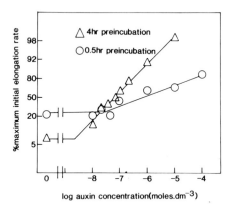

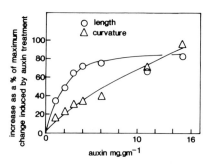

Fig. 4a Variation of initial elongation
rate of excised wheat coleoptile
sections preincubated for 0.5 or 4 hours
before auxin addition. Elongation rates
have been expressed as a % maximum
(nominally 98%) and plotted on a
probability scale to linearise the
normal S shaped curve. Data calculated
from McDowall and Sirois (1977) and note
similar data in Vesper and Evans (1978).

Fig. 4b Effect of auxin on the growth
rate of curvature of intact coleoptiles.
Growth rate and curvature expressed as
% maximum observed. Data calculated
from Bastin et al. (1986).

are normally only used for quantal responses (e.g. a seed does or does not germinate) but if we hypothesise a certain growth process as resulting from permanent occupation of a certain percent of receptors (a receptor is or is not occupied, and summed over a period of time this is a reasonable view) then ordinary growth responses can be drawn in the same way. I have done this later because it clarifies the assessment of information. Fig. 3a (the 61 day and 25 day pretreatment) is included to show that only slight changes in probit slope are the result of the very considerable changes in sensitivity to control shown in Fig. 2b.

Egley's group (Schonbeck and Egley, 1980, 1981a,b) have examined the effects of a number of seed treatments on ethylene responsiveness. Conditions under which sensitivity is enhanced (i.e. steeper dose response) are burial in the imbibed state, inappropriate temperatures for germination and low water availability for germination. These are all poor growth conditions since all can induce secondary dormancy. However ethylene is coupled to certain growth events in early germination. The implication is that ethylene maintains these growth events in seeds which germinate under conditions normally inimical to their progress. The data of Fig. 2 show that seeds prepare for this eventuality by metabolic changes leading to sensory adaptation. Thus the use of ethylene widens the ecological circumstances under which Amaranthus seeds can germinate. Burdett (1972) showed that lettuce seeds with high temperature pretreatments synthesise ethylene at only a 3-4 fold higher rate (compare this with a 20-fold change at least in sensitivity to control). The biosynthetic pathway and responsiveness to ethylene are clearly always present in these seeds. Only under appropriate condition does sensory adaptation occur to make ethylene a meaningful control. These poor growth conditions may simply impair respiration leading to ATP deprivation. There is a necessity for accelerating reactions which circumvent this critical limitation in order for radicle protrusion to commence (Trewavas, 1986a).

2 Coleoptile Growth and Auxin

Fig. 4a shows dose-response curves of excised coleoptile section growth to auxin when freshly excised sections are preincubated either half-an-hour or four hours (McDowall and Sirois, 1977). The latter are markedly more sensitive to auxin and I interpret this to be the result of starvation induced by excision from the seed. Excised sections incubated on their own in the absence of auxin can resume growth after 2-3 hours at a rate little short of optimal auxin effects (see data for example in Kutschera and Schopfer, 1985). This results from a change in sensitivity to auxin (Vesper and Evans, 1978), not in auxin content as mistakenly referred to by Kutschera and Schopfer (1985). Skoog (1937) showed that deseeding (i.e. starving) oat seedlings for 24 hours increased their subsequent sensitivity to auxin by an order of magnitude.

The half-hour curve is probably representative of the sensitivity of the (relatively) well-nourished intact coleoptile on the seedling. All those who have applied auxin to intact plants find it necessary to use very high concentrations (about 10^{-4} moles.dm^{-3}) to get an effect (e.g. Ball and Dyke, 1956). From the dose response data of Baskin et al., 1986 the response (70 and 85% of maximum growth) between 1 and 10 mg gm^{-1} auxin almost exactly matches the last 2 points on the half-hour line. Hatfield and Lamotte (1984) used decapitated but otherwise intact coleoptiles and could only demonstrate growth promotion at high auxin concentrations, mimicking the half-hour dose-response curve of McDowall and Sirois (1977) and others. In an intact (relatively) well-nourished coleoptile auxin is therefore an essential but insensitive control of growth. This was concluded by Mer (1969) many years ago (note that Mer (1959) obtained only a total of 10% increase in coleoptile length after many days incubation of oat seedlings in auxin solutions).

Under starvation conditions, probably not an infrequent state for a seedling which has experienced lengthy buried dormancy, competition between the shoot and root for endosperm growth resources is intensified. Etiolated stem tissues put their growth resources into height rather than thickness under these conditions. The stem becomes thinner (Trewavas, 1986a and references in Gould et al., 1934) and root growth is diminished. Coleoptile sections grown in the absence of carbohydrate have thinner cell walls (Ray, 1962). Starvation, then, initiates sensory adaptation making auxin a sensitive contribution to the growth of the shoot. Auxin is coupled to the vertical polarity of shoot growth, ensuring the better maintenance of height but at the expense of thickness and root growth. This is a clear cut example of phenotypic plasticity.

Fig. 4b shows the dose-response data of Baskin et al. (1986) for either coleoptile elongation or curvature induced by auxin applied to intact coleoptiles. It should be compared with Fig. 2a. Curvature is clearly much less sensitive than growth to auxin application and this highlights the difficulty in identifying a highly mobile molecule, like auxin, with a function (differential growth) which would be better served by relative immobility. Fig. 4b shows that very substantial gradients of auxin are necessary to get reasonable curvature. If, as frequently proposed, gradients of auxin of 2:1 across tropically stimulated tissues are sufficient to mimic the bending response, proponents (e.g. Pickard, 1985) should show that application of such a gradient will induce the appropriate curvature. These results imply that much more is needed than a simple auxin gradient.

3 Amylase Production by the Aleurone

Fig. 5 shows dose responses of barley aleurone amylase production to gibberellin in seed grown under malting conditions (partly anaerobic and lower temperature) and normal aerobic laboratory conditions (Groat and Briggs, 1969). Malting conditions are generally poor for embryo growth and Fig. 5 shows that sensory adaptation occurs under these conditions making the aleurone much more sensitive to gibberellin control. (These poor metabolic conditions might be mimicked by, for example, aleurone protoplast preparation). Treatment of intact barley seed with gibberellin under good aerobic germination conditions leads to only slight increases in accumulated amylase (Briggs, 1968); as would be expected if gibberellin is an essential but insensitive control under these circumstances.

There are many cases known where amylase production cannot be easily related to gibberellin variations (e.g. de-embryonated seeds with synthesise amylase, (Naylor, 1983) or parental environmental treatments which obviate gibberellin control in the subsequent seed (Nicholls, 1982) and others (Trewavas, 1982)). At various times carbohydrates, amino acids, fatty acids and minerals have all been shown to affect amylase production (Jones and Armstrong, 1971; Buller et al., 1976; Trewavas, 1982). More significantly the scutellum has been shown to secrete enzymes which will modify the endosperm level of all of these (Dure, 1960; Okamoto et al., 1980; Gibbons, 1981; Fujikura and Baisted, 1983). In addition the scutellum can provide up to 50% of the amylase (Gibbons, 1981) and the synthesis is gibberellin independent (Simpson, 1966). Briggs (1968) showed that scutellar amylase synthesis is far less sensitive to water deprivation than aleurone amylase. Aleurone dose-response curves to abscisic acid could prove informative if carried out on water-deprived half seeds.

The function of gibberellin in controlling aleurone activity is obviously far more subtle than the blunt reserve-mobilising function often quoted. If is one of a complex mixture of substances controlled and secreted by the scutellum which are concerned with events in early germination. But under normal aerobic conditions it is an insensitive control. Aerobically germinating barley and oat embryos both synthesise gibberellic acid (Groat and Briggs, 1969; Metzger, 1983).

4 Embyro Growth, Gibberellin and Carbohydrate Starvation

Fig. 6a shows dose response curves of coleoptile growth of excised oat embryos responding to gibberellin in the presence and absence of sucrose (Simpson, 1965).

This early coleoptile growth is much more sensitive to control by gibberellin when starved of carbohydrate. In the absence of sucrose, gibberellin-induced growth was virtually confined to the shoot; in its presence shoot and root growth was about equal. Thus when competition for carbohydrate resources is severe, shoot growth with its additional gibberellin component is maintained, aiding an eventual search for light. This is accomplished by sensory adaptation following starvation, making gibberellin a sensitive control.

Freshly-germinating cereal seeds frequently show a dip in soluble carbohydrate in the endosperm about 24 hours after imbibition (Trewavas, 1982). After long periods of imbibed dormancy the freely-available carbohydrate for rapid germination may be even lower. Embryo carbohydrate starvation may thus represent a recurring metabolic problem in some germinating grass seeds.

There is evidence that the presence of sugar impairs gibberellin synthesis in isolated (i.e. starved) embryos (Radley, 1967) by about 2-fold, with a slightly bigger effect on scutellar gibberellin. The presence of an embryo axis, a sink for carbohydrate and a tissue which rapidly converts sugar to starch during imbibition (Trewavas, 1982) increases gibberellin synthesis by the scutellum (Radley, 1969).

Naylor and Simpson (1961) provide evidence that gibberellin-coupled growth reactions in Avena fatua involve a 'carbohydrate-sparing' effect. Embryos given gibberellin metabolise far less sucrose than their untreated counterparts. We would expect gibberellin-coupled processes to represent a sensitive control of growth only when carbohydrate is short. A gibberellin requirement for germination of Avena fatua could also be lowered 3-4 orders of magnitude by addition of sucrose (Naylor and Simpson, 1961).

Fig. 6b shows dose response curves of barley aleurone amylase production in the presence or absence of an osmoticum (PEG) (Jones, 1969). It is known that PEG mimics the accumulation of very substantial carbohydrate levels in the endosperm (up to 0.5 M) in early germination. In the absence of carbohydrate (carbohydrate starvation), then gibberellin becomes a more sensitive control of aleurone amylase synthesis. Jones and Armstrong (1971) show that the presence of substantial carbohydrate levels in the endosperm leads to sensory adaptation of the aleurone, reducing responsiveness to gibberellin.

5 Stomatal Closure and Abscisic Acid

Fig. 7 shows a dose response curve of stomatal aperture to abscisic acid of cotton plants grown under normal conditions or deficient in N or P (Radin et al., 1982; Radin, 1984). Deficiency of these two elements increases sensitivity to ABA by an order of magnitude. In addition ABA-induced stomatal closure is remarkably sensitive to antagonism by cytokinin (total dose-response an order of magnitude) but only in the deficient plants. High temperature also increases stomatal aperture sensitivity to abscisic acid.

Although a great deal of work associates stomatal aperture with abscisic acid there is good reason to doubt any simple relationship. In all short-term stress treatments (most of which are experimentally vigorous, excessive and unlike field water-stress conditions) stomata close before detectable changes in abscisic acid level (Trewavas, 1981; Radin and Ackerson, 1982). Attempts to explain this difficulty by a re-partitioning of ABA are frankly not very convincing, involving assumptions that 50% changes are significant. The important point is that there are alternative methods of closing stomata in water-stressed leaves. One of these is change in sensitivity to abscisic acid itself. Both Davies (1978) and Ackerson (1980) clearly show that water stress makes stomata more sensitive to abscisic acid in the short term. Longer term changes resulting from water stress seem to make stomata more resistant to closure during subsequent periods of water stress. Plants deficient in N and P seem to suffer continual slight water stress and it could be this that potentiates the responsiveness shown in Fig. 7. Deficiency of N

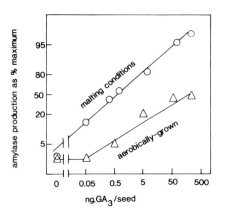

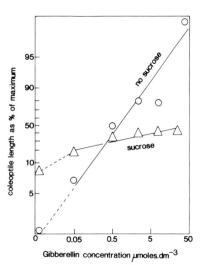

Fig. 5 Variation of barely aleurone amylase production against logarithm of gibberellin (applied as droplets) on de-embryonated but otherwise intact barley seed. Seed pretreated either under malting conditions or germinated aerobically. Amylase production calculated as % maximum (nominally 98%) and plotted on a probability scale. Data calculated from Groat and Briggs (1969).

Fig. 6a Variation in coleoptile length of excised embryos of Avena fatua grown in the presence and absence of 4% sucrose and various gibberellin concentrations. Coleoptile length expressed as % maximum and plotted on a probability scale against logarithm gibberellin concentration. Data calculated from Simpson (1965).

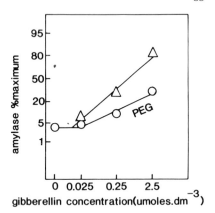

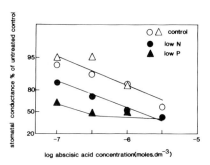

Fig. 6b Variation of barley aleurone amylase production against gibberellin concentration. Aleurones incubated in the presence or absence of polyethylene glycol (PEG). Amylase expressed as % maximum (nominally 95%) and plotted on a probability scale against lograithm gibberellin concentration. Data calculated from Jones (1969).

Fig. 7 Variation of stomatal conductance against abscisic acid concentration of cotton plants grown in low N or P. Stomatal conductance expressed as % maximum aperture (100%) and plotted on a probability scale against lograrithm applied abscisic acid. Data calculated from Radin et al. (1982) and Radin (1984).

28

increases ABA levels by only some 50% (Radin et al., 1982).

The stomatal aperture/ABA hypothesis leans heavily on excised leaf experiments for its assumption of sensitive control by ABA. But it takes little account of the possible metabolic perturbations which this experimental treatment involves. Excision of leaves initiates stomatal aperture fluctuations potentiating the system towards change (Heber et al., 1986). Placing petioles in 10^{-4} moles.dm^{-3} ABA leads to stomatal closure within 5-10 minutes. But after a further 2-3 hours incubation, stomata re-open even though leaf ABA levels are maximal (Dorffling et al., 1979). At the least this observation suggests that ABA on its own is an unsuitable molecule for long term stomatal aperture control and suggests sensory adaptation to ABA making control insensitive. Other metabolic changes (i.e. sensitivity) are necessary to accommodate water stress phenomena and keep stomata closed. It also suggests that excision initiates leaf metabolic adaptation rather in the same way an excised coleoptile section will show a growth resurgence after 2-3 hours. Leaf excision initiates new programmes of development, leading to senescence (which can be inhibited by N), and the appearance of sensitivity to cytokinin of this process. Some of these metabolic changes may partially mimic the effects of nutrient stress themselves. Taken at its face value the data of Jones and Mansfield (1970) suggest stomata of excised leaves to be far more sensitive to abscisic acid than stomata on leaves of intact plants.

Stomatal aperture change may merely by an experimental reflection of a much more profound metabolic and physiological adaptation to lowered water availability. Some plants which are water-stressed undergo a variety of growth adjustments which lead to fewer, smaller, xeromorphic type leaves, a reduction of shoot growth (with a thicker stem) and increased root development. The normal competition between root and shoot growth for water tilts in favour of root growth, perhaps using the excess photosynthate released from inhibited shoot growth. The xeromorphic type leaf is thicker, with reduced aerenchyma content and leaf area, the cells have thicker walls, are smaller with reduced vacuolation and an accumulation of solutes. These are identical to the changes described by us as initiated by ABA application to Spirodela, a water plant (Smart and Trewavas, 1983). In part, they may simply result from an emphasis on the vertical polarity of leaf growth at the considerable expense of the horizontal area polarity. Potamageton plants treated with ABA show a similar production of much thicker, smaller leaves (Anderson, 1978); Seidlova et al., (1981) showed a similar change towards the thickness polarity in the ABA treated shoot apex. Abscisic acid coupled-reactions help arbitrate resource allocation between these (competitive) growth polarities when the complex of metabolic reactions associated with water starvation are initiated.

Plants deficient in N share some similar morphological changes with water-stressed plants (increased apical dominance, with fewer, smaller leaves, and stems shorter and thicker) but there are differences, (N deficient plants have thinner leaves, for example) (Hunt et al., 1985).

6 Pea Internode Elongation and Gibberellin

Figs. 8a and b show dose-response curves for dwarf pea internode elongation to gibberellin in conditions of nutrient starvation or in comparing green to etiolated stems. Both (green) starved and etiolated tissues are clearly more sensitive. Etiolated tissues generally have a poorly-developed vascular system and the growing region of pea epicotyls, remote as it is from the cotyledons, will probably experience starvation for growth resources. A simple interpretation of this is that gibberellin is used to arbitrate resource diversion between pea leaves and stem when resources are scarce, e.g. in low-light intensity. The critical resource starvation may be for carbohydrate and the presence of gibberellin ensures some maintenance of height at the expense of leaf growth. However, this set of events involves sensory adaptation to gibberellin making gibberellin a sensitive control. Both etiolated and green pea tissues synthesise gibberellin (Sponsel, 1986) with little difference, qualitatively, and slightly higher quantities in de-etiolated

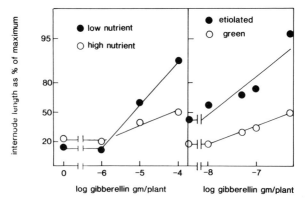

Fig. 8a Internode length of dwarf peas treated with gibberellin grown on high and low nutrient levels. Data calculated from Sprent (1966).

Fig. 8b Internode length of etiolated or red light grown dwarf peas against gibberellin GA_1 concentration. Etiolated plants treated with AMO 1618 before assay. Data calculated from Sponsel (1986). In both Figs. 8a and b internode length calculated as % maximum (nominally 95%) and plotted on a probability scale against logarithm applied gibberellin.

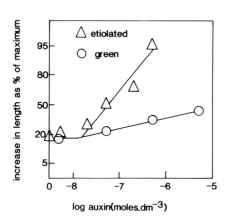

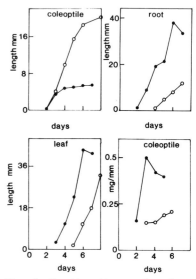

Fig. 8c Variation of excised pea internode length of green and etiolated peas grown in various auxin concentrations. Data calculated from Galston and Kaur and Length expressed as % maximum (nominally 95%) and plotted on a probability scale against logarithm auxin concentration.

Fig. 9 Growth patterns of various tissues of rice seedlings grown under water (open symbols) or in moist air (filled symbols) at 25°. Note the thinner pattern of growth in the coleoptile grown under water.

peas. Gibberellin is coupled to the processes of vertical growth polarity (Sommer, 1961; Shibaoka, 1972, 1974) rather than horizontal (thickness) polarity. Treatment of dwarf peas with gibberellin leads to thinner stems. This is likewise a characteristic of infection by Gibberella fujikuroi.

Gibberellin is not the only substance capable of promoting length in pea. Broughton and McComb (1971) showed that gibberellin effects on internode length could be mimicked by many sugars. However careful examination of their data shows that sugar-promoted growth produces a thicker internode than gibberellin. Such observations complicate any facile conclusion concerning biochemical differences between talls and dwarfs based on grafting data (e.g. Reid et al., 1983). Whether dwarfs and talls differ radically in gibberellin synthetic capability seems at present controversial, since the types of gibberellin and their approximate amounts in both types seem to be the same, although their metabolism may be different (Sponsel, 1986). However talls and dwarfs differ markedly in their response to GA_{20} (Sponsel, 1986). In the absence of information concerning the sterospecific capabilities of the gibberellin receptive site, it seems as likely that a change in sensitivity to gibberellin may be responsible for the dwarf/tall difference as any other. The most active gibberellin in the dwarf pea is GA_3 so the receptive site cannot have the absolute discrimination for GA_1 often claimed.

There are many observations that morphogenetically-active light changes the sensitivity of plant tissues to applied growth substances. The literature is too extensive to include here but Fig. 8c shows one example.

7 Other Examples of Change in Sensitivity

There are many other cases in the literature, where we can anticipate dose-response analysis will show some form of specific starvation to initiate sensory adaptation when it is carried out. Thus young attached fruits, abscission zones, or attached flowers seem far less sensitive to ethylene than their excised counterparts (Burg and Burg, 1965; Beyer, 1975; Halevy and Mayak, 1981) since they synthesise ethylene at a rate which would induce ripening, abscission, or senescence after excision. In this context the very different climacteric characteristics between attached and detached fruit should be noted (Hulme and Rhodes, 1971). The sensitivity of petal and corolla abscission or pollinated flowers to ethylene is much higher than unpollinated flowers (Halevy et al., 1984; Mor et al., 1985). Mature cells in an intact plant are insensitive to division initiation by auxin but are much more sensitive when induced to divide by wounding. Differential sensitivity to auxin is shown by the upper and lower petiole halves of leaves (Palmer, 1985). Attached leaves are insensitive to cytokinin compared to detached leaves (Trewavas, 1986a). Many other examples of clear sensitivity change during development have been detailed elsewhere (Trewavas, 1981; Trewavas, 1982).

THE RICE COLEOPTILE AS AN EXAMPLE OF THE FUNCTIONING OF GROWTH SUBSTANCES IN DEVELOPMENT

To draw together the threads of the argument I have chosen a case history which exemplifies many of the points made earlier. This is the germinating rice seedling, grown either in air or under water. The root and various shoot tissues of seedlings grown in air show some competitive character between themselves for endosperm-derived resources. If the growth of one is reduced the others increase. When grown in stagnant water, (a condition involving partial anaerobiosis), the amylase system functions poorly and competition for endosperm resources is intensified. It is the coleoptile and mesocotyl whose growth is maintained under these latter conditions. These continue growth (the coleoptile can be 3 times longer than air-grown equivalents) until the water surface is breached and the well-known snorkel effect permits the passage of oxygen to the root (Wada, 1961; Kordan, 1974; Takahashi, 1978). The main features of the growth pattern are shown in Fig. 9a-c. Vlamis and Davis (1943) used various partial pressures of oxygen below ambient and demonstrated that as the growth of the root diminished, in almost mirror image, the growth of the shoot was enhanced. This is a well-characterised example of phenotypic plasticity.

Ethylene is coupled as a promotive substance only to the growth of the mesocotyl/coleoptile and not (at this stage) to the leaf or roots. There are little dose-response data of growth against ethylene concentration but what are available show that under low partial pressures of oxygen, coleoptile growth rates are much more sensitive to ethylene control than growth rates of aerobically-grown coleoptiles (Ku et al., 1970). The dose-response curve is quite evidently steeper. But ethylene-coupled reactions still contribute to the growth of air-grown coleoptiles. This has been shown by the effects of AVG, ethylene removal and by the promotion of elongation by added ethylene. But overall growth is much less sensitive (Ishizawa and Esashi, 1983, 1984). Coleoptiles grown in stagnant water are 2-fold longer than those grown in static air but the ethylene content is only 50% higher (Ishizawa and Esashi, 1984), emphasising the contribution of a change in sensitivity. It should not be thought that ethylene is the only component of altered growth. Auxin, gibberellin, unknown effects of immersion, CO_2, K^+ and various amino acids and sugars contribute (Wada, 1961; Kefford, 1962; Ishizawa and Esashi, 1983, 1984).

What then is the function of ethylene in this system? Is it simply to arbitrate resources between the growth of the shoot and root? Careful examination of the data suggests that the critical function may be what is indicated in Fig. 9d. The anaerobically-grown coleoptile is thinner than its aerobically-grown counterpart. We have measured it; it is 0.16 mm compared to 0.22 mm in air. In addition it is full of aerenchyma. The data of Atwell et al. (1982) suggest this may be a specific function of ethylene acting as an arbitrator of resource diversion between the vertical and horizontal components of growth. Thus inhibition of ethylene-coupled reactions by silver ions inhibits length more than weight. Therefore when competition for resources is intense, ethylene-coupled reactions function to maintain the vertical growth polarity but at the expense of the horizontal. Maximal length is achieved (the ecological requirement) but at the expense of thickness. Many experiments show the polarity-altering effects of ethylene but the direction regulated is clearly tissue and plant specific (Marinos, 1960; Roberts et al., 1985). The primary environmental conditions invoking ethylene-sensitive growth is low oxygen tension. The metabolic effects of this environmental perturbation are extensive, with numerous qualitative changes in protein synthesis and the production of a cell wall structure specifically reduced in certain components (Zarra and Masuda, 1979). No doubt these are involved in the sensory adaptation to ethylene which accompanies immersion.

What we are dealing with here are very different metabolic and physiological situations; adaptation to different growth conditions, a situation in which respiratory resources (i.e. ATP) are limited (plants have a very poor Pasteur effect) and in which ethylene becomes a sensitive contributor, maintaining a vital growth component at the expense of others. But the system exhibits the characteristics described earlier which can now be generalised (Trewavas, 1986a). Phenotypic and developmental plasticity occurs as a result of physiological/metabolic adaptation in response to particular resource imbalances or resource competition. These plastic responses require the diversion of resources to one component of growth of one, or a number of, tissues so that leaf area or shoot height may be maintained at the expense of thickness (or vice versa). Alternatively shoot growth may be maintained at the expense of roots and so on. Growth substances are coupled to specific facets of growth to arbitrate resources between the two basic polarities and usually in specific tissues. Sensory adaptation under poor growth conditions enhances the contribution of growth substances to growth but the events they are normally coupled to are also expressed in well-nourished plants. Under these latter conditions they are, however, an insensitive control on the whole developmental event.

It may be possible to identify gibberellin with carbohydrate limitation, cytokinin with nitrate starvation (nitrogen starved plants have thinner leaves, effects which can be mimicked appropriately by cytokinins), and abscisic acid with water starvation, ethylene with ATP starvation and auxin with both carbohydrate and amino acid starvation (Trewavas, 1986a). Changes in growth polarities induced by growth substances are well-documented. The result is a co-ordinated set of growth and developmental changes designed to maximise resource capture or survival and thus eventual reproductive yield.

CONCLUSION

I have tried in this article to emphasise the necessity for sensitive controls of development in the context of growth substances. This can be justified from the optimality principles which underpin much of our biological thinking. These suggest that if there are a variety of ways of accomplishing the same result then natural selection will ensure the adoption of the most efficient. In this context the most sensitive means of control are optimal, and the conditions which elicit them, those in which endogenous growth substances function sensibly. Much confusion could be avoided if insistence was placed on demonstrating that a developmental effect produced by the modification of a growth regulator level represented a sensitive control. This could clearly only be defined in the context of measurements carried out on plants or tissues metabolically adjusted to a variety of circumstances. Dose-response curves expressed as shown here will help to define the optimal circumstance and thus clarify much of the apparent mystique behind present growth regulator concepts.

When some bacterial cells are starved they accumulate cyclic AMP effecting an active response. In this uncompartmentalised organism, cyclic AMP and the appropriate receptor have been evolved to fill a simple co-ordinating function. In the highly-compartmentalised plant cell an equivalent co-ordinate activation of even a few compartments would necessitate molecules with the facility of being easily distributed through intracellular membrane and aqueous phases. Chemically, growth substances are ideally designed for such intracellular 'growth factor' functions, although changes in sensitivity rather than growth substance level seem to predominate.

REFERENCES

Ackerson, R.C. (1980). Stomatal response of cotton to water stress and abscisic acid as affected by water stress history. Plant Physiology **65**, 455-459.

Anderson, L.W.J. (1978). Abscisic acid induces the formation of floating leaves in the heterophylous aquatic angiosperm Potamageton. Science **201**, 1135-1138.

Atwell, B.J., Waters, I. and Greenway, H. (1982). The effect of oxygen and turbulence on elongation of coleoptiles of submergence-tolerant and intolerant rice cultivars. Journal of Experimental Botany **33**, 1030-1044.

Ball, N.G. and Dyke, I.J. (1956). The effects of indole-3-acetic acid and 2,4 dichlorophenoxy acetic acid on the growth rate and endogenous rhythm of intact Avena coleoptiles. Journal of Experimental Botany **7**, 25-41.

Baskin, T.I., Briggs, W.R. and Iino, M. (1986). Can lateral redistribution of auxin account for phototropism of maize coleoptiles? Plant. Physiology **81**, 306-309.

Beyer, E.M. (1975). Abscission. The initial effect of ethylene is in the leaf blade. Plant Physiology **55**, 322-327.

Beyer, E.M. (1975). Abscission. The initial effect of ethylene is in the leaf blade. Plant Physiology 55, 322-327.

Briggs, D.E. (1968). α-amylase in germinating decorticated barley. Phytochemistry 7, 539-554.

Broughton, W.J. and McComb, A.J. (1971). Changes in the pattern of enzyme development in gibberellin-treated pea internodes. Annals of Botany 35, 213-228.

Buller, D.C., Parker, W. and Reid, J.S.G. (1976). Short chain fatty acids as inhibitors of gibberellin-induced amylolysis in barley endosperm. Nature 260, 169-170.

Burdett, A.N. (1972). Ethylene synthesis in lettuce seeds: its physiological significance. Plant Physiology 50, 719-722.

Burg, S.P. and Burg, E.A. (1965). Ethylene action and the ripening of fruits. Science 148, 1190-1196.

Davies, W.J. (1978). Some effects of abscisic acid and water stress on stomata of Vicia faba. Journal of Experimental Botany 29, 125-182.

Dorffling, K., Teitz, D., Streich, J. and Ludewig, M. (1979). Studies on the role of abscisic acid in stomatal movements. In "Plant Growth Substances 1979" (F. Skoog ed.), pp 274-289. Springer-Verlag, Berlin.

Dure, L.S. (1960). Site of origin and extent of amylases in maize germination. Plant Physiology 35, 925-934.

Fujikura, Y. and Baisted, D. (1983). Changes in starch bound lysophospholipids and lysophospholipase in germinating glacier and amylose glacier barley varieties. Phytochemistry 22, 865-868.

Galston, A.W. and Kaur, P. (1961). Comparative studies on the growth and light sensitivity of green and etiolated pea stems. In "Light and Life" (W.D. McElroy and B. Glass eds.), pp 687-708. John Hopkins Press, Baltimore.

Gibbons, G.C. (1981). On the relative role of the scutellum and aleurone in the production of hydrolases during germination of barley. Carlsberg Research Communications 46, 215-225.

Gould, G.A., Pearl, R., Edwards, T.I. and Miner, J.R. (1934). On the effects of partial removal of the cotyledons upon the growth and duration of life of Canteloup seedlings without exogenous food. Annals of Botany 48, 575-599.

Groat, J.I. and Briggs, D.E. (1969). Gibberellins and amylase formation in germinating barley. Phytochemistry 8, 1615-1627.

Halevy, A.H. and Mayak, S. (1981). Senescence and post-harvest physiology of cut flowers. Horticultural Reviews 3, 59-77.

Halevy, A.H., Whitehead, C.G. and Kofranek, A.M. (1984). Does pollination induce corolla abscission of cyclamen flowers by promoting ethylene production? Plant Physiology 75, 1090-1093.

Hatfield, R.D. and Lamotte, C.E. (1984). IAA induced growth response of decapitated corn seedlings. Plant Physiology 74, 302-306.

Heber, U., Neimanis, S. and Lange, O.L. (1986). Stomatal aperture, photosynthesis and water fluxes in mesophyll cells as affected by the excision of leaves. Planta 167, 554-563.

Hulme, A.C. and Rhodes, M.J.C. (1971). Pome Fruits. In "Biochemistry of Fruits and Their Products" (A.C. Hulme ed.), Volume 2, pp 333-373. Academic Press, London.

Hunt, E.R., Weber, J.A. and Gates, D.M. (1985). Effects of nitrate application on Amaranthus pomelli. Plant Physiology 79, 609-613.

Ishizawa, K. and Esashi, Y. (1983). Cooperation of ethylene and auxin in the growth regulation of rice coleoptile segments. Journal of Experimental Botany 34, 74-82.

Ishizawa, K. and Esashi, Y. (1984). Gaseous factors involved in the enhanced elongation of rice coleoptiles under water. Plant, Cell and Environment 7, 239-245.

Jones, R.J. and Mansfield, T.A. (1970). Suppression of stomatal opening in leaves treated with abscisic acid. Journal of Experimental Botany 21, 714-719.

Jones, R.L. (1969). Inhibition of gibberellic acid induced amylase formation by polyethylene glycol and mannitol. Plant Physiology 44, 101-104.

Jones, R.L. and Armstrong, J.E. (1971). Evidence for osmotic regulation of hydrolytic enzyme production in germinating barley seeds. Plant Physiology 48, 137-142.

Kefford, N.P. (1962). Auxin-gibberellin interaction in rice coleoptile elongation. Plant Physiology 37, 380-386.

Ketring, D.L. (1977). Ethylene and seed germination. In "The Physiology and Biochemistry of Seed Dormancy and Germination" (A.A. Khan ed.), pp 157-178. Elsevier/North Holland Biomedical Press, Amsterdam.

Kordan, H.A. (1974). Patterns of shoot and root growth in rice seedlings germinating under water. Journal of Applied Ecology 11, 685-690.

Ku, H.G., Suge, H., Rappaport, L. and Pratt, H.K. (1970). Stimulation of rice coleoptile growth by ethylene. Planta 90, 333-339.

Kutschera, V. and Schopfer, P. (1985). Evidence against the acid-growth theory of auxin action. Planta 163, 483-494.

Marinos, N.G. (1960). Some responses of Avena coleoptiles to ethylene. Journal of Experimental Botany 11, 227-235.

McDowall, F. and Sirois, J.C. (1977). Importance of time after excision and of pH on the kinetics of response of wheat coleoptile segments to added indole acetic acid. Plant Physiology 59, 405-410.

Mer, C.L. (1959). A study of the growth and photoperceptivity of etiolated oat seedings. Journal of Experimental Botany 10, 220-232.

Mer, C.L. (1969). Plant growth in relation to endogenous auxin with special reference to cereal seedings. New phytologist 68, 275-294.

Metzger, J.D. (1983). Role of endogenous plant growth regulators in seed dormancy of Avena fatua. Plant Physiology 73, 791-795.

Mor, Y., Halevy, A.H., Spiegelstein, H. and Mayak, S. (1985). The site of 1-amino-cyclopropane 1-carboxylic acid synthesis in senescing carnation petals. Physiologia Plantarum **65**, 196-202.

Naylor, J.M. (1983). Studies on the genetic control of some physiological processes in seeds. Canadian Journal of Botany **61**, 3561-3567.

Naylor, J.M. and Simpson, G.M. (1961). Dormancy studies in seed of Avena fatua. Canadian Journal of Botany **39**, 281-295.

Nicholls, P.B. (1982). Influence of temperature during grain growth and ripening of barley on the subsequent response to exogenous gibberellic acid. Australian Journal of Plant Physiology **9**, 373-383.

Nissen, P. (1985). Dose responses of auxins. Physiologia Plantarum **65**, 357-374.

Okamoto, K., Kitano, H. and Akazawa, T. (1980). Biosynthesis and excretion of hydrolases in germinating cereal seeds. Plant and Cell Physiology **21**, 201-204.

Palmer, J.H. (1985). Epinasty, hyponasty and related topics. In "Hormonal Regulation of Development III. Role of Environmental Factors", Encyclopaedia of Plant Physiology" New Series Vol. 11 (R.P. Pharis and D.M. Reid eds.), pp 139-168. Springer-Verlag, Berlin.

Pickard, B.G. (1985). Role of hormones, protons and calcium in geotropism. In "Hormonal Regulation of Development III. Role of Environmental Factors", Encyclopaedia of Plant Physiology New Series Vol. 11 (R.P. Pharis and D.M. Reid eds.), pp 193-282. Springer-Verlag, Berlin.

Radin, J.W. (1984). Stomatal responses to water stress and abscisic acid in phosphorus deficient cotton plants. Plant Physiology **76**, 392-394.

Radin, J.W. and Ackerson, R.C. (1982). Does abscisic acid control stomatal closure during water stress. What's New in Plant Physiology **13**, 9-12.

Radin, J.W., Parker, L.L. and Guinn, G. (1982). Water relations of cotton plants under nitrogen deficiency. Plant Physiology **70**, 1066-1070.

Radley, M. (1967). Site of production of gibberellin-like substances in germinating barley embryos. Planta **75**, 164-171.

Radley, M. (1969). The effect of the endosperm on the formation of gibberellin by barley embryos. Planta **86**, 218-223.

Ray, P.M. (1962). Cell wall synthesis and cell elongation in oat coleoptile tissue. American Journal of Botany **49**, 928-939.

Reid, J.B., Murfet, I.C. and Potts, W.C. (1983). Internode length in Pisum. Journal of Experimental Botany **34**, 349-364.

Roberts, I.N., Lloyd, C.W. and Roberts, K. (1985). Ethylene induced microbtubule reorientation; mediation by helical arrays. Planta **164**, 439-447.

Schonbeck, M.W. and Egley, G.H. (1980). Effects of temperature, water potential and light on germination responses of redroot sigweed seeds to ethylene. Plant Physiology **65**, 1149-1154.

36

Schonbeck, M.W. and Egley, G.H. (1981a). Changes in sensitivity of <u>Amaranthus</u> <u>retroflexus</u> seeds to ethylene during preincubation. II. Effects of alternating temperatures and burial in soil. <u>Plant, Cell and Environment</u> **4**, 237–242.

Schonbeck, M.W. and Egley, G.H. (1981b). Changes in sensitivity of <u>Amaranthus</u> <u>retroflexus</u> seed to ethylene during preincubation. I. Constant temperatures. <u>Plant, Cell and Environment</u> **4**, 229–235.

Seidlova, F., Kohli, R.K. and Pavlova, L. (1981). Effects of abscisic acid on the growth pattern of the shoot apical meristem and on flowering in <u>Chenopodium</u> <u>rubrum</u>. <u>Annals of Botany</u> **48**, 777–785.

Shibaoka, H. (1972). Gibberellin–colchicine interaction in elongation of bean epicotyl sections. <u>Plant and Cell Physiology</u> **13**, 461–469.

Shibaoka, H. (1974). Involvement of wall microtubules in gibberellin promotion and kinetin inhibition of stem elongation. <u>Plant and Cell Physiology</u> **15**, 255–263.

Simpson, G.M. (1965). Dormancy studies in seed of <u>Avena fatua</u>. <u>Canadian Journal</u> <u>of Botany</u> **43**, 793–816.

Simpson, G.M. (1966). The suppression by CCC of synthesis of a gibberellin–like substance by embryos of <u>Avena fatua</u>. <u>Canadian Journal of Botany</u> **44**, 115–116.

Skoog, F. (1937). A deseeded <u>Avena</u> test method for small amounts of auxin and auxin precursors. <u>Journal of General Physiology</u> **20**, 311–334.

Smart, C.C. and Trewavas, A.J. (1983). Abscisic acid induced turion formation in <u>Spirodela polyrrhiza</u>. II. Ultrastructure of the turion; a stereological analysis. <u>Plant, Cell and Environment</u> **6**, 515–522.

Sommer, N.F. (1961). Longitudinal and lateral response of etiolated pea sections to indoleacetic acid, gibberellin, kinetin, sucrose and cobaltous chloride. <u>Physiologia Plantarum</u> **14**, 741–749.

Sponsel, V. (1986). Gibberellin in dark and red–light grown shoots of dwarf and tall cultivars of <u>Pisum sativum</u>. <u>Planta</u> **168**, 119–129.

Sprent, J.I. (1966). The effect of nutrient factors on the response of peas to gibberellic acid. <u>Annals of Botany</u> **30**, 779–790.

Stiles, W. (1950). "An Introduction to the Principles of Plant Physiology." Methuen and Co. Ltd. London.

Takahashi, N. (1978). Adaptive importance of mesocotyl and coleoptile growth in rice under different moisture regimes. <u>Australian Journal of Plant Physiology</u> **5**, 511–517.

Trewavas, A.J. (1981). How do plant growth substances work? <u>Plant, Cell and</u> <u>Environment</u> **4**, 203–228.

Trewavas, A.J. (1982). Growth substance sensitivity: the limiting factor in plant development. <u>Physiologia Plantarum</u> **35**, 60–72.

Trewavas, A.J. (1986a). Resource allocation under poor growth conditions. A major role for growth substances in developmental plasticity. <u>In</u> "Plasticity in Plants" (D. Jennings and A.J. Trewavas eds.). <u>Symposium Society for Experimental Biology</u> XXXX, pp 31–77. Company of Biologists, London.

Trewavas, A.J. (1986b). Understanding the control of plant development and the role of growth substances. <u>Australian Journal of Plant Physiology</u> **13** , 447–457.

Vesper, M.J. and Evans, M.L. (1978). Time dependent changes in the auxin sensitivity of coleoptile segments. Plant Physiology **61**, 204-208.

Vlamis, J. and Davis, A.R. (1943). Germination, growth and respiration of rice and barley seedlings at low oxygen pressures. Plant Physiology **18**, 685-692.

Wada, S. (1961). Growth patterns of rice coleoptiles grown on water and under water. Scientific Reports of Tohuku University. Series IV (Biology) **27**, 199-207.

Zarra, I. and Masuda, Y. (1979). Growth and cell wall changes in rice coleoptiles growing under different conditions. Plant and Cell Physiology **20**, 1117-1124.

REQUIREMENTS FOR HORMONE INVOLVEMENT IN DEVELOPMENT AT DIFFERENT LEVELS OF ORGANIZATION

Peter W. Barlow

University of Bristol, Department of Agricultural Science, Long Ashton Research Station, Long Ashton, Bristol, BS18 9AF, England.

Plants consist of hierarchically organized levels that range from the cellular to the organismal; molecules and the community represent the lower and upper boundaries of the hierarchy, respectively. Each level of the hierarchy contains an interacting two-fold aspect of structure and function. Hormones that affect structural aspects, particularly at the tissue or organ levels of the hierarchy, are termed 'regulators'; they either (i) maintain a particular developmental state, or (ii) promote developmental change. Hormones that act upon functional activities are termed 'enablers'; they link processes within one level of the hierarchy. Examples of each of these categories of hormone action are given.

There may be advantages in analysing further the hierarchical nature of plant structure and the functional systems that support the hierarchy. One outcome might be a more precise clarification of the rôles of hormones at each level and a better appreciation of how their activities are integrated in the organization of the whole plant. Recently devised analytical tools for formalizing plant development at two different levels are outlined to which results of hormone research may be related in the future.

INTRODUCTION

The concepts implicit in the title of this chapter are those which developmental biologists and physiologists alike encounter in their search for an understanding of the rôle of hormones in plant development. Firstly, what are hormones, and what sets them apart from other naturally-occurring chemicals that participate in plant metabolism? The word 'hormone' is used in an operational sense. It is derived from the Greek ὁρμῶν (urging on) and, according to the Oxford English Dictionary, means 'a substance formed in an organ serving to excite some vital process'. Another commonly accepted feature of hormones, though one which was first suggested for hormones of animals, is that they (or their precursors) are made in one part of the organism and transported to other parts where they produce their effects. By common consent, the group of chemicals collectively known as auxins, gibberellins, and cytokinins, are held to be plant hormones since they do indeed excite two most vital processes - cell expansion and cell division - and they can also be transported between different parts of the plant. Abscisic acid and ethylene, which are unique molecules, also enjoy hormonal status as they, too, can modify growth processes and are mobile. Sometimes each of these classes of hormones, when supplied to plants have similar effects. For example, all of the classes can stimulate cell enlargement (R.E. Cleland, 1986). But at certain times during development one or other of the classes can have a response not shared by the others, or can counter some of their effects. Therefore, in appraising the rôle of hormones in plant development one might suspect that their unique properties are of more consequence for development than those that are shared; the shared properties may be of importance for maintaining particular functions or structures.

Secondly, the title speaks of 'the requirement for the involvement of hormones in development' thereby implying that certain criteria must be met (Jacobs, 1959) before it can be accepted that a hormone has 'urged on' some vital process. We should ask, therefore, whether there are any developmental events that cannot occur unless a hormone is present and, conversely, whether there are developmental events that can occur without the participation of a hormone.

Thirdly, the phrase 'different levels of organization' introduces the concept of a hierarchy. A hierarchical system is constructed of a graded set of levels, each level consisting of a specific set of entities. The limits to the structure, and the consequent function of each assemblage of entities, represent the boundary separating one level in the hierarchy from the next. A hierarchy is asymmetrical: the levels can be ordered in a sequence of increasing complexity, where complexity is defined as the minimum algorithm required for the unambiguous specification of the level in question. The hierarchy of levels in the living plant emerges from the atomic and molecular levels, which are characteristic of all matter, and proceeds through the cellular and organ levels to that of the whole plant. Plants are part of a community which represents yet another hierarchical level, but one that transcends the individuality of its members. A more detailed discussion of the living plant hierarchy is set out in another publication (Barlow, 1987a). It is important to realise that plants are constructed in a hierarchically organized way and that they themselves are units within a level of another type of hierarchy. The reason is that the explanation of any phenomenon at a given level, and an understanding of its significance, can only be properly appreciated with reference to the levels above and below the one in question. Thus, 'explanations' derived from analysis of the molecular level are not explanations at all unless they can be related to properties of the cellular level; similarly, properties of the whole plant, though they may be analysed at its component lower levels, can only be understood by setting them in the context of the community in which the plant lives.

The fourth concept, 'development', is perhaps the one most familiar to biologists. Development involves an increase in complexity (as defined above) with the passage of time brought about by the reading of the genetic information contained within the zygote. Genetic information resides at the relatively simple level of the molecule, while its potentialities are most fully expressed at the highest level for the plant - its structure as an individual, and its function as a reproductive member of the community. The whole plant and the plant community, as well as the hierarchically ordered assemblages of molecules, cells, etc., each have a two-fold aspect, the structural (form) and the functional (organization of parts), and both increase in complexity with time. These features might, then, be useful bases from which to explore the rôle of hormones in plant development.

The structural and functional domains at any level have subtle interrelationships for structure is the product of function, and function in turn depends upon structure. This interdependency also takes place across different levels since processes in one level can determine the structure of the next level (e.g. the properties of molecules and the processes in which they engage determine the structure of cells). The rôle of hormones is to assist this interplay of structure and function. For example, in the water-mould, Achlya, the steroid hormones antheridiol and oogoniol (Bilderback, 1985) are products of the reproductive organs (a structure) and encourage the process of fertilization (a function); the resultant progeny thereby increase the span of the community, which is a higher level of organization than either of the parents alone.

Hormones can, perhaps, be viewed in two ways: as 'regulators' of structural development, and as 'enablers' of functional organization. Since the processes initiated by hormones must first occur at the molecular level, these two groups of regulator and enabler relate to (i) the number of levels through which their reactions subsequently ascend, and (ii) whether the outcome of hormone action is viewed in structural or functional terms. Given that development has a particular tempo and direction, then a hormonal 'regulator' of structure can be viewed in two ways. One view of a regulator is that it maintains a predetermined developmental programme (rather as a governor of a piece of machinery maintains the rate of a process by correcting deviations from the desired rate); the other is that it brings about a change in the course of structural development. Change may be a response to an outside circumstance and the hormonal regulator may be able to transduce the information present in the outside environment and help to transform it into information which the plant can use to modify its form. By 'outside environment' is meant 'not contained within the hierarchical level in question'. It could be the ambient environment if one is considering the whole plant, the tissue environment in the case of cells, or the cellular environment if the molecular (e.g. genetic) level is being considered. The 'outside' may thus be a component of a level higher than the one in which the change comes about. The various courses of differentiation of plant cells in culture in response to changes in the environment at the levels of the cell, its organellar compartments, and the surrounding culture medium have been explored by Glock and Gregorius (1984).

The hormone as 'enabler' of function might allow processes to link with each other, perhaps by serving as an intermediary in a sequence of metabolic reactions. Here the enabler co-operates with components of processes within the same structural level to enhance the span of that level. Hence, the enabler increases the functional complexity of that level. Many enabling actions inevitably occur at the level occupied by the hormone itself (i.e. the molecular), but some may also occur at higher levels, e.g. the tissue level (hormonally directed source-sink relations being an example), or indeed at the community level if they enable a function such as reproduction.

The participation of hormones in developmental processes can be summarised and tabulated in the two complementary groups, regulators and enablers, with the features described above, as follows (Table 1).

Table 1 Hormones and developmental processes

Hormonal Category	Domain of Action	Property
Regulator	Structural	Developmental Conformity
Regulator	Structural	Developmental Change
Enabler	Functional	Link Processes Within a Level

Can the categories listed in Table 1 be useful in analysing hormone action in plant development? In the following section, selected examples indicate that each of these categories has an actual counterpart. It might even be possible to find that certain hormones are associated either with certain of the categories, or with certain processes at one or other of the structural levels. This will be briefly discussed in a later section.

CATEGORIES AND LEVELS

Hormones as Regulators

Regulators as maintainers of developmental conformity The rate of plant development is sensitive to environmental factors such as light, temperature, and degree of aeration, but the resulting structure maintains a fairly constant form (e.g. Barlow, 1987b). Nowhere is the ability to maintain a constancy of high-level structure more evident than in cases of regeneration following loss of, or damage to, parts of an organ. A convincing example of hormonal involvement in regeneration is shown by the re-establishment of vascular tissue around a wounded stele (reviewed by Sachs, 1981). Severance of the stele of roots and shoots induces surrounding parenchymatous cells to develop as xylem and phloem elements. Their redifferentiation is regulated in such a way that the new types of cells link end to end to form channels that functionally compensate for the damaged tissue. The spatial pattern of new xylem elements looks as though it traces the flow of a signal for differentiation through the parenchyma. Where a wound is made in the stem near young leaves and the leaves are then removed, the number of vessels which differentiate is reduced (Jacobs, 1952). Auxin applied to the side of an unwounded stem of pea or Coleus also induces redifferentiation of parenchymatous cells so that rows of xylem vessels form and link the existing vasculature to the site of auxin application. Grafting a bud onto the stem promotes a similar pattern of additional vessel formation (Sachs, 1981). These and many other experiments have led Sachs (1978, 1981) to propose that the new vessels are induced by auxin and that their pattern is an indication of the pathway taken by auxin through the tissue. Auxin also appears to facilitate its own transport through the parenchyma (Sachs, 1975). It thus seems to have a strong canalizing influence on cell differentiation in the wounded plant.

Examples where polarized auxin transport is reduced are also instructive because they present evidence that contrasts with the foregoing. Shoot tip cultures of carnation, Dianthus caryophyllus, provide one such example. About 50% of cultured apices acquire a 'glassy' phenotype that is associated with lower rates of basipetal auxin transport in their leaves; these, in turn, have correspondingly reduced vascular development (Gersani et al., 1986). This observation also supports the idea that auxin and its transport canalizes xylem development.

Facilitated transport and the subsequent differentiation of xylem strongly suggest that auxin may also canalize and regulate xylem development in the intact plant (Sachs, 1975; Mitchison, 1980). In apices of roots and shoots, xylem cells are sources of auxin (either because they transport it, or synthesise it) and the meristems can be sinks (Sheldrake, 1971; Bowen et al., 1972). Thus, auxin, on leaving the cell at the distal end of a file of xylem, would pass into contiguous undifferentiated cells where it would facilitate auxin flow through them, and eventually cause them to differentiate as new xylem. Continuity of the xylem cell file would thus be assured. Such a system is autocatalytic, the differentiation of young cells being the result of homeogenetic induction by older, already differentiating cells in the same cell file.

From these examples auxin emerges as a powerful inducer of developmental conformity - 'like inducing like', and in the above cases operates at the cellular and tissue levels. It may also induce conformity at the organ level as, for example, in leaf initiation. Phyllotactic patterns, and the positioning of their structural precursors, the incipient leaf primordia, have been proposed as being due to the pattern of procambial strands within the apex (Larson, 1983). The evidence is that the spatial pattern of procambial strands in the shoot apex corresponds to the phyllotactic pattern, even in zones of the apex where no leaf primordia are yet visible. While it is possible that the sites of prospective leaf primordia have been defined (but at a lower level of organization, e.g. at the level of the cells) before they actually become visible on the apical dome and could therefore arise independently of the procambium, they might nevertheless also be determined by a facilitated flow of auxin directed towards the shoot surface from the ends of the procambial strands. Upon reaching the shoot surface auxin might redirect the polarity of cell growth and thus induce a primordium. The incipient primordia could even be secondary sites of auxin production, the sites being defined by means of one of the numerous mechanisms that have been proposed to underlie phyllotactic patterning (Schwabe, 1984). The relation of vascular patterning to phyllotaxis could then be the result of two sources of auxin - the invisible primordium and the procambial strand - becoming linked by means of facilitated transport.

A final example of developmental conformity is one that operates at the level of the whole plant. It concerns tropisms (mentioned further in the chapter by I.R. Macdonald and J.W. Hart in this volume). Here the perturbing influence can be either light or gravity acting upon a shoot or a root, the response being photo- or gravitropism. Ignoring the complexities of stimulus perception, the point of

interest is that a deviation between the organ axis and the direction of
is believed to be corrected by a redistribution of hormone. In both type
whether in shoots or roots, there is evidence for the involvement of au
the case of root gravitropism there is the possibility that ABA is an ¿
even an alternative, signal.

In these examples the hormonal regulator manifests its effects
structural organization (tissue, organ, whole plant) which have already ᵃᵘⁿ⁻⁻⁻
stable developmental states. The perturbation of these higher level states (by
wounds, for example) requires regulation in a correspondingly highly organized way.
Perturbation of lower levels, e.g. molecular or metabolic defects, is not necessarily
restored by molecules that include hormones. Hormones, and auxin in particular, may
be able to regulate the reorganization of higher structural levels through long-range
transport effects that involve cell polarity and intercellular fluxes.

Regulators as promoters of developmental change   Plant development is a continuous
process accompanied by irreversible changes of form.   It is an axiom of the
contemporary concept of development that genes become active at different stages of
the plant's life cycle (Haldane, 1932; Sheridan and Neuffer, 1981), the switch
between inactive and active states and back again occurring either at particular
times (e.g., after a certain number of cell divisions have been accomplished) or at
particular positions in the body of the plant. Many aspects of development are
related to the growth of apical meristems; and some phenotypic characters, such as
leaf shape, may gradually change as the apex ages. But rather more abrupt changes of
form can occur. Flowering is one example of such a change; here, the apex switches
from producing one set of appendages (leaves) to producing another, more modified,
set (floral organs). At the same time, the individual's future is reoriented from
continuous vegetative growth to reproduction and possible death (in monocarpic
species). The hormonal and physiological basis of flowering are poorly understood
(C.F. Cleland, 1982), probably because of the many levels of organization that have
to be reset by the flowering stimulus, which itself must sometimes be a complex set
of environmental signals.

Another example of the redirection of form (but one less complex than flowering) is
the dimorphism of roots and leaves of certain species. Aquatic members of the family
Onagraceae possess two types of root, upward-growing and downward-growing. The
downward-growing roots of Ludwigia peploides have a compact cortex and a smooth
surface covered with root hairs, while the upward-growing roots are hairless and have
an aerenchymatous cortex composed of radially oriented cells. Each type of root
grows at characteristic locations around the horizontal stem (Ellmore, 1981). The
primordia at these locations are committed only in so far as they will become roots;
which of the two forms of root will be adopted by an emerging primordium is probably
determined by the hormonal milieu at the site of the primordium. This involvement of
hormones in root form has been investigated in the related species, Jussiaea repens,
where about 80% of all roots on shoot cuttings are downward-growing; the remaining
20% are upward-growing (Samb and Kahlem, 1983). Auxin (naphthyleneacetic acid (NAA))
and gibberellic acid (GA) separately overcome the upward-growing tendency and all
primordia develop as downward-growing roots. By contrast, the cytokinin, benzylamino
-purine, causes many more upward-growing roots to develop and can suppress the
downward-inducing effects of NAA (Samb and Kahlem, 1983). In the natural environment
there must be comparable signals determining the fate of the primordia, although what
they are has not been established; leaves and light seem to play some rôle in the
phenomenon.   Somewhat similar in structure to the above types of roots are the
contractile and fibrous roots of geophytes, the former having cortical cells with a
radial rather than an axial polarity (i.e. resembling upward-growing roots). The
frequency of contractile roots in Gladiolus can be modified by hormones and
environmental signals (Halevy, 1986). Fluctuating soil temperatures normally induce
contractile root formation, but application of auxin (indolebutyric acid) can be
substituted for this requirement when the soil temperature is held constant. Auxin
presumably transduces information inherent in this environmental signal into a
developmental response.

43

hese systems of root dimorphism offer excellent opportunities to investigate the regulation of alternative forms of an organ, the commitment of primordia, and the rôle of hormones in these phenomena. Perhaps significantly, alterations of cell polarity are involved in producing the two distinct forms of root, and it may be at this level that the auxin regulator operates.

A counterpart of root dimorphism is found in shoots producing different-shaped leaves (heterophylly) in response to different environments. Aquatic angiosperms are sometimes heterophyllous: apices of submerged shoots produce linear or dissected leaves (water forms - WF), whereas apices above the water level produce broader or entire leaves (land forms - LF). Heterophylly in Callitriche heterophylla has been experimentally analysed and the results support a rôle for hormones in the developmental modification of its leaves (Deschamp and Cooke, 1985). In this species WF and LF leaves have different length/width ratios and stomatal densities. Emergence of the shoot from water causes the apex to switch from producing WF to LF leaves. Application of 10^{-5}M GA to an emerged apex causes it to revert to producing WF leaves. Conversely, applying 10^{-5}M abscisic acid (ABA) to a submerged apex (producing WF leaves), or growing submerged plants at 30°C as opposed to the usual 23°C, induces LF leaves. Although the form of the leaves is varied by these treatments, not all the other features (such as turgor pressure, number of veins, total number of cells) associated with LF or WF leaves show corresponding changes. However, WF leaves induced by GA on emerged shoots do have a turgor pressure typical of WF leaves on submerged shoots (Deschamp and Cooke, 1983) suggesting that this hormone is able to override completely the environmental influence that would otherwise cause the apex to produce LF leaves. Thus, relatively high GA levels may be a natural determinant of leaf form, at least in the submerged plant.

Gibberellin can also influence the form of leaves of the land plant Taraxacum officinale. When GA_3 is applied to the shoot apex of whole plants, or to apices in culture, entire rounded leaves are formed, while the absence of GA favours a runcinate, or toothed, leaf form (Pomar et al., 1986). The transition from the entire to the runcinate form also occurs naturally as the plant ages. The rounded form of either the young leaf or the GA-treated leaf of Taraxacum might at first sight seem dissimilar to both the elongated form of the WF leaf and those produced by the GA-treated emerged apex of Callitriche. However, in Taraxacum, young primordia on the GA-treated apex actually grow more in length than in width (Cogliatti and Guitman, 1984) just as occurs in the WF leaf primordia of Callitriche. On the other hand, the suppression of toothing by GA is due to the continued isodiametric expansion of all cells at the margin of the leaf, a feature which makes it similar to the more rounded LF leaf of Callitriche.

Obviously the relation between GA, polarity of cell growth, and final leaf form is not straight forward. The common denominator in both the cases described above is that the type of leaf induced by GA has a juvenile form. Thus, it is possible that the association of GA with juvenility is related more to an ability of GA to reset the primordium to a juvenile state, whose properties are subsequently expressed at many levels of structure, than to its effect at one particular level or process, such as that of the cell and its polarity. Support for this possibility comes from the well known 'phase' phenomenon in shoots of English ivy, Hedera helix (Wareing and Frydman, 1976). Leaf shape is an outward indicator of the phase of the shoot apex, juvenile leaves being lobed whereas adult leaves are entire (cf. Taraxacum). Juvenility can be restored to an adult apex by application of GA (Robbins, 1957) - an effect which can be suppressed by ABA (Rogler and Hackett, 1975) (cf. the suppression of WF leaves by ABA in Callitriche). But juvenility is expressed in terms other than leaf shape alone: also typical of juvenile shoots are the size of the apical dome, phyllotaxy, growth habit (juvenile shoots are horizontal, adult shoots are upright) (Stein and Fosket, 1969), as well as certain cellular and molecular features such as nuclear chromatin structure and DNA composition (Nagl, 1979). Differences in a heritable feature such as the organization of the DNA could explain the perpetuation of a particular phase by continued meristematic activity over long periods of time.

Developmental changes associated with hormonal status may be more complex than can be envisaged at present. The stimuli for change may cause differences in intra- or inter-cellular hormonal compartmentation and thus bring about a hormonal profile that serves as the first message in a sequence that ultimately affects development. At present we do not know at which level the message is perceived and transduced in order to bring about the change. For instance, not all developmental changes may be a result of hormonal messengers directly affecting gene activity; certain changes could be a result of alterations in hormone distribution within a primordium, some tissues responding with altered rates or planes of growth more strongly than others. This would be perception of hormonal messengers at an organ, rather than at a molecular, level.

Hormones as Enablers

Enablers as links within an organizational level In the early years of hormone research attention was given to the structure that would confer hormonal activities on certain types of molecules. The molecular configurations of some auxin-like compounds result in biological activity, while those of others do not. The same is true of cytokinins and gibberellins. These studies were (and still are) a prelude to the discovery of molecules to which hormones bind with kinetics and configurations relevant to ensuing developmental changes (Venis, 1985; see also the chapter by M. A. Venis in this volume). The chain of events that a hormone/receptor interaction initiates at the molecular level may be the starting point for developmental changes expressed at higher levels. Nevertheless, molecular interaction is a hormonal property in its own right and constitutes the enablement of a process that leads to a change of function.

Cytokinins offer examples of this category of enabling action at a molecular level. There is evidence that cytokinins interact with a protein receptor and that the resulting complex influences RNA transcription (Kulaeva, 1981). Furthermore, cytokinins and another type of protein receptor can interact with polysomes and thereby influence RNA translation (Fosket and Tepfer, 1978; Szweykowska et al., 1981). Neither of these events alone need have developmental significance since they may not cause any change in complexity at the cellular level in which they occur. This is particularly true if the reactions contribute only to the maintenance of the prevailing functional processes. In this case enablers act as links within one structural level and may be said to extend the span of the functional processes at that level. The reactions become significant only when the RNA transcribed, or the protein synthesised, promotes some function from which arise changes in structural development or functional complexity.

Which of these two rôles does the cytokinin enabler play? Is it simply a cofactor in RNA and protein syntheses required by every cell engaged in these activities, or can it modulate the quality of these activities in certain circumstances? That cytokinin does have activities other than maintenance is evident from its inhibition of the synthesis of certain proteins (Felix and Meins, 1985) and its stimulation of others which are apparently important for the completion of mitosis in cultured cells (Jouanneau, 1970). The appearance of these qualitatively different proteins which have been tentatively assigned a rôle in mitosis provides a partial explanation for the frequent observation that cytokinins promote cell division in tissue culture. Moreover, the progress of a cell through its division cycle seems to be linked in turn to cytokinin synthesis, for when synchronized cultured cells of tobacco enter mitosis the amount of extractable cytokinins increases fivefold (Nishinari and Syōno, 1980). How these different effects are integrated in the control of cell division is not clear, though the situation has the makings of a feed-forward control system: cytokinin made in a dividing cell promotes conditions necessary for the subsequent division of the two daughter cells and thereby causes a recurrence of the process.

Pardee and colleagues (1981) have suggested three criteria by which an enabler of cell division can be recognised, namely the 'transformation test', the 'availability test,' and 'the arrest test'. Although their proposals were made with animal cells in mind, the same criteria apply to plant cells. Cytokinins satisfy the first two criteria (for example, transformed tumour cells are self-sufficient for cytokinin; and cytokinins are ubiquitous, naturally-occurring compounds), but not the third. According to the latter criterion, removal of a putative enabler should arrest the cell cycle at a specific point. The apparent involvement of cytokinins at the G_2/mitosis boundary suggests that removal of cytokinin should block the cycle at G_2. In the case of a suspension culture of sycamore cells dependent on cytokinin for its growth, removal of cytokinin does indeed arrest the cycle, but not at any particular stage (Wang et al., 1981). However, this result is not unexpected if the culture has other activities that also depend on cytokinin.

Cytokinins are enablers of some process(es) that leads to cell division, but they are not enablers of cell division per se because this process is a property of a higher level (the cell) than the one at which the enabler functions (the molecular). The cell is a complex of metabolic and structural molecules, and their functions must be integrated by the enabler for division to be accomplished.

The interface between two different levels of organization is of great interest for development, particularly if cell division is involved. Hormones can facilitate this interaction. For example, through the interaction of a regulator of cell growth (e.g. auxin) and an enabler of cell division (e.g. cytokinin) the cell is capable of developmental change. Cell growth and division can be coupled in such a way that one-dimensional chains of cells can be transformed into two- or three-dimenensional cellular arrays which are then open to opportunities for histogenesis and morphogenesis. Thus, with this increased step in complexity, other levels of structure and degrees of organization (tissues, organs) become possible.

HORMONES AND COMPLEXITY

Space limits a consideration of every class of hormone in the context of the categories mentioned in Table 1. However, in some way to compensate for this, and also in order to make a general summary, it is of interest to speculate (admittedly in broad and tendentious terms) whether any of the classes of hormones play distinct rôles in bringing about different stages of development of the whole plant in much the same way that auxin, cytokinin and gibberellin have been claimed to exert sequential effects during the growth of a single organ (e.g. the coleoptile of wheat (Wright, 1961; though for a re-examination of this work see Firn, 1986)). In other words, do particular hormones facilitate transitions from one level of complexity to another, thus performing a developmental 'gating' function? For example, epidermal cells removed from the stem of a tobacco plant and placed in culture show an increasing capacity to form flower primordia the higher their initial location on the stem (Tran Thanh Van, 1973); this observation could indicate that the potentiality to form flowers in vivo is gated by the status of a particular hormone in or around potentially receptive cells, and that the hormonal milieu of the cells changes as a function of cellular age or position.

As enablers of function, some hormones can influence the fundamental processes of protein and nucleic acid metabolism by acting as cofactors. They can act in either a promotive or an antagonistic sense in any cell to which they have access and in which these processes are able to occur. As regulators, hormones determine form and promote increased structural complexity. They may also be quite specific in the timing of their action. For example, gibberellins are notably associated with early stages of plant growth. The most juvenile stage of the sporophyte generation is the embryo, and gibberellins are most abundant and active in stages leading up to embryo formation (e.g. in flowering and gametogenesis) as well as during the subsequent embryonic growth, germination and seedling stages. It may be significant that GA_3 is also able to modify the structure and composition of DNA (Schafer and Neumann, 1978) and in some cells it can reduce the amount of differentially replicated AT-rich DNA (Nagl and Rücker, 1976). Thus, it might be that GA can direct the genetic material towards a juvenile mode so that genes concerned with early development are activated and hence evoke the development of sexual organs and germination. With regard to the former pathway, it may be no coincidence that gibberellins are structurally similar to the antheridium-inducing factor, antheridiogen, of ferns (Nakanishi et al., 1971) suggesting that sexuality and gibberellins have had a long, and perhaps interconnected, history.

Abscisic acid generally has retarding functions: it acts, therefore, as a developmental brake. By retarding germination it can delay the onset of development; by retarding root and shoot growth, and bringing about apical dormancy, it can periodically (i.e. seasonally) terminate development. As a senescence factor, it can abolish growth and metabolism and consequently permit decomposition of highly developed parts into their lowest hierarchical elements (molecules). At the same time, this brings about the removal of an element (the individual) from the highest hierarchical level, the plant community.

Ethylene is a regulator also capable of reducing structural complexity. By stimulating leaf and fruit abscission, for example, it is instrumental in removing organs from plants; and by its induction of aerenchyma in stems and roots it partially removes tissues from organs.

Auxins and cytokinins seem to be all-pervasive in plant development. Perhaps this is a feature of their uncomplicated origin from a ubiquitous amino acid and nucleotides, respectively. Their stimulation of cell division, promotion of cell growth, and influence on cell polarity and differentiation can regulate the basic cellular framework from which developmental complexity can emerge. And by their mobility through tissues they have the power to integrate the functions of spatially separated parts.

The majority of hormone research is concerned with responses of the sporophyte generation, but it is not without interest to enquire about the relation of hormones to the gametophyte generation, or indeed whether this generation has its own specific hormone complement. Brassinolide, a steroid, is found on the surface of pollen grains (Grove et al., 1979) and stimulates the growth of pollen tubes at concentrations an order of magnitude lower than any other class of hormone (Hewitt et al., 1985). Thus, brassinolide might be a candidate for a gametophytic hormone. With its presumed rôle in reproduction, it could exert an enabling effect at the highest level of plant organization, the whole plant/community boundary.

NEW APPROACHES TO PLANT DEVELOPMENT

Viewing the plant as a hierarchical structure may have some commendable features. It not only permits a categorization of the various structural levels and the systems needed for their functional organization (Barlow, 1987a; Fukshansky and Wagner, 1985) but also prompts an analysis of the conditions necessary for the advancement of functional complexity and structural development. A hierarchy also reconciles reductionist and holistic attitudes towards growth and development (for further discussion see Bartholomew, 1986). But, in consequence, it is necessary to learn more about the structure of each level in the hierarchy and how the structure and function of one level influence those of the next. Since hormones clearly have important rôles in integrating the development of the individual parts of a plant, as well as in buffering development from the exigencies of the environment, it may be profitable to pursue those analytical methods that can be applied to hierarchical structures in order to learn whether hormones have some unique rôle in permitting transitions from one level to another, or whether they simply integrate or modulate activities within one particular level. For example, xylem formation in cell or tissue culture systems seems to be regulated by the same hormones as it is in the whole plant (Roberts, 1976). An important question, therefore, is how the hormonal controls of xylogenesis are deployed and integrated at both the cellular and the whole plant levels to give correctly structured tissues. One way is through quantitative controls: high levels of auxin can favour numerous small xylem vessels, whereas lower levels favour fewer larger vessels (Aloni and Zimmermann, 1983; Saks and Aloni, 1985).

One analytical tool that seems to have the power to formalize developmental interactions at the level of the whole plant is the net theory developed by C.A. Petri (Peterson, 1977). The formalism of Petri nets has so far been applied in a biological context only in the analysis of interactive processes in vegetative development of Tradescantia cuttings (Lück et al., 1983). The Petri net does not determine cause and effect, but shows the interactions between structural states. Within the net there are conditions (nodes) that must be fulfilled if the net is to be complete. The net is a diagram of potentialities, but at the same time there is a direction to the arcs of the net; the necessity for directionality implies the contingent condition of causality. An analysis of nets formalizing plant development could be of great value in determining whether the nodes and arcs of the net have a correspondence with any physiological parameters. It would obviously be of interest to see whether hormones uniquely substitute for certain of the nodes. Other analytical tools are formalisms such as L-systems (Lindenmayer, 1975) and the related graph grammars (Lück and Lück, 1983), both of which can define interactions at the cellular level. They offer challenging and exciting concepts with which to advance an understanding of plant development. They are more than just descriptive devices, for not only do they make explicit the important principles of structural morphology but they also draw attention to the physiological processes necessary for the initiation and development of plant structure. For example, the algorithms of L-systems that have been applied to patterns of cell division draw attention to the properties of cell walls and their underlying cytoskeleton in determining the site of future walls. The arrangement of walls, in turn, specify tissue boundaries. These structural properties inherent to cells may also relate to underlying patterns of hormone action that pervade the cellular arrays. Similarly, algorithms that formalize inflorescence development (e.g. Frijters, 1978; Lindenmayer, 1984) demonstrate the principles necessary for floral organ development and, furthermore, they make definite predictions about the correlative activities of physiological factors (possibly hormones) that normally govern the sequence of flowering in an inflorescence.

An understanding of a hierarchical system such as a plant increases only by exploration of its different levels and the linkage between them. The main thrust of plant development should now be to obtain more detailed explanations of the workings of each level and how these are integrated throughout the hierarchy. Plant hormones are likely to serve as one of the links by which levels in the hierarchy communicate.

REFERENCES

Aloni, R. and Zimmermann, M.H. (1983). The control of vessel size and density along the plant axis. A new hypothesis. Differentiation **24**, 203-208.

Barlow, P.W. (1987a). The hierarchical organization of plants and the transfer of information during their development. Postepy Biologii Komorki (in press).

Barlow, P.W. (1987b). The cellular organization of roots and its response to the physical environment. In "Root Development and Function" (P.J. Gregory, J.V. Lake and D.A. Rose eds.), pp 1-26. Cambridge University Press, Cambridge.

Bartholomew, G.A. (1986). The role of natural history in contemporary biology. BioScience **36**, 324-329.

Bilderback, D.E. (1985). Regulators of plant reproduction, growth and differentiation in the environment. In "Encyclopedia of Plant Physiology, New Series, vol. **11**. Hormonal Regulation of Development III. Role of Environmental Factors" (R.P. Pharis and D.M. Reid eds.), pp 653-706. Springer, Berlin.

Bowen, M.R., Wilkins, M.B., Cane, A.R., and McCorquodale, I. (1972). Auxin transport in roots VIII. The distribution of radioactivity in the tissues of Zea root segments. Planta 105, 273-292.

Cleland, C.F. (1982). The chemical control of flowering - a status report. In "Plant Growth Substances 1982" (P.F. Wareing ed.), pp 635-644. Academic Press, London.

Cleland, R.E. (1986). The role of hormones in wall loosening and plant growth. Australian Journal of Plant Physiology 13, 93-103.

Cogliatti, D.H. and Guitman, M.R. (1984). Some observations on the effect of gibberellic acid on the shape of Taraxacum officinale leaf primordia. Journal of Plant Physiology 115, 97-103.

Deschamp, P.A. and Cooke, T.J. (1983). Leaf dimorphism in aquatic angiosperms: significance of turgor pressure and cell expansion. Science 219, 505-507.

Deschamp, P.A. and Cooke, T.J. (1985). Casual mechanisms of leaf dimorphism in the aquatic angiosperm Callitriche heterophylla. American Journal of Botany 71, 319-329.

Ellmore, G.E. (1981). Root dimorphism in Ludwigia peploides (Onagraceae): development of two types of roots from similar primordia. Botanical Gazette 142, 525-533.

Felix, G. and Meins, F. (1985). Purification, immunoassay and characterization of an abundant, cytokinin-regulated polypeptide in cultured tobacco tissues. Evidence the protein is a β-1, 3-glucanase. Planta 164, 423-428.

Firn, R.D. (1986). Growth substance sensitivity: the need for clearer ideas, precise terms and purposeful experiments. Physiologia Plantarum 67, 267-272.

Fosket, D.E. and Tepfer, D.A. (1978). Hormonal regulation of growth in cultured plant cells. In Vitro 14, 63-75.

Frijters, D. (1978). Principles of simulation of inflorescence development. Annals of Botany 42, 549-560.

Fukshansky, L. and Wagner, E. (1985). Anwendung von Variationsprinzipien zur Beschreibung der hierarchischen Organisation des Energiestoffwechsels. Berichte der Deutschen Botanische Gesellschaft 98, 25-34.

Gersani, M., Leshem, B., and Sachs, T. (1986). Impaired polarity in abnormal plant development. Journal of Plant Physiology 123, 91-95.

Glock, H. and Gregorius, H.-R. (1984). Differentiation - A consequence of idiotype-environment interaction. BioSystems 17, 23-34.

Grove, M.D., Spencer, G.F., Rohwedder, W.K., Mandava, N., Worley, J.F., Warthen, J.D., Steffens, G.L., Flippen-Anderson, J.L., and Cook, J.C. (1979). Brassinolide, a plant growth-promoting steroid isolated from Brassica napus pollen. Nature 281, 216-217.

Haldane, J.B.S. (1932). The time of action of genes and its bearing on some evolutionary problems. American Naturalist 66, 5-24.

Halevy, A.H. (1986). The induction of contractile roots in Gladiolus grandiflorus. Planta 167, 94-100.

Hewitt, F.R., Hough, T., O'Neill, P., Sasse, J.M., Williams, E.G., and Rowan, K.S. (1985). Effect of brassinolide and other growth regulators on the germination and growth of pollen tubes of Prunus avium using a multiple hanging-drop assay. Australian Journal of Plant Physiology 12, 201-211.

Jacobs, W.P. (1952). The role of auxin in differentiation of xylem around a wound. American Journal of Botany 39, 301-309.

Jacobs, W.P. (1959). What substance normally controls a given biological process? I. Formulation of some rules. Developmental Biology 1, 527-533.

Jouanneau, J.P. (1970). Renouvellement des proteins et effect spécifique de la kinetine sur des cultures de cellules de Tabac. Physiologia Plantarum 23, 232-244.

Kulaeva, O.N. (1981). Cytokinin action on transcription and translation in plants. In "Metabolism and Molecular Activities of Cytokinins" (J. Guern and C. Péaud-Lenöel eds.), pp 218-227. Springer, Berlin.

Larson, P.R. (1983). Primary vascularization and the siting of primordia. In "The Growth and Functioning of Leaves" (J.E. Dale and F.L. Milthorpe eds.), pp 25-51. Cambridge University Press, Cambridge.

Lindenmayer, A. (1975). Developmental algorithms for multicellular organisms: a survey of L-systems. Journal of Theoretical Biology 54, 3-22.

Lindenmayer, A. (1984). Positional and temporal control mechanisms in inflorescence development. In "Positional Controls in Plant Development" (P.W. Barlow and D.J. Carr eds.), pp 461-486. Cambridge University Press, Cambridge.

Lück, J. and Lück, H.B. (1983). Generation of 3-dimensional plant bodies by double wall map and steromap systems. Lecture Notes in Computer Science 153, 219-231.

Lück, J., Raoul, F., and Lück, H.B. (1983). Le déterminisme de la ramification chez Tradescantia fluminensis a la lumière des réseaux de Petri. Actes 3eme Séminaire de l'Ecole de Biologie Théorique du CNRS, pp 27-39.

Mitchison, G.J. (1980). A model for vein formation in higher plants. Proceedings of the Royal Society of London B207, 79-109.

Nagl, W. (1979). Differential DNA replication in plants: a critical review. Zeitschrift für Pflanzenphysiologie 95, 283-314.

Nagl, W. and Rücker, W. (1976). Effects of phytohormones on thermal denaturation profiles of Cymbidium DNA: indication of differential DNA replication. Nucleic Acids Research 3, 2033-2039.

Nakanishi, K., Endo, M., Näf, U., and Johnson, L.F. (1971). Structure of the antheridium-inducing factor of the fern Anemia phyllitidis. Journal of the American Chemical Society 93, 5579-5581.

Nishinari, N. and Syōno, K. (1980). Identification of cytokinins associated with mitosis in synchronously cultured tobacco cells. Plant and Cell Physiology 21, 383-393.

Pardee, A.B., Cherington, P.V., and Medrano, E.E. (1981). On deciding which factors regulate cell growth. Progress in Clinical and Biological Research 66A, 495-502.

Pomar, M.C., Slabnik, E., Caso, O.H., and Díaz, H. (1986). Leaf dimorphism in Taraxacum officinale during in vitro culture of shoot tips. Journal of Plant Physiology 122, 413-421.

Peterson, J.A. (1977). Petri nets. Computing Surveys **9**, 223-252.

Robbins, W.J. (1957). Gibberellic acid and the reversal of adult Hedera to a juvenile state. American Journal of Botany **44**, 743-746.

Roberts, L.W. (1976) "Cytodifferentiation in Plants. Xylogenesis as a Model System". Cambridge University Press, Cambridge.

Rogler, C.E. and Hackett, W.P. (1975). Phase change in Hedera helix: stabilization of the mature form with abscisic acid and growth retardants. Physiologia Plantarum **34**, 148-152.

Sachs, T. (1975). The induction of transport channels by auxin. Planta **127**, 201-206.

Sachs, T. (1978). Patterned differentiation in plants. Differentiation **11**, 65-73.

Sachs, T. (1981). The control of the patterned differentiation of vascular tissues. Advances in Botanical Research **9**, 151-262.

Saks, Y. and Aloni, R. (1985). Polar gradients of tracheid number and diameter during primary and secondary xylem development in young seedlings of Pinus pinea L. Annals of Botany **56**, 771-778.

Samb, P.I. and Kahlem, G. (1983). Déterminisme de l'organogénèse racinaire de Jussiaea repens L. Zeitschrift für Pflanzenphysiologie **109**, 279-284.

Schafer, A. and Neumann, K.-H. (1978). The influence of gibberellic acid on reassociation kinetics of DNA of Daucus carota L. Planta **143**, 1-4.

Schwabe, W.W. (1984). Phyllotaxis. In "Positional Controls in Plant Development" (P.W. Barlow and D.J. Carr eds.), pp 403-440. Cambridge University Press, Cambridge.

Sheldrake, A.R. (1971). Auxin in the cambium and its differentiating derivatives. Journal of Experimental Botany **22**, 735-740.

Sheridan, W.F. and Neuffer, M.G. (1981). Maize mutants altered in embryo development. In "Levels of Genetic Control in Development" (S.Subtelny and U.K. Abbott, eds.), pp 137-156. Liss, New York.

Stein, O.L. and Fosket, E.B. (1969). Comparative developmental anatomy of shoots of juvenile and adult Hedera helix. American Journal of Botany **56**, 546-551.

Szweykowska, A., Gwóźdź, E., and Spychała, M. (1981). The cytokinin control of protein synthesis in plants. In "Metabolism and Molecular Activities of Cytokinins" (J. Guern and C. Péaud-Lenöel eds.), pp 212-217, Springer, Berlin.

Tran Thanh Van, M. (1973). Direct flower neoformation from superficial tissue of small explants of Nicotiana tabacum L. Planta **115**, 87-92.

Venis, M. (1985). "Hormone Binding Sites in Plants". Longman, New York.

Wang, T.L., Everett, N.P., Gould, A.R., and Street, H.E. (1981). Studies on the control of the cell cycle in cultured plant cells. III. The effects of cytokinin. Protoplasma **106**, 23-35.

Wareing, P.F. and Frydman, V.M. (1986). General aspects of phase change, with special reference to Hedera helix L. Acta Horticulturae **56**, 57-69.

Wright, S.T.C. (1961). A sequential growth response to gibberellic acid, kinetin and indolyl-3-acetic acid in the wheat coleoptile (Triticum vulgare L.). Nature **190**, 699-700.

HORMONE RECEPTOR SITES AND THE STUDY OF PLANT DEVELOPMENT

Michael A. Venis

Institute of Horticultural Research, East Malling, Maidstone, Kent, ME19 6BJ, England

Plant development is likely to be governed both by hormone concentration and by tissue sensitivity to the hormone. Sensitivity presumably relates to the abundance and/or affinities of hormone receptors. Many hormone binding systems have been described in plants, but only a few of these have any credibility as receptors. Developmental mutants with reduced hormone sensitivity have been described and some of these may be receptor mutants, but their evalution has been hampered by an inability to detect appreciable hormone binding in the wild types. There are one or two reports of a plant hormone apparently regulating its own binding sites and several more instances where binding sites seem to be developmentally regulated. Receptors have been sought both in membranous and in 'soluble' (nuclear/cytoplasmic) fractions, as mediators of rapid (e.g. ion flux) and transcriptional responses respectively. Binding sites with receptor characteristics have been located in membrane fractions both for auxins and for auxin transport inhibitors (phytotropins). Whereas the latter sites can be readily detected both in monocotyledon and dicotyledon shoots (and have been immunolocalised), convincing auxin binding has so far only been shown in monocotyledon membranes, usually in maize. The auxin binding sites in maize membranes have been solubilised, purified and shown to have appropriate receptor properties. Attempts are being made to raise antibodies, to use as probes of receptor localisation and developmental regulation.

INTRODUCTION

Investigations on the role of plant hormones in development can be carried out at several different levels, e.g:

1. the way in which the hormonal signal is first recognised, i.e. the nature of hormone-receptor interaction;

2. the nature and mechanism of stimulus-response coupling;

3. identification of the primary response;

4. identification of hormone-regulated gene products;

5. characterisation of end physiological effects.

Research effort has been largely concentrated at level 5, which has led to a preoccupation with multiple effects of individual hormones, with the ability of different hormones to produce somewhat similar end-effects in some circumstances, and most of all with a bewildering array of interactive effects of different hormones. Much of this effort has obscured rather than illuminated primary hormone action. A greater research input into characterisation of hormone receptors in plants and mechanisms of signal transduction is called for.

53

RECEPTOR CHARACTERISTICS

A receptor is a specific cellular recognition site (e.g. for a hormone, drug or neurotransmitter) that binds the ligand and in consequence instructs the cell to respond in the appropriate manner to the particular chemical signal. The precision of the recognition process can probably only be accommodated in a macromolecular structure and all known hormone receptors are proteins. When studying a putative receptor system, it is necessary to evaluate the properties of the system in relation to the behaviour that might be expected of a true receptor:

1. Binding should be reversible, of high affinity, and of finite capacity, in order that the physiological effect can be regulated and be responsive to changes in hormone concentration.

2. The saturation range of binding should be consistent with the concentration range over which the physiological response saturates.

3. Binding specificity for different hormone analogues should be approximately in accordance with the relative biological activities of the compounds. A given receptor should not bind hormones of another class.

4. Binding should lead to a hormone-specific biological response. (This is inevitably the most difficult criterion to establish, and is rarely addressed.)

5. Binding may be confined to hormone-responsive tissues.

There can, however, be frequent exceptions to these criteria. Thus, in a system where the response is dependent upon the generation of a second messenger, it can be shown that the hormone concentration required for half-maximum biological response will be lower than that required for half maximal receptor saturation (Strickland and Loeb, 1981), leading to the displacement between response and receptor saturation curves observed in some animal hormone systems. Next, factors other than intrinsic activity can contribute towards net physiological activity, e.g. transport to site of action, susceptibility to metabolism, lipophilicity.

Again, the normal experience with animal hormones is that receptors are confined to specific target organs, and it might be anticipated that receptors for plant hormones would be localised in hormone-responsive tissues, hence governing tissue sensitivity. While this may be so, it is not always clear what constitutes a hormone-responsive system. Simplistically, it is often equated to growth responsiveness in some form, but this neglects not only the known diversity of plant hormone effects, but also the less overt hormone-dependent biochemical changes of which we may be unaware. As an example, the auxin-induced N-acyl-aspartate synthetase of peas is inducible not only in the growth-responsive third internode, but also in non-elongating tissue from the first internode (Südi, 1966). The latter tissue, while not responding to auxin in terms of growth, must nevertheless clearly be regarded as auxin responsive biochemically, and can be presumed to contain auxin receptors. It may be that the tissue does not contain membrane-bound receptors essential for a growth response, or it could simply be that receptors are present, but that growth of the more mature zone is limited by other constraints such as cell wall structure. Similarly, Zurfluh and Guilfoyle (1982 a, b) have found that auxin induces comparable mRNA species in both elongating (apical) and non-elongating (basal) regions of soybean hypocotyl, showing that at least some auxin-regulated changes in gene expression are common to organs with very different growth responses.

RECEPTOR MODULATION IN DEVELOPMENT

The thesis of growth substance sensitivity as a factor in determining plant development, advanced in particular by Trewavas (1981) essentially draws attention to the receptor component in the system.

Hormone + Receptor $\rightleftarrows$ Hormone-Receptor complex ------------------→ Response

Changes in sensitivity, i.e. the ability of a tissue to respond to a given concentration of hormone, can be equated to some change in receptor properties - their number or their hormone binding affinity. In animal systems there are many mechanisms, both covalent and non-covalent for regulating receptors and biological responsiveness (see e.g. Sibley and Lefkowitz, 1985). In plants, comparable evidence is only fragmentary, with no detailed information on possible mechanisms. There are, nevertheless, several indications that plant receptors may be hormonally and/or developmentally regulated. Thus Bhattacharyya and Biswas (1982) reported that a high affinity particulate IAA-binding site (Kd 0.68 μM) was induced in wheat roots by 1 h pretreatment in 50 μM IAA, adding to the lower affinity site (Kd 7 μM) already present in control roots. Earlier, Trewavas (1980) noted the induction by 2,4-D pretreatment (24 h) of IAA-binding sites (Kd ca. 1 μM) in membrane preparations from artichoke tuber slices. In tobacco cultures there is evidence that auxin binding both to particulate (Vreugdenhil et al., 1981) and cytoplasmic sites (Oostrom et al., 1980) is modulated during the growth cycle. In addition Maan et al. (1985) found that in both suspension cultures and callus cultures of tobacco, auxin binding to membranes disappears if 2,4-D replaces NAA plus kinetin in the culture medium. There was a possible connection with rooting ability, since calli on solid media with 2,4-D were unable to generate roots, whereas those on NAA plus kinetin did produce roots.

The best-studied auxin binding sites (discussed later) remain those in monocotyledonous membranes - generally examined in maize coleoptiles, but present also in maize mesocotyls and in oat coleoptiles. These provide several examples relating binding activity with tissue responsiveness:

1. As coleoptiles increase in size (age), auxin binding and auxin responsiveness in maize decrease in parallel (Kearns, 1982). This has more recently been confirmed by Vesper (personal communication), who finds that a change in affinity rather than in the number of binding sites is involved.

2. Auxin binding and auxin-induced elongation also decrease in parallel down the length of the maize mesocotyl (Walton and Ray, 1981). The same authors also observed that exposure to red light reduced auxin responsiveness and auxin binding activity of mesocotyls (but not coleoptiles) with a similar time course and to a similar extent. In this case, reduced NAA binding was brought about by a decrease in site number without influencing binding affinity, corresponding to the way in which red light inhibited growth, which was to reduce the maximum response to NAA without affecting the concentration at which half-maximal response was obtained.

3. Apical 1 cm sections of oat coleoptiles are far more auxin-sensitive and show higher auxin binding than basal sections. Conversely, in maize coleoptiles basal sections are more responsive than apical sections, but they also have greater auxin binding activity (Kearns, 1982).

4. Finally, in maize specifically, there are endogenous modulators of auxin-binding site interaction (benzoxazinones), which might have a role in growth regulation (Venis and Watson, 1978).

In addition, there is one example of hormonal modulation of another regulator's binding sites. High affinity binding of the fungal toxin fusicoccin, a mimic of some aspects of auxin action, has been located in the plasma membrane of several species, both monocotyledons and dicotyledons. Aducci et al. (1986) have recently found that pretreatment of maize coleoptiles (10-90 min) in 1-10 μM IAA (or other auxins) leads to an increase (up to 100%) in the number of microsomal fusicoccin-binding sites without affecting their affinity. Auxin-binding and fusicoccin-binding sites are quite independent and most plant cells do not normally encounter fusicoccin. It is possible, therefore, that the fusicoccin sites normally bind an as yet unidentified endogenous ligand, for which there is some evidence (Aducci et al., 1980). It also appears that the fusicoccin sites may be phosphorylated glycoproteins, subject to hydrolytic inactivation (Aducci et al., 1984). The auxin effect (which is not observed in isolated membranes) may thus represent an example of induced covalent modification of receptor activity, and it is tempting to speculate that this might have close bearing on the mode of action of auxin itself.

RESPONSE MUTANTS

In principle, mutants differing in hormone responsiveness constitute a powerful means of examining receptor function. Several mutants with reduced sensitivity to various hormones have been described, e.g. to abscisic acid in maize (Robichaud et al., 1980), Arabidopsis (Koornneef et al., 1984), tobacco cultures (Wong and Sussex, 1980) and barley (Ho et al., 1980); to gibberellin in certain dwarf wheats (Ho et al., 1981) and in barley (Ho et al., 1980); to cytokinins and to auxin in the moss Physcomitrella (Ashton et al., 1979), and to auxins in Arabidopsis (Maher and Martindale, 1980). Whilst reduced hormone sensitivity could arise for several reasons, in many of the above cases the evidence suggests that the mutation is receptor-related. To exploit any of these systems, however, the first hurdle that must be overcome is detection of hormone binding in the wild type. Thus Lomax-Reichert et al. (1982) were interested in using auxin-insensitive Physcomitrella mutants, but auxin binding in the wild type was barely detectable, and even then only after sucrose gradient fractionation of the total membrane preparations. Auxin binding has been detected at a low level in Arabidopsis particulate fractions, but binding in an auxin-resistant mutant was quantitatively as great as in the wild type (C. Bell, personal communication). In tomatoes very little difference was found between normal plants and non-ripening mutants nor and rin in terms of ethylene binding affinity or site concentration in either fruit or leaves (Sisler, 1982). If, therefore, the binding sites are receptors, it must be concluded that failure to ripen is not a consequence of defective binding of ethylene to its receptors. Mutant receptors might be able to bind ethylene, but have some lesion in response coupling - or the binding sites may just not be receptors. Possibly, mutants with enhanced rather than attenuated hormone sensitivity should be sought. Alternatively, mutant maize lines could be explored for putative auxin receptor mutants, given that in coleoptile membranes auxin binding is readily detectable and well-characterised.

Mention was made above of the gibberellin insensitivity of certain dwarf (Rht 3) wheats. However, sensitivity of such de-embryonated seeds or aleurones to gibberellin can be restored by pre-incubation at low temperature (Singh and Paleg, 1984). The characteristics of this effect suggested that the treatment somehow increases the availability of active receptor sites. In normal (tall) wheat, the aleurone layers only acquire gibberellin sensitivity 40-50 days post-anthesis. This change appears to depend upon the water content of the tissue, since sensitivity can be induced by drying immature grains to a water content of about 25% (Armstrong et al., 1982). Again, this phenomenon is suggestive of a membrane structural change influencing receptor activity or availability. In both these systems, the ability to manipulate experimentally hormone sensitivity presents obvious attractions for studies of receptor operation. Regrettably, no-one has yet demonstrated convincingly binding of a gibberellin to any fraction in cereal grains.

BINDING SITES AND RECEPTORS

In the foregoing, the term 'binding site' has been used almost exclusively when referring to specific systems, since in many cases no evidence other than binding is available as to receptor activity. However, there is little doubt that fusicoccin-binding sites represent receptors, though for what precisely is as yet uncertain. Similarly, there are high affinity plasma membrane receptors for the phytotropin group of synthetic auxin transport inhibitors, and these are readily detectable in both monocotyledons and dicotyledons. Again, the presumed normal endogenous ligand for these sites is unknown, but their function certainly seems connected with auxin transport. They have been detected immunohistochemically, and their localisation at the basal ends of vascular parenchyma cells in pea internodes (Jacobs and Gilbert, 1983) is entirely compatible with the preferential basal location of auxin efflux carriers required by the chemiosmotic model of auxin transport (Rubery and Sheldrake, 1974).

When it comes to known, native plant growth regulators, the position is somewhat less satisfactory. Various binding sites for gibberellins and for cytokinins have been described, without any one emerging as a clearly defined receptor candidate. High affinity binding sites for ethylene, showing many of the characteristics of receptors, have been intensively studied in bean cotyledons by the Aberystwyth group. This tissue has no <u>known</u> physiological response to ethylene, though as noted earlier in the context of auxin responses, this does not necessarily mean that the tissue is <u>not</u> ethylene responsive. A more detailed discussion of these various binding sites can be found elsewhere (Venis, 1985).

Auxin binding sites in maize coleoptile membranes, first studied by Hertel et al. (1972), have been extensively investigated in several laboratories and appear to fulfil many of the criteria expected of genuine receptors (Venis, 1985). Comparable binding sites have not yet been clearly detected in auxin-responsive dicotyledonous shoots, but this is likely to be a problem of methodology and/or lower site abundance. Examination of binding specificity has revealed a reasonable correlation between biological activity of auxin analogues and their apparent Kd values, one of the main discrepancies being the relatively low binding affinity for highly active phenoxyacetic acids such as 2,4-D. The use of general group-modifying reagents and site-directed irreversible inhibitors has pointed to several of the amino acids likely to be involved at the active auxin-binding site. The maize sites can be readily solubilised from the membranes without detergent and partly purified by various means, revealing a native molecular weight of 40-45 kilodaltons.

The various correlations listed earlier relating tissue responsiveness and binding activity provide indirect evidence in support of a receptor function for the auxin binding sites in maize membranes. In addition, there are two rather more direct pieces of evidence pointing to a receptor role. First, the solubilised, partly-purified binding proteins have been reconstituted in a synthetic bilayer lipid membrane, where they elicited an auxin- and ATP-dependent electrochemical response consistent with H$^+$ translocation (Thompson et al., 1983). Second, by an ingenious though involved sequence involving affinity and immunoaffinity chromatography, Löbler and Klämbt (1985a) were able to derive both a purified binding protein (a dimer of 20 kilodalton subunits) and a monospecific antiserum fraction. Using this antiserum, the binding sites appeared to be confined to the auxin-responsive outer epidermal cells. Moreover, by pre-incubation with the antiserum it was possible to block an auxin-dependent growth response (Löbler and Klämbt, 1985b), supporting the suggestion that the binding sites have a receptor function and indicating that auxin receptors involved in cell expansion are located at the outer face of the plasma membrane. This is not to say that similar or identical receptors, perhaps mediating other auxin responses, do not also occur intracellularly. Indeed, there is general agreement between laboratories that an abundant class of maize auxin binding sites is located on endoplasmic reticulum - these could, of course, be precursors to the plasma membrane sites.

RECEPTOR PURIFICATION

Ingenious though the Löbler and Klämbt purification protocol is, it is a laborious procedure and, moreover, it is not a method that one could guarantee to reproduce successfully. We have, therefore, been seeking more direct means of preparing extensively-purified or homogenous receptors for the generation of monoclonal and polyclonal antibodies respectively. Chromatography on DEAE Bio-Gel is a useful initial step, giving around 10-fold purification. The post-DEAE fraction is then subjected to FPLC, first by gel filtration on Superose 12 and then by anion exchange on Mono Q (Fig. 1). SDS gel electrophoresis (Fig. 2) reveals band enrichment

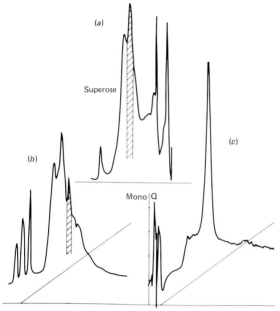

Fig. 1 <u>Purification of post-DEAE receptor by FPLC</u>. The active eluate from Superose 12 (shaded) was applied to Mono Q in piperazine (b) and eluted in a 0-0.35 M NaCl gradient. Binding activity eluted at 0.12-0.14 M NaCl (shaded) and rechromatographed (c) as a single absorbance peak.

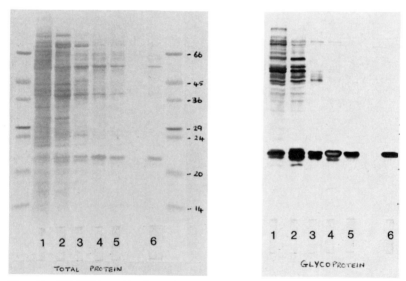

Fig. 2 <u>SDS-PAGE monitoring of receptor purification</u>. Identical 12% SDS gels were blotted and stained either for total protein or for glycoprotein. Fractions from: 1. DEAE Bio-Gel. 2. Superose 12. 3, 4. Mono Q in piperazine, adjacent active fractions. 5. Mono Q in phosphate. 6. Rechromatography of 5 under same conditions.

58

predominantly in a 22 kilodalton polypeptide, slightly larger than the 20 kilodaltons reported by Löbler and Klämbt (1985a). In agreement with Löbler et al. (1986), this polypeptide is highly glycosylated and in the most purified fractions (Fig. 2, track 6) it represents the sole concanavalin A-binding glycoprotein. In fractions from Superose and from Mono Q run in piperazine, the 22 kilodalton band is associated with a less abundant polypeptide at 21 kilodaltons, which is also highly glycosylated. This is in general agreement with a very recent report from Shimomura et al. (1986) whose protocol incorporated a carbodiimide-coupled NAA affinity column, and who obtained a preparation with subunit molecular weights of 21,000 (major) and 20,000 (minor).

CONCLUDING REMARKS

With scaling up and minor modification of the procedure summarised in Fig. 1, we expect soon to proceed to preparation of auxin receptor antibodies, as also do other laboratories. These will be invaluable in addressing such questions as subcellular and tissue localisation, number of binding proteins, and inter-species cross-reactivity, as well as aiding in immunoaffinity purification, exploration of receptor structure, function and signal transduction and in screening of cDNA libraries. In the near future, therefore, there is the prospect for the first time of having molecular probes to examine the role of a plant hormone receptor in development.

REFERENCES

Aducci, P., Ballio, A., Fiorucci, L. and Simonetti, E. (1984). Inactivation of solubilised fusicoccin-binding sites by endogenous plant hydrolases. Planta 160, 422-427.

Aducci, P., Ballio, A. and Marra, M. (1986). Incubation of corn coleoptiles with auxin enhances in-vitro fusicoccin binding. Planta 167, 129-132.

Aducci, P., Federico, R. and Ballio, A. (1980). Fusicoccin receptors. Evidence for an endogenous ligand. Planta 148, 208-210.

Armstrong, C., Black, M., Chapman, J.M., Norman, H.A. and Angold, R. (1982). The induction of sensitivity to gibberellin in aleurone tissue of developing wheat grains. I. The effect of dehydration. Planta 154, 573-577.

Ashton, N.W., Grimsley, N.H. and Cove, D.J. (1979). Analysis of gametophytic development in the moss, Physcomitrella patens using auxin and cytokinin resistant mutants. Planta 144, 427-435.

Bhattacharyya, K. and Biswas, B.B. (1982). Induction of a high affinity binding site for auxin in Avena root membrane. Phytochemistry 21, 1207-1211.

Hertel, R., Thomson, K-St. and Russo, V.E.A. (1972). In vitro auxin binding to particulate cell fractions from corn coleoptiles. Planta 107, 325-340.

Ho, T.H.D., Nolan, R.C. and Shute, D.E. (1981). Characterization of a gibberellin-insensitive dwarf wheat, D6899. Plant Physiology 67, 1026-1031.

Ho, T.H.D., Shih, S.C. and Kleinhofs, A. (1980). Screening for barley mutants with altered hormone sensitivity in their aleurone layers. Plant Physiology 66, 153-157.

Jacobs, M. and Gilbert, S.F. (1983). Basal localisation of the presumptive auxin transport carrier in pea stem cells. Science 220, 1297-1300.

Kearns, A.W. (1982). The search for the auxin receptor. D.Phil. thesis, University of York.

Koornneef, M., Reuling, G. and Karssen, C.M. (1984). The isolation and characterization of abscisic acid-insensitive mutants of Arabidopsis thaliana. Physiologia Plantarum 61, 377-383.

Löbler, M. and Klämbt, D. (1985a). Auxin-binding protein from coleoptile membranes of corn. I. Purification by immunological methods. Journal of Biological Chemistry 260, 9848-9853.

Löbler, M. and Klämbt, D. (1985b). Auxin-binding protein from coleoptile membranes of corn. II. Localisation of a putative auxin receptor. Journal of Biological Chemistry 260, 9854-9859.

Löbler, M., Klämbt, D. and Simon, K. (1986). Auxin-binding in target tissue. Journal of Cellular Biochemistry 10B (Suppl.), 11.

Lomax-Reichert, T., Ashton, N.W. and Ray, P.M. (1982). Naphthaleneacetic acid and fusicoccin binding to membrane fractions of the moss Physcomitrella patens. In "Plasmalemma and Tonoplast: Their Functions in the Plant Cell". (D. Marme, E. Marre and R. Hertel, eds.), pp 303-310. Elsevier Biomedical Press, Amsterdam - New York - Oxford.

Maan, A.C., Van der Linde, P.C.G., Harkes, P.A.A. and Libbenga, K.R. (1985). Correlation between the presence of membrane-bound auxin binding and root regeneration in cultured tobacco cells. Planta 164, 376-378.

Maher, E.P. and Martindale, S.J.B. (1980). Mutants of Arabidopsis thaliana with altered responses to auxins and gravity. Biochemical Genetics 18, 1041-1053.

Oostrom, H., Kulescha, Z., Van Vliet, T.B. and Libbenga, K.R. (1980). Characterization of a cytoplasmic auxin receptor from tobacco-pith callus. Planta 149, 44-47.

Robichaud, C.S., Wong, J. and Sussex, I.M. (1980). Control of in vitro growth of viviparous embryo mutants of maize by abscisic acid. Developmental Genetics 1, 325-330.

Rubery, P.H. and Sheldrake, A.R. (1974). Carrier-mediated auxin transport. Planta 118, 101-121.

Shimomura, S., Sotobayashi, T., Futai, M. and Fukui, T. (1986). Purification and properties of an auxin-binding protein from maize shoot membranes. Journal of Biochemistry 99, 1513-1524.

Sibley, D.R. and Lefkowitz, R.J. (1985). Molecular mechanisms of receptor desensitization using the β-adrenergic receptor-coupled adenylate cyclase system as a model. Nature (London) 317, 124-129.

Singh, S.P. and Paleg, L.G. (1984). Low temperature induction of hormonal sensitivity in genotypically gibberellic acid-insensitive aleurone tissue. Plant Physiology 74, 437-438.

Sisler, E.C. (1982). Ethylene binding in normal, rin, and nor mutant tomatoes. Journal of Plant Growth Regulation 1, 219-226.

Strickland, S. and Loeb, J.N. (1981). Obligatory separation of hormone binding and biological response curves in systems dependent upon secondary mediators of hormone action. Proceedings of the National Academy of Sciences USA 78, 1366-1370.

Südi, J. (1966). Increases in the capacity of pea tissue to form acyl-aspartic acids specifically induced by auxins. New Phytologist 65, 9-21.

Thompson, M., Krull, U.L. and Venis, M.A. (1983). A chemoreceptive bilayer lipid membrane based on an auxin receptor ATPase electrogenic pump. Biochemical and Biophysical Research Communications 110, 300-304.

Trewavas, A. (1980). An auxin induces the appearance of auxin-binding activity in artichoke tubers. Phytochemistry 19, 1303-1308.

Trewavas, A. (1981). How do plant growth substances work? Plant, Cell and Environment 4, 203-228.

Venis, M.A. (1985). Hormone-binding Sites in Plants. Longman, Harlow.

Venis, M.A. and Watson, P.J. (1978). Naturally occurring modifiers of auxin-receptor interaction in corn: identification as benzoxazolinones. Planta 142, 103-107.

Vreugdenhil, D., Burgers, A., Harkes, P.A.A and Libbenga, K.R. (1981). Modulation of the number of membrane-bound auxin-binding sites during the growth of batch-cultured tobacco cells. Planta 152, 415-419.

Walton, J.D. and Ray, P.M. (1981). Evidence for receptor function of auxin binding sites in maize. Plant Physiology 68, 1334-1338.

Wong, J.R. and Sussex, I.M. (1980). Isolation of abscisic acid resistant variants from tobacco cell cultures II. Selection and characterization of variants. Planta 148, 103-107.

Zurfluh, L.L. and Guilfoyle, T.J. (1982a). Auxin-induced changes in the population of translatable messenger RNA in elongating sections of soybean hypocotyl. Plant Physiology 69, 332-337.

Zurfluh, L.L. and Guilfoyle, T.J. (1982b). Auxin- and ethylene-induced changes in the population of translatable messenger RNA in basal sections and intact soybean hypocotyl. Plant Physiology 69, 338-340.

DO PLANT HORMONES REGULATE GENE EXPRESSION DURING DEVELOPMENT?

D.C. Baulcombe

Plant Breeding Institute, Maris Lane, Trumpington, Cambridge CB2 2LQ, England

Plant hormones modify plant development – developmental changes are associated with changes in gene expression. It is not surprising therefore that hormonal changes are often associated with gene expression. Two types of system in which this effect is well characterised are auxin stimulated growth in soybean and pea shoots and the gibberellin effect on cereal aleurone cells. From both of these systems various hormone regulated genes have been cloned and characterised. This step is leading to an understanding of the association between the primary hormone interaction and the mechanism of gene regulation. Eventually it will be possible from this work to provide an answer to the question of the title.

INTRODUCTION

This article describes an analysis of plant hormone action which is characterised by a single major feature. This is the contention that, in order to unravel the action of plant hormones, it is not necessary to focus on the primary events of hormone action. Instead, the emphasis should be on hormone associated changes in growth, which are susceptible to molecular analysis. The molecular approach is considered important, as this includes the most powerful techniques available for biologists interested in mechanisms which underlie the processes of development. The power of these techniques is exemplified most spectacularly in the context of animal development by the analyses on animal homeotic genes. These are genes which, having been known for some time as abstract activities of genetic loci, have now been isolated as DNA clones (North, 1985). From the clones it is proving possible to unravel how and when these genes are expressed, and how they might act. The approach proposed in this paper is a variation on that, in which the intention is to isolate genes which show modified activity as a result of hormone action and then to determine how the hormone (either primarily or secondarily) affects those genes. Subsequently it will be possible to trace events back to the primary interaction of the plant cell with the hormone. This is an attractive prospect when, as is true with plant hormones, the nature of the primary receptor molecules is still unknown (Venis, this volume) or when the biochemical changes associated with hormonal effects are not well characterised.

The particular molecular events considered in this paper involve regulation of gene expression. There are two reasons for this. Firstly, it has been shown that shifts in the number and type of genes expressed are characteristic of developmental transitions in plants (Kamalay and Goldberg, 1980). It is quite likely therefore that the changes in gene expression associated with plant hormone action might well be involved in either the causation or maintenance of the resultant change in growth or development. The second reason is that, following from the pioneering work in other systems, the molecular technology associated with analysis of gene regulation is particularly well developed.

At the most basic level this technology allows the recognition of changes in the expression of a particular gene. At a more advanced level, and in a few examples of plant, animal and fungal genes it is possible to identify the elements within and around a gene which control its expression and to identify cellular components ("trans-acting factors") which interact with the elements to effect the changes in

expression (Sassone-Corsi and Borrelli, 1986). Most hormonal systems in plants
where gene expression has been investigated are at the first, characterisation,
level. Furthermore, since the studies were often stimulated by earlier biochemical
analyses of the systems, the genes being investigated are abundant enzymic or
structural proteins which are most likely to characterise the hormone induced state
rather than to bring about that state. However, there are in some hormonally
regulated systems a number of uncharacterised genes which show modified expression
and which may have a causal role in the hormone modified growth.

At least two of these experimental systems have been developed beyond the basic
characterisation stage. The aim of this paper is to review the progress in these
experimental systems and to describe the prospects for obtaining a definitive answer
to the question posed by the title.

AUXIN MODIFIED GENE EXPRESSION IN SOYBEAN AND PEA

For some time the notion that changes in gene expression might be a component of
auxin modified growth was not universally accepted despite the large amount of data
suggesting the existence of growth limiting RNAs in auxin stimulated cells (Key et
al., 1967). The reasons for this included the (false) assumption that gene
expression would not be modified quickly enough to cause modified growth rates and
also the ascendancy of the acid growth hypothesis (Evans, 1985). This proposed that
auxin stimulated proton extrusion caused the observed rapid changes in elongation
growth. Recently, however, it has been shown that features of proton stimulated
growth do not correlate with those of auxin stimulated growth, for example in
kinetics and external cation requirements (Terry and Jones, 1981; Kutschera and
Schopfer, 1985). In addition, the acid-growth hypothesis is not relevant to auxin
stimulated division growth. Appreciation of these points lead several groups to
reappraise the effect of auxin on gene expression using newer molecular techniques.

Initially, the analysis on 1D and 2D gels of in vitro translation products of mRNA
was used to show that in both soybean hypocotyl and pea epicotyls, auxin modified
growth was accompanied by quantitative and qualitative changes in the mRNA
populations (Baulcombe et al., 1979; Zurfluh and Guilfoyle, 1982; Theologis and Ray,
1982). These involved both increases and decreases in mRNA levels, although
Baulcombe and Key (1980) showed with the soybean hypocotyl system that the most
prominent changes involve a decrease in the level of two or three different mRNAs.
These sequences were cloned as cDNA, the clones being identified by differential
hybridisation to RNA of auxin stimulated or control hypocotyls. Subsequently, a
similar approach was used to isolate cDNA clones of auxin up-regulated mRNAs in
soybean and in pea (Walker and Key, 1982; Hagen et al., 1984; Theologis et al.,
1985). Other cDNA clones of auxin regulated mRNAs, those for ribosomal proteins
were isolated by Gantt and Key (1985) using an immunological cloning method.

One important series of control experiments by Walker et al. (1985) showed that the
upward change in the level of mRNAs of cDNA clones JCW1 and JCW2 were not a
pleiotropic consequence of the auxin-mediated growth. They showed that fusicoccin
induced growth, which is induced via a different mechanism from auxin stimulated
growth, had no influence on the level of these mRNAs. Conversely, they showed that
cytokinins, which inhibit the auxin enhanced growth could not reverse the auxin
effect on the JCW1 and JCW2 mRNAs.

An equally important control is to show that the mRNA species showing an auxin
effect in an experimental system, are regulated during development of the plant.
The developmental changes should be consistent with the likely changes of auxin
stimulated growth during development, although, since little is known about changes
in auxin responsiveness of plant cells during development, this is difficult to
predict with accuracy. This notwithstanding, Baulcombe et al. (1981) showed that
the auxin repressed mRNAs were all expressed at the lowest level in the apical zones
of soybean shoots and roots. These, of course, are the zones where the auxin

response is probably most active in the intact plant.

The Role of Auxin-regulated Genes

Although it is not the major theme of this paper, it should be mentioned in passing how the isolation of these clones could facilitate understanding of auxin-controlled growth separately from addressing the link-up of auxin action and gene control. This is because the availability of the clones provides a method of characterising the encoded proteins and therefore the effects on growth downstream of the auxin effects on gene expression.

In the example of the ribosomal proteins (Gantt and Key, 1985), for which cDNA clones were identified immunologically, it is likely that their availability could affect the increased ribosome synthesis effect of auxin in soybean hypocotyl. This would have a knock-on quantitative effect on all aspects of growth mediated by increased rate of protein synthesis.

From the other, as yet anonymous, proteins encoded by auxin regulated mRNAs, the first information will come from sequence analysis. Key et al. (1986) have described in a preliminary report how one developmentally and auxin regulated mRNA encodes a protein with a repeat motif characteristic of some cell wall proteins.

In due course this kind of information will appear for other auxin-regulated mRNAs. Subsequently, the whole array of plant transformation and mutagenesis procedures will be used also to unravel the role of these proteins. In addition, it will be possible to carry out a biochemical analysis of auxin-regulated proteins using directly the recombinant proteins expressed in E. coli or indirectly using antibodies raised against them.

The Mechanism of Auxin-regulated Gene Expression

Having established that the expression of some genes can be modified by an auxin response, it then becomes necessary to establish the level, transcriptional or post-transcriptional, of this control. This can be considered as the next step in tracing back towards the primary interaction of auxin with the cell.

So far, the results from 2 systems have produced quite different results, and reflect at the molecular level how auxins can trigger different types of growth process.

Using the soybean hypocotyl system, Baulcombe et al. (1981) analysed nuclear RNA for the precursors of mRNA sequences which decrease following auxin treatment. It was reasoned that the level of these precursors would reflect the equilibrium of the specific mRNA synthesis and decay within the nucleus. Perturbation of either of these processes would cause the level of mRNA precursor to change. However, the observation was that the level of precursor remained more or less constant following auxin stimulation. This finding suggested that the large auxin-induced decrease in the level of these mRNAs was mediated by a post-transcriptional process, possibly acting at a post-nuclear level, for example affecting the stability of cytoplasmic mRNA.

The different finding came from the work of Hagen and Guilfoyle (1985), working with auxin-stimulated mRNAs in excised soybean hypocotyls from the elongating zone. They used a sensitive assay in which isolated nuclei are incubated with labelled ribonucleotide triphosphates and the specific mRNA transcript is assayed by hybridisation with specific cloned probes. In these experiments, when there is no initiation of RNA synthesis and no breakdown of RNA in the isolated nuclei, the amount of RNA which hybridises to the probe reflects the number of polymerase molecules on the specific gene. From these experiments it was shown that in the auxin treated hypocotyls there were more run-off transcripts from the auxin-stimulated genes than in the control nuclei, indicating regulation at the transcriptional level. A second interesting and highly relevant finding of this work was that the stimulation of transcription could be detected within 15 minutes of the beginning of auxin treatment. The question of the timing of auxin-stimulated expression of certain genes has been addressed also by Theologis et al. (1985) who showed that there is an increase in even the steady state level of some mRNA species as soon as five minutes after the application of auxin. So much for the objections raised by exponents of the acid growth hypothesis that synthesis of growth limiting RNAs could not account for rapid auxin induced growth!

GA REGULATED GENES IN CEREAL ALEURONES

The cereal aleurone system was the first in which plant hormone action was associated with a specific effect on the expression of an identifiable gene. The gene of course is α-amylase and the plant hormone, gibberellic acid (GA). The earlier work in which the effect of gibberellin on α-amylase gene expression was characterised using density labelling, inhibitor and in vitro translation experiments has been reviewed many times (e.g. Akazawa and Miyata, 1982). The intention in this paper is to describe some recent work, both published and unpublished, which will trace the connection between gene regulation and hormone action.

Gibberellic Acid Regulates Many Genes in Cereal Aleurones

The earlier in vitro translation analyses of aleurone mRNA had suggested that mRNAs other than those for α-amylase are regulated by GA (Higgins et al., 1976; Mozer, 1980). This was proved conclusively when cDNA clones of GA-regulated mRNA species were isolated which were, by several criteria, not α-amylase mRNA (Baulcombe and Buffard, 1983). Two GA down-regulated mRNAs were also identified in this manner from aleurones of wheat, although in this instance it was not clear whether the observed effect implies a mechanism which is targetted on these genes. An equally likely possibility is that these represent abundant mRNAs from an earlier developmental stage, the decay of which is accentuated in the GA stimulated aleurone cells.

It was not possible on the basis of in vitro translation analyses to identify the function of the GA stimulated mRNAs. However, now that clones are available it has been possible to deduce the protein sequence encoded by these mRNAs. Global search computer programmes have identified three of these sequences as various types of protease. This is especially gratifying as early experiments by Jacobsen and Varner (1967) had suggested that de novo synthesised protease is a consequence of GA action in barley aleurones.

Two of these mRNAs encode sulphur proteases homologous to cathepsin H (Rogers et al., 1985) and cathepsin B (Murphy and Baulcombe, 1987) from animal sources. The third protease mRNA in wheat aleurones has very good homology with carboxypeptidase Y of yeast (Baulcombe et al., 1987a). One tangential conclusion from these findings is that it may be possible to identify genes from a range of organisms if the protein sequence is known from only one organism. This may apply especially if the known sequence includes the active site, since in these 3 proteases and also in α-amylase (Rogers, 1985), the active site protein sequences are highly conserved between plants and animals or fungi or even bacteria.

In addition, the comparison of sequences of proteins from diverse (phylogenetically) sources may lead to new findings about structure-function relationships in proteins. For example, in the carboxypeptidase-like gene of wheat there are several domains of homology with the yeast enzyme (Baulcombe et al., 1987a). Some of these domains had been identified previously as having an important role in the active site or substrate binding. However, other conserved domains had not been recognised previously as having functional significance.

A second level at which GA regulates several genes derives from the multiple nature of many genes in higher plants. This and the resulting complications is illustrated quite well by the α-amylase genes of wheat and barley. These are encoded at multiple loci on chromosomes 1 and 6 (barley) (Muthukrishnan et al., 1984) or group 6 and group 7 chromosomes of wheat (Lazarus et al., 1985). Furthermore, it has been shown by isozyme analysis and direct analysis of clones of nuclear DNA (Huttly and Baulcombe, 1986) that each locus contains multiple alleles. To add to the complexity of the situation, it is now known that the different alleles are not all expressed equally. For example, the α-Amy2 genes (located on the group 7 chromosomes of wheat) are expressed later in germination than the α-Amy1 genes (on the group 6) chromosomes (Lazarus et al., 1985). This is most likely not because othe GA response is initiated asynchronously on the different genes, but because expression of the α-Amy2 genes is more prolonged. In barley the same situation exists in that the expression of the chromosome 1 encoded genes is more prolonged than the chromosome 6 genes (Rogers, 1984). In addition, Deikman and Jones (1985) have shown a differential effect of calcium on the expression of the group 1 and group 6 chromosome α-amylase genes. Expression of the α-amylase genes from the group 1 chromosomes is independent of calcium, whereas the group 6 genes require calcium, possibly for efficient translation. There may be also other differences between the expression of α-amylase genes from the two loci, in terms of sensitivity to gibberellin concentration.

These results were obtained because the use of cloned cDNA or genomic DNA probes provides a sensitive means of measuring expression from a group of homologous genes or even an individual gene independently of related genes. In the examples described above, use was made of the variation between α-amylase genes in the 5' and 3' sequences which flank the protein coding sequence. The same techniques were applied to an analysis of transcription of an unusual α-amylase gene encoded on the group 5 chromosomes (Baulcombe et al., 1987b). It was found that this gene was not expressed at all during germination, but that it was expressed soon after anthesis in the developing grain. Expression of a subset of the α-Amy2, but not the α-Amy1 genes at this time has been recorded previously. Because the features of this gene (chromosomal location, expression and also sequence) distinguish it from the better characterised α-Amy1 and α-Amy2 genes it is now assigned to a new α-amylase locus, α-Amy3. These findings illustrate how the differential expression of multigene families can allow an organism to express a protein at different times in development, when different control mechanisms operate. In addition they show how it is not necessarily accurate to draw conclusions from developmental studies in which an enzyme activity is measured. It may well be that, as with α-amylase genes, different alleles are active at different stages.

The Mechanism of GA Regulated Expression in Aleurones

From the description above it should be clear that explanations of how GA action affects gene expression in the cereal aleurone must account for effects on multiple, unrelated genes. If there is a single mechanism acting on all genes the effect must be close to transcription, so that secondary effects could account for differences between α-Amy1 and a-Amy2 expression and also variation in timing between expression of the α-amylase genes and the various non-α-amylase genes. The alternative would be that the stimulated expression is mediated through several mechanisms acting variously on the different genes.

To date, the results are not conclusive, but clearly the way is open for a detailed mechanistic understanding of the regulatory processes.

Two groups, using nuclear run-off experiments described above, have shown that the regulation is at the transcriptional level in both barley and oat aleurone layers (Jacobsen and Beach, 1985; Zwar and Hooley, 1986). In addition, the group working with barley have shown that another, still anonymous gene, is also regulated transcriptionally. However, such experiments do not indicate necessarily that different genes are regulated co-ordinately by a single mechanism.

To address this point, we have sought to identify regulatory sequence elements close to α-amylase and other gibberellin responsive genes. The approach has involved a simple sequence analysis of the isolated and cloned genes combined with a hybridisation analysis to identify the transcribed regions of the genes. This analysis has yielded several findings:

(1) In different members of the wheat α-amylase (α-Amy2) gene family, the homology breaks off at about 250 bp on the 5' side of the transcriptional start point. This implies that the regulatory sequences are located inside that sequence (Huttly and Baulcombe, 1986).

(2) There are short homologous domains shared between different α-amylase genes, which might be regulatory sequences controlling expression in either the aleurone, or in the developing grain (Baulcombe et al., 1987b). However, in no case has it been possible to detect sequence elements which are shared between both types of GA-regulated α-amylase gene and the carboxypeptidase gene (Baulcombe et al., 1987a). There could be several reasons for this. It may be that regulatory sequence elements have a composition which is outside the scope of DNA sequence analysis algorithms currently in use. Alternatively, it may be that despite the apparent co-regulation of the α-amylase and other genes in cereal aleurones, there are multiple regulatory mechanisms acting on the genes.

There is only one way to resolve these problems. The promoters from the GA regulated genes will be coupled to a suitable reporter gene and reintroduced into aleurone or equivalent cells. The activity of the promoters either intact or in modified form would be assayed independently of the endogenous genes. The regulatory regions could be located then from the position of promoter modifications which affect regulated production of the reporter activity.

Already several different genes from higher plants have been analysed in this way, although not as yet hormonally regulated genes (Goldberg, 1986). Beyond this there is the prospect to use regulatory DNA elements to probe for regulatory proteins in the cell and again there are preliminary indications that the appropriate techniques, which are well established for analysis of animal genes, are also being used successfully for plant genes (Maier et al., 1987). It is my expectation that, when the experimental systems described in this article have reached that point, hormone research will begin to reap the benefit. Not only will it be possible to address directly the question posed by my title, but other fundamental questions will become accessible. For example, having identified cellular components which mediate hormonal responses it will be possible to ask why different plant tissues and cells produce such diverse responses to a single hormone.

REFERENCES

Akazawa, T. and Miyata, S. (1982). Biosynthesis and secretion of α-amylase and other hydrolases in germinating cereal seeds. In "Essays in Biochemistry" (P.N. Campbell and R.D. Marshall, eds), pp 41-78. Academic Press, London, New York.

Baulcombe, D.C., Barker, R.F. and Jarvis, M.G. (1987a). A gibberellin responsive wheat gene has homology to yeast carboxypeptidase Y. Submitted for publication.

Baulcombe, D.C. and Buffard, D. (1983). Gibberellic-acid-regulated expression of α-amylase and six other genes in wheat aleurone layers. Planta **157,** 493-501.

Baulcombe, D.C., Giorgini, J. and Key, J.L. (1979). The effect of auxin on the polyadenylated RNA of soybean hypocotyls. In "Genome Organisation and Expression in Plants" (C.J. Leaver, ed.). Plenum Press, New York and London.

Baulcombe, D.C., Huttly, A.K., Martienssen, R.A., Barker, R.F. and Jarvis, M.G. (1987b). A novel α-amylase gene (α-Amy3). Submitted for publication.

Baulcombe, D.C. and Key, J.L. (1980). Polyadenylated RNA sequences which are reduced in concentration following auxin treatment of soybean hypocotyls. The Journal of Biological Chemistry 255, 8907-8913.

Baulcombe, D.C., Kroner, P.A. and Key, J.L. (1981). Auxin and gene regulation. In "Levels of Genetic Control in Development" (S. Subtelny and U.K. Abbott, eds.), pp 83-97. Alan R. Liss, Inc., New York.

Deikman, J. and Jones, R.L. (1985). Regulation of the accumulation of mRNA for α-amylase isoenzymes in barley aleurone. Plant Physiology 80, 672-675.

Evans, M.L. (1985). The action of auxin on plant cell elongation. CRC Critical Reviews in Plant Science 2, 317-365.

Gantt, J.S. and Key, J.L. (1985). Coordinate expression of ribosomal protein mRNAs following auxin treatment of soybean hypocotyls. The Journal of Biological Chemistry 260, 6175-6181.

Goldberg, R.B. (1986). Regulation of plant gene expression. Philosophical Transactions of the Royal Society of London, Series B 313, 343-353.

Hagen, G. and Guilfoyle, T.J. (1985). Rapid induction of selective transcription by auxins. Molecular and Cellular Biology 5, 1197-1203.

Hagen, G., Kleinschmidt, A. and Guilfoyle, T. (1984). Auxin-regulated gene expression in intact soybean hypocotyl 1 and excised hypocotyl 1 sections. Planta 162, 147-153.

Higgins, T.J.V., Zwar, J.A. and Jacobsen, J.V. (1976). Gibberellic acid enhances the level of translatable mRNA for α-amylase in barley aleurone layers. Nature 260, 166-168.

Huttly, A.K. and Baulcombe, D.C. (1986). Subfamily organisation in the α-Amy2 genes of wheat. Biochemical Society Transactions 14, 1099.

Jacobsen, J.V. and Beach, L.R. (1985). Control of transcription of α-amylase and rRNA genes in barley aleurone protoplasts by gibberellin and abscisic acid. Nature 316, 275-277.

Jacobsen, J.V. and Varner, J.E. (1967). Gibberellic acid-induced synthesis of protease by isolated aleurone layers of barley. Plant Physiology 42, 1596-1600.

Kamalay, J.C. and Goldberg, R.B. (1980). Regulation of structural gene expression in tobacco. Cell 19, 935-946.

Key, J.L., Barnett, N.M. and Lin, C.Y. (1967). RNA and protein biosynthesis and the regulation of cell elongation by auxin. Annals of the New York Academy of Sciences 144, 49-62.

Key, J.L., Kroner, P., Walker, J., Honey, J., Ulrich, T., Ainley, W., Gantt, J.S. and Nagao, R.T. (1986). Auxin regulated gene expression. Philosophical Transactions of the Royal Society of London, Series B 314, 427-440.

Kutschera, U. and Schopfer, P. (1985). Evidence against the acid-growth theory of auxin action. Planta 163, 483-493.

Lazarus, C.M., Baulcombe, D.C. and Martienssen, R.A. (1985). α-amylase genes of wheat are two multigene families which are differentially expressed. Plant Molecular Biology 5, 13-24.

Maier, U.-G., Brown, J.W.S., Toloczyki, C. and Feix, G. (1987). Binding of a nuclear factor to a consensus sequence in the 5' flanking region of zein genes from maize. The EMBO Journal **6**, 17-22.

Mozer, T.J. (1980). Control of protein synthesis in barley aleurone layers by the plant hormones gibberellic acid and abscisic acid. Cell **70**, 479-485.

Murphy, G.J.P. and Baulcombe, D.C. (1987). A gibberellin regulated gene of wheat aleurones has homology to cathepsin B of mammalian cells. Submitted for publication.

Muthukrishnan, S., Gill, B.S., Swegle, M. and Chandra, G.R. (1984). Structural genes for α-amylases are located on barley chromosomes 1 and 6. The Journal of Biological Chemistry **259**, 13637-13639.

North, G. (1985). Drosophila development: homing in on homoeo boxes. Nature **318**, 605-606.

Rogers, J.C. (1984). Two barley α-amylase gene families are regulated differently in aleurone cells. The Journal of Biological Chemistry **260**, 3731-3738.

Rogers, J.C. (1985). Conserved amino acid sequence domains in alpha-amylases from plants, mammals, and bacteria. Biochemical and Biophysical Research Communications **128**, 470-476.

Rogers, J.C., Dean, D. and Heck, G.R. (1985). Aleurain: a barley thiol protease closely related to mammalian cathepsin H. Proceedings of the National Academy of Science U.S.A. **82**, 6512-6516.

Sassone-Corsi, P. and Borrelli, E. (1986). Transcriptional regulation by trans-acting factors. Trends in Genetics **2**, 215-219.

Terry, M.E. and Jones, R.L. (1981). Effect of salt on auxin-induced acidification and growth by pea internode sections. Plant Physiology **68**, 59-64.

Theologis, A., Huynh, T.V. and Davis, R.W. (1985). Rapid induction of specific mRNAs by auxin in pea epicotyl tissue. Journal of Molecular Biology **183**, 53-68.

Theologis, A. and Ray, P.M. (1982). Early auxin-regulated polyadenylylated mRNA sequences in pea stem tissue. Proceedings of the National Academy of Science, U.S.A. **79**, 418-421.

Walker, J.C. and Key, J.L. (1982). Isolation of cloned cDNAs to auxin-responsive poly(A)+ RNAs of elongating soybean hypocotyl. Proceedings of the National Academy of Science, U.S.A. **79**, 7185-7189.

Walker, J.C., Legocka, J., Edelman, L. and Key, J.L. (1985). An analysis of growth regulator interactions and gene expression during auxin-induced cell elongation using cloned complementary DNAs to auxin-responsive messenger RNAs. Plant Physiology **77**, 847-850.

Zurfluh, L.L. and Guilfoyle, T.J. (1982). Auxin-induced changes in the population of translatable messenger RNA in elongating sections of soybean hypocotyl. Plant Physiology **69**, 332-337.

Zwar, J.A. and Hooley, R. (1986). Hormonal regulation of α-amylase gene transcription in wild oat (Avena fatua L.) aleurone protoplasts. Plant Physiology **80**, 459-463.

SECTION II

GENETICAL PROBING OF HORMONE ACTION IN DEVELOPMENT

GIBBERELLIN-DEFICIENT MUTANTS OF MAIZE AND PEA AND THE MOLECULAR

ACTION OF GIBBERELLINS

J. MacMillan

School of Chemistry, University of Bristol, Bristol, BS8 1TS, England

Evidence is presented to support the view that GA_1 is a plant hormone regulating stem elongation in maize and pea. Possible approaches to the identification of GA_1 receptor(s) in shoots of maize and pea are outlined.

INTRODUCTION

The gibberellins (GAs) are natural plant constituents which elicit a range of developmental responses when applied to growing plants in g amounts. For example, certain dwarf mutants respond by showing normal stem elongation. This response is unique to the GAs; no other known chemical treatment will substitute for GAs. Stem elongation and the role of GAs is the main theme of this paper. This topic is used as a vehicle to discuss the controversy over the hormonal concept of GAs, to present the case that GA_1 is a hormone for stem elongation, and to discuss some current studies on the molecular basis of GA action.

GENERAL CONSIDERATIONS

Trewavas (for example, 1981, 1982) has questioned the thesis that GAs, cytokinins, auxins, abscisic acid and ethylene are plant hormones. His main criticisms are:
(1) Does-response curves for these compounds span 4–5 orders of magnitude in growth substance concentration in contrast to mammalian hormones for which the range is 1–2 orders of magnitude.
(2) There is no evidence of "action at a distance".
(3) Plant responses are not dependent on the concentration of these substances but only on the sensitivity of the plant system. He states that "The system is designed to resist or buffer against changes in concentration (of the natural growth substance) in terms of the response".

Point (1) can be answered at two levels. Firstly, the selection of response data, used by Trewavas, was limited. Drawing on a much wider selection Firn (unpublished), has shown that a more typical range for plant growth substances is 2 orders of magnitude. Secondly, in the case of the gibberellins, whole plant growth responses have been compared with mammalian enzyme responses. A more meaningful comparison is between the induction of α-amylase synthesis in aleurone protoplasts by GAs (Hooley, 1981 and unpublished data) and the induced protein synthesis by oestradiol in the rat uterus (Katzenellenbogen and Gorski, 1972). As shown in Fig. 1 the concentration range for the saturation of response occurs from 10^{-7} – 10^{-9}M for the GA and 10^{-8} – 10^{-10}M for the steroid. It must be concluded that the responses occur over a similar order of magnitude for plant and animal systems.

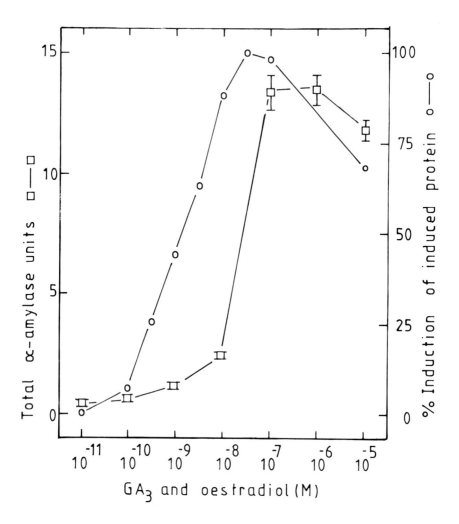

Fig.1 Dose-response curves

□ - □ GA$_3$ and total α-amylase synthesis in protoplasts from aleurone cells of Avena fatua (R. Hooley, unpublished results).

0 - 0 Oestradiol and induced protein synthesis in rat uteri (re-drawn from Katzenellenbogen and Gorski, 1972).

Point (2) may be true on the strict classical definition of a mammalian hormone. But, as Trewavas points out, plants are not animals and plants may adopt a different hormonal strategy. For example, the hormone might be synthesised in the target cells from a precursor which was synthesised distant from, and transported

74

to, the target cells. Indeed there are indications that this may occur in mammalian systems; aldosterone is synthesised in the adrenal cortex and converted in the liver to more polar metabolites which may be the true hormones for Na^+ and K^+ homeostasis (Morris et al., 1983). Evidence that a similar situation may also exist in pea stem elongation is presented later.

Point (3) can now be answered, with regard to GAs and stem elongation, from studies using tall maize and pea plants and GA-deficient dwarf mutants of these two species. The approach involved:
(a) identification of the native GAs in the normal genotypes of these two species;
(b) determination of the GA metabolic pathways of the native GAs in the tall plants and the position of the metabolic blocks in the dwarfs;
(c) identification of the active native GA for stem elongation;
(d) investigation of the relationship between the concentration of the active GA and the stem elongation response.

For the successful outcome of this experimental approach it was necessary to use definitive analytical methods such as capillary GC-MS with a data processing system. In addition, detailed metabolic studies were required using synthesised GA- substrates, doubly labelled with a radio-isotope and a stable isotope (MacMillan, 1984, 1985a,b). This is not to indulge in "an obsessive chemical approach to complex biological problems" as stated by Trewavas (1985). Also challenged are the statements attributed to Schrader by Vanderhoef and Kosuge (1984) that "there should not be so much attention paid to the metabolism of plant hormones" and that "the metabolic reactions should be considered to be of secondary importance in understanding the mode of plant hormone action". It is only by establishing the native metabolic pathways that the active compound can be identified. There are many examples of this in mammalian biochemistry. For example it has been established that calcium metabolism in the intestine and bone is not controlled by cholecalciferol (vitamin D3) but by its metabolite 1,25-dihydroxycholecalciferol (Lawson et al., 1971; Norman et al., 1971). The successful application of this chemical and metabolic approach, combined with the use of stem-elongation dwarfs of Pisum sativum (pea) and Zea mays (maize) is now reviewed.

NATIVE GAs IN SHOOTS OF PEA AND MAIZE

In pea, GAs were first identified in seeds. In a series of papers Frydman and MacMillan (1973), Frydman et al. (1974) and Sponsel and MacMillan (1978) identified GA_9, GA_{17}, GA_{20}, GA_{29}, GA_{44}, GA_{51} and GA_{29}-catabolite by GC-MS. Subsequently the same GAs plus GA_{19}, GA_1 and GA_8 have been identified by GC-MS in shoots of tall peas by Davies et al. (1982), Ingram et al. (1983, 1984) and Gaskin et al. (1985).

In maize GAs were initially identified in the tassels by GC-MS, (Hedden et al., 1982; Heupel et al., 1985). These were: GA_{53}, GA_{17}, GA_{19}, GA_{20}, GA_1 and GA_8. Subsequently, the same GAs have also been identified in the shoots of normal tall maize by Spray et al., (1984) and Phinney et al. (unpublished).

METABOLIC PATHWAYS IN SHOOTS OF PEA AND MAIZE

The identification of these GAs in the shoots of pea and maize enabled the metabolic pathway, shown in Fig. 2, to be constructed. This pathway was based originally on evidence for an early 13-hydroxylation pathway from the common GA-biosynthetic intermediate, GA_{12}-aldehyde, in seeds of pea (Frydman and MacMillan, 1975; Sponsel and MacMillan, 1977, 1978 and 1980; Kamiya and Graebe, 1983).

The present evidence for this pathway in shoots of pea and maize is derived from metabolic studies of the isotopically-labelled, native GAs and their ent-kaurenoid precursors applied to normal and dwarf genotypes, combined with the bio-activities of these compounds. The results have been reviewed for pea by MacMillan (1985a,b) and for maize by Phinney (1984; Phinney et al., 1986). The salient points are:
(a) the dwarf-1 mutant of maize is blocked at the step between copalyl pyrophosphate and ent-kaurenoic acid (Hedden and Phinney, 1979);
(b) the nana-mutant of pea is also blocked for GA biosynthesis at an early step before GA_{12}-aldehyde (Potts and Reid, 1983);
(c) the dwarf-2 and dwarf-3 mutants of maize are blocked at the steps between GA_{12}-aldehyde and GA_{53} (Phinney and Spray, 1982);
(d) the dwarf-1 mutant of maize and the le mutant of pea are blocked at the step between GA_{20} and GA_1 (Spray et al., 1984; Ingram et al., 1984).

Thus, both the dwarf-1 of maize and the le mutant of pea are blocked late in the pathway shown in Fig. 2. These late metabolic blocks were of crucial importance in identifying GA_1 as the only native GA which is necessary per se for stem elongation in maize and pea. The evidence for the position of these blocks was obtained by methods which Trewavas (1985) has described as an "obsessive chemical approach". $[^3H,^{13}C]$Gibberellin A_{20} was prepared and fed to normal and dwarf seedlings of pea and maize. The $[^3H,^{13}C]$metabolites were identified by HPLC-radiocounting and capillary-GC-MS. In the case of pea, Ingram et al. (1984) found that $[^3H,^{13}C]GA_{20}$ was metabolised to $[^3H,^{13}C]GA_1$, and also to $[^3H,^{13}C]GA_8$ and $[^3H,^{13}C]GA_{29}$, in all Le genotypes. In all plants homozygous for the le gene the only product was $[^3H,^{13}C]GA_{29}$ and, in one case, $[^3H,^{13}C]GA_{29}$-catabolite; no $[^3H,^{13}C]GA_1$ or other 3- hydroxylated $[^3H,^{13}C]GAs$ were detected. The same results were obtained irrespective of the genotype at the Na locus. In all Na lines, however, the $[^3H,^{13}C]$metabolites were diluted by endogenous $[^{12}C]GAs$ indicating that the applied $[^3H,^{13}C]GAs$ and the endogenous GAs were metabolised in the same way. In contrast there was no dilution of the $[^{13}C]$ label in the na lines, confirming that the na mutants do not biosynthesise C_{19}-GAs. Similar results were obtained for maize by Spray et al. (1984). Thus in normal and dwarf-5 seedlings $[^3H,^{13}C]GA_{20}$ was metabolised to $[^3H,^{13}C]GA_1$ and either $[^3H,^{13}H]GA_{29}$ or $[^3H,^{13}]GA_{29}$-catabolite. In dwarf-1 the only metabolite was $[^3H,^{13}C]GA_{29}$. As expected from the position of the block in dwarf-5 early in the biosynthetic pathway, there was no dilution of the $[^{13}C]$ in the recovered GA_{20} or the GA_{29} from this mutant. These results established that GA_{20} is converted into GA_1 in normal plants and in mutants in which the biosynthetic blocks occur before GA_{20} and that this conversion does not occur in the le mutant of pea or in the dwarf-1 mutant of maize.

IDENTIFICATION OF GA_1 AS THE NATIVE GA FOR STEM ELONGATION IN MAIZE AND PEA

These mutants, blocked at known steps in the GA-biosynthetic pathway (Fig. 2), were then used to test the biological activities of those GAs which are members of the pathway of the normal genotype. In this way it was determined which of the GAs in the pathway were required for stem elongation per se and not through conversion to a GA later in the pathway.

For maize mutants, Phinney and Spray (1982) obtained the comparative bioassay data, summarised in Table 1. In addition, Tamura et al. (1966) have reported that GA_{19} showed similar activity to GA_1 on dwarfs-2 and -5 but very low activity on dwarf-1. Also Yokota et al. (1971) found that GA_{29}, formed by 2β -hydroxylation of GA_{20}, and GA_8, the immediate metabolite of GA_1, showed no or little activity on dwarfs-1, -2 and -5. Hoad and Kuo (1970) found that GA_{17}, the branch metabolite of GA_{19}, was inactive on dwarfs-1, -2 and -5.

Table 1 Relative activities of native GAs and their precursors in dwarf-1, dwarf-2, dwarf-3 and dwarf-5 bioassays. (Data from Phinney and Spray, 1982).

Mutant	ent-kaurene	GA_{12}-aldehyde	GA_{53}-aldehyde	GA_{53}	GA_{20}	GA_1
dwarf-5	1	5	10	10	100	100
dwarf-3	0	0	10	10	100	100
dwarf-2	0	0	0	10	100	100
dwarf-1	0	0	0	1	1	100

For the na and le mutants of pea similar, if less extensive, bioassay data are available. For example, Ingram et al. (1983) found that Le lines responded equally to GA_{20} and GA_1 irrespective of the genotype at the Na locus. In contrast these authors found that genotypes, homozygous for the le allele, respond much less (1-10%) to GA_{20} than to GA_1. This differential response was most clearly illustrated using the Le/na and le/na segregates, since the untreated plants of each genotype had the same initial stem length because of the presence of the na allele (Reid et al., 1983). In the cultivar Progress No. 9, homozygous for the le allele, GA_{17} and GA_{19} showed very low activity (Hoad and Kuo, 1970; Tamura et al., 1966) as did GA_{29}, GA_{29}-catabolite, GA_8, and GA_8-catabolite (Yokota et al., 1971; Sponsel, 1983).

These bioassay results established that GA_1 is the only native GA of maize and pea that shows high activity in dwarf-1 and the le mutants. The branch metabolites and the metabolites after GA_1 in the pathway (Fig. 2) are inactive in all the mutants. The precursors of GA_1 showed high activity only in those mutants that are blocked at steps in the pathway preceeding their position in the pathway. In the dwarf-1 mutant of maize GA_{53}, GA_{19} and GA_{20} do show about 1% of the activity of GA_1 and GA_{20} does show 1-10% of the activity of GA_1 in le mutant of pea. There are two explanations for the observed activities of these

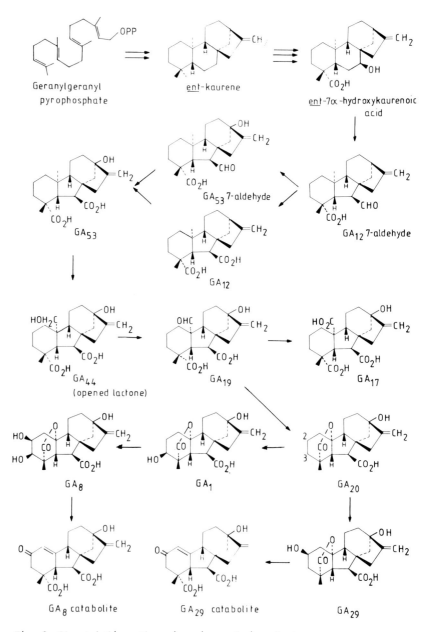

Geranylgeranyl
pyrophosphate

ent-kaurene

ent-7α-hydroxykaurenoic
acid

GA$_{53}$ 7-aldehyde

GA$_{12}$ 7-aldehyde

GA$_{53}$

GA$_{12}$

GA$_{44}$
(opened lactone)

GA$_{19}$

GA$_{17}$

GA$_8$

GA$_1$

GA$_{20}$

GA$_8$ catabolite

GA$_{29}$ catabolite

GA$_{29}$

Fig. 2 GA-metabolic pathway in maize and rice shoots.

precursors of GA_1 in the dwarf-1 and le mutants. The first is that the precursors possess inherent biological activity. The other explanation is that the mutations at the D-1 and the Le loci are "leaky". That is, they result in an altered 3 β-hydroxylase that can still convert GA_{20} to GA_1, albeit inefficiently. To distinguish between these two possibilities Ingram et al., (1986) fed very high levels of $[^3H,^{13}C]GA_{20}$ to the uppermost expanding leaves of 20-day old seedlings of the genotypes nale and naLe; the presence of the na mutation ensured only traces of endogenous C_{19}-GAs in both genotypes. After 6 days the metabolites in the tissue above the treated internode were identified by GCMS. In the na/le genotype the major metabolites were $[^3H,^{13}C]GA_{29}$ and $[^3H,^{13}C]GA_{29}$-catabolite, as expected from previously described results (Ingram et al., 1984). In addition, however, traces of $[^3H,^{13}C]GA_1$, that 3-epi-$[^3H,^{13}C]GA_1$ and $[^3H,^{13}C]GA_8$ were also identified showing that the le mutation is "leaky".

Thus it must be concluded that GA_1 is the only native GA in maize and pea that is required for stem elongation in these two species and that other members of the pathway (Fig. 2) are only active by virtue of their conversion to GA_1. These conclusions provide an explanation for previously reported inconsistencies, referred to by Trewavas (1981), over the quantitative comparisons of the GA-content of tall and GA-responding dwarf plants. When extracts of dwarf and tall plants are bioassayed on dwarf mutants a quantitative difference in response may or may not be observed. It depends on which dwarf mutant is extracted and which dwarf mutant is used for the bioassay. For example, the extracts of dwarfs-1, -2 and -3 may well give a similar response as extracts of tall plants using a dwarf-5 bioassay but not using a dwarf-1 assay. It is not the total GA-like content, but the GA_1 content, that relates to phenotype.

QUANTITATIVE RELATIONSHIP BETWEEN GIBBERELLIN A_1 AND STEM ELONGATION

As mentioned earlier, Trewavas (1982) has advanced the view that it is plant sensitivity, and not the concentration of "gibberellic acid" (sic), that controls, inter alia, stem elongation. The shortened internode length of GA-responding dwarfs suggests otherwise. The existence (Reid, 1986) of double mutants of pea, such as na/lh and na/ls with even shorter internodes than their corresponding single mutants, reinforces the view that GAs are quantitatively required for stem elongation. With the identification of GA_1 as the native GA required for stem elongation in maize and pea, attention can now be directed to the quantitative relationship between GA_1 and stem elongation.

As described in the previous section, Ingram et al. (1986) have provided evidence that the le mutation is "leaky". This finding has been used to examine the relationship between GA_1 concentration and stem elongation in two sets of experiments. Firstly treatment of seedlings of na/le and na/Le mutants with a range of amounts of $[^3H]GA_{20}$ on the uppermost fully expanded leaves gave, for both genotypes, a straight line relationship between the logarithm of the amount of $[^3H]GA_8$, formed in the expanded region above the treated internode, and internode extension. Secondly, the same relationship was observed for the three genotypes le^d, le and Le; the le^d allele confered a more severe dwarfing phenotype than the le allele (Ross and Reid, 1987). Unfortunately in these experiments a direct correlation between internode elongation and the amount of GA_1 was not possible; although $[^3H]GA_1$ was formed, it could not be completely separated from the relatively larger amounts of $3-\underline{epi}-[^3H]GA_1$ that was also formed from $[^3H]GA_{20}$. Nevertheless the results provide evidence that stem elongation and GA_1 concentration are directly related. Using an inhibitor of GA-biosynthesis, Lenton et al. (this volume) have shown that GA_1 levels and stem length are also correlated in wheat.

LOCALISED BIOSYNTHESIS OF GIBBERELLIN A_1

The question of the localised biosynthesis and site of primary action of GAs can be considered in a more critical way than Trewavas (1981) has done. Attention can now be focussed on GA_1 as the true native GA for stem elongation in maize and pea and earlier work can be interpreted in terms of the known position of the blocks of the metabolic pathways in each of the mutants.

The expression of the Le gene for the conversion of GA_{20} to GA_1 appears to be confined to the immature expanding region of the stem. In the Le genotype, Potts et al. (1982) found that a GA_1-like compound, subsequently identified as GA_1 by Ingram et al. (1983), was present in the young apical region but absent, or at very low levels, in the mature stem and leaf tissue. In grafting studies with peas, Reid et al. (1983) confirmed the previous findings by McComb and McComb (1970) and by Lockhart and Grunwald (1970) that there was no promotion of stem elongation in le scions on Le stocks. This would be the expected result if GA_1 were not present in mature shoot tissue. However, Reid et al. (1983) did observe a large promotion (up to 10-fold increase in internode length) of stem elongation of na scions grafted to Na stocks with foliar leaves. The response was induced by mature stem and leaf tissue since grafts with a leafy interstock of Le genotype caused the na scion to elongate in a similar manner to na scions where the entire basal part was derived from the Na genotype. This result shows that the Na genotype produces a graft-transmissible precursor of GA_1. The implication from these grafting results, together with the identification of GA_1 in the expanding apical region of the shoot but not in the mature tissue, is that GA_1 is biosynthesised only in the immature apical region from a precursor that is formed in the mature tissue.

Evidence for graft transmissible GA-like compounds in maize has been provided by Katsumi et al. (1983). Using approach grafts they showed stem elongation was promoted in dwarf-1 and dwarf-5 members of normal/dwarf-1 and normal/dwarf-5 grafts. Also in some cases increased elongation was observed in the dwarf-1 and dwarf-5 members, especially the dwarf-5 member of dwarf-1/dwarf-5 grafts. These results demonstrate the movement of native GAs in the pathway (Fig. 2) including GA_1 since the dwarf-1 member of the dwarf-1/normal grafts showed a response. The difference between maize and pea with respect to the graft transmissibility of GA_1 is interesting and may reflect an intrinsic difference between monocotyledons and dicotyledons. Perhaps the finding can be anticipated that the biosynthesis of GA_1 is confined to the expanding region at the nodal base in maize.

The graft transmissibility of GA-like substances in maize and pea and the localisation of the formation of GA_1 in the expanding apical region of the pea shoot meet two further criticisms of Trewavas (1981) concerning the hormonal role of GAs.

THE HORMONAL ROLE OF GIBBERELLIN A_1 IN STEM ELONGATION OF MAIZE AND PEA

Evidence has been presented showing that GA_1 is the only native GA in maize and pea that has intrinsic activity in promoting stem elongation in these species. Evidence has also been presented that stem elongation in pea is directly related to the concentration of GA_1. There is also evidence to support the view that the formation of GA_1 is localised in the young expanding tissue of pea shoots and that GA_1 is formed there from a precursor formed outside the apical region. It seems reasonable therefore to regard GA_1 as a plant hormone for stem elongation. The relationship shown in Fig. 2 (cf. Trewavas, 1981), can now be reconsidered in that light.

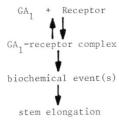

Fig. 3   Sequence from GA_1-recognition to stem elongation.

The assertion by Trewavas (1982) that plant growth responses are not regulated by GA concentration cannot be sustained for GA_1 in relation to stem elongation in maize and pea. It follows that many of Trewavas's arguments that sensitivity is the only limiting factor are invalid. That is not to deny that GA-receptor molecules (which Trewavas arguably equates to sensitivity) are essential components in the GA-regulation of stem elongation of maize and pea.

GIBBERELLIN A_1 RECEPTORS IN STEMS OF MAIZE AND PEA

There is little information on GA-receptors. In the case of GA_1-induced stem elongation the immediate difficulty is that of recognising a GA-receptor. Nothing is known of the biochemical events that occur between GA recognition and stem elongation. There is therefore no biochemical event(s) by which GA-receptor interaction can be monitored in stems. The situation is different in aleurone cells in which the de novo synthesis of α-amylase is a biochemical marker for GA-receptor interaction. But that is another topic. In the case of stem elongation, the isolation of GA-binding fractions and characterisation of them on the basis of reversible, high-affinity binding, correlated with biological activity, is a hazardous undertaking in the absence of an in vitro biochemical response for stem elongation.

Unfortunately there are no characterised receptor mutants of maize or pea. The Dwarf-8 of maize, like the Rht mutants of wheat (Lenton et al., this volume), does not respond to GA_1, and GA_1 has been shown by Phinney et al. (unpublished

Table 2 Gibberellin Monoclonal Antibodies

Antigen	Type	Affinity for GA hapten ($l\,mol^{-1}$)	Recognition Groups required	Groups interfering
(structure) OH, =CH$_2$, CO, H, CO$_2$H, OC, (CH$_2$)$_2$CONHKLH	IgM	7.5×10^7	7-CO$_2$H 13-OH 16-ene	1β-OH 15β-OH
(structure) =CH$_2$, CO, H, CO$_2$H, OC, (CH$_2$)$_2$CONHKLH	IgG	1.1×10^9	7-CO$_2$H 13-H 16-ene	2-ene 15β-OH
(structure) CH$_2$, S, (CH$_2$)$_3$, S, CO, HO, CO$_2$H, KLHNHCOCH$_2$CHCO$_2$H	IgG$_{2a}$	1.1×10^{10}	7-CO$_2$H 19,10-lactone 3β-OH	1β-OH 2β-OH
(structure) CH$_2$, S, (CH$_2$)$_3$, S, CO, CO$_2$H, KLHNHCOCH$_2$CHCO$_2$H	IgM	1.2×10^8	7-CO$_2$H 19,10-lactone	1β-OH 2β-OH 3β-OH 2-ene

results) to accumulate in Dwarf-8 to levels that are approximately 8 times greater than in normal plants. Recently, Reid and Potts (1986) have reported a new lk mutant of pea that is GA_1-insensitive and is therefore also a putative receptor mutant. However, there is no published evidence to indicate that the maize Dwarf-8 and the pea lk mutants are receptor mutants. A detailed investigation of these potential receptor mutants is now timely.

In the absence of biochemical markers for stem elongation and receptor mutants, we are exploring indirect methods for the localisation and identification of GA_1 receptors in immature tissue of pea. For example immunohistochemical localisation of the sites of GA_1 synthesis from GA_{20}, and of GA_1 metabolism to GA_8, may provide information on the site of GA_1 primary action (GA_1 receptor). For this purpose monoclonal antibodies to the 2β- and 3β-hydroxylases which catalyse these conversions (Fig. 2) are currently being prepared (Smith and Knox, unpublished work) and several monoclonal antibodies to the free GAs have been prepared (Knox et al., 1986). To obtain GA-epitope specific antibodies, the strategy outlined by Beale et al. (1986) is being used. Thus GA-antigens have been prepared by linking keyhole limpet haemocyanin (KLH) to different parts of the GA-molecule, thereby exposing different epitopes of GA-haptens. Some of the GA-monoclonals that have been characterised are shown in Table 2. The preparation of anti-iodiotypic monoclonal antibodies to some of these GA-antibodies is in progress.

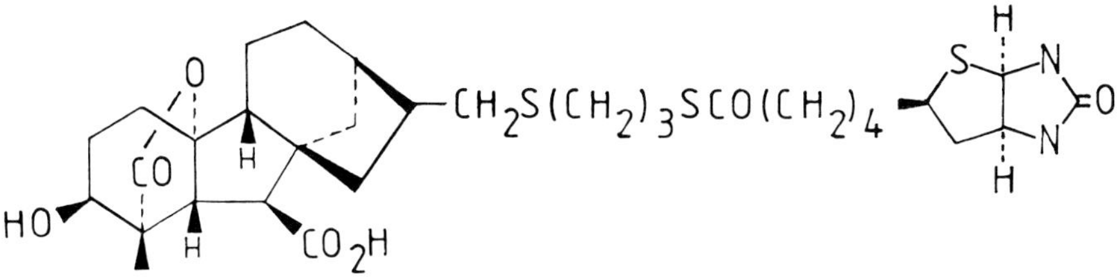

Fig. 4 GA_4-biotin conjugate.

Gibberellin-biotin conjugates, such as the GA_4-biotin conjugate (Fig. 4), recently prepared by Beale (unpublished work), are potentially useful probes for GA-binding protein(s). The GA_4 portion of this conjugate (Fig. 4) binds to one of the antibodies of Table 2 and the biotin portion can then be recognised by avidin-binding. The use of such conjugates, together with monoclonal antibodies to the GA-metabolising enzymes, should prove useful in the detection and characterisation of GA-binding protein(s) from immature stem tissue of normal GA-responding dwarfs and putative GA_1-receptor mutants.

REGULATION OF GIBBERELLIN A$_1$ LEVELS IN MAIZE AND PEA

There are many possible, but unknown, mechanisms for the regulation of GA$_1$ formation in maize and pea plants. The identification of GA$_1$ as the hormonal regulator of stem extension directs attention to the crucial step in which GA$_1$ is formed by 3β-hydroxylation of GA$_{20}$. The isolation and characterisation of the 3β-hydroxylase from pea by direct isolation (Smith, unpublished work) or from maize using the Robertson Mutator-1 (Phinney et al., 1986) is therefore an important step in the study of the regulation of expression of the Le and D-1 genes in pea and maize respectively.

CONCLUSION

From studies with the GA-responding stem-length mutants of maize and pea, GA$_1$ has been identified as the only native GA that is qualitatively and quantitatively required for stem elongation. Although further investigations are required on the localisation of the biosynthesis of GA$_1$ and its precursors, GA$_1$ can be regarded as a plant hormone for stem elongation in these two plant species. Attention can perhaps now be re-directed from semantic discussions on the hormonal rôle of GAs in stem elongation to studies of the GA$_1$ receptor and the regulation of GA$_1$ biosynthesis.

ACKNOWLEDGEMENTS

Drs. M.H. Beale, B.O. Phinney, V.A. Smith, V.M. Sponsel and C.L. Willis are warmly thanked for their constructive criticisms of the manuscript. The permission, readily given, by Drs. R. Hooley, J.B. Reid and B.O. Phinney to disclose their unpublished data is much appreciated.

REFERENCES

Beale, M.H., Hooley, R. and MacMillan, J. (1986). Gibberellins: Structure-activity relationships and the design of molecular probes. In "Plant Growth Substances 1985" (M. Bopp, ed.), pp 65-73. Springer-Verlag, Berlin.

Davies, P.J., Emschwiller, E., Gianfagna, T.J., Proebsting, W.J., Noma, M. and Pharis, R.P. (1982). The endogenous gibberellins of vegetative and reproductive tissues of G2 peas. Planta, **154**, 222-272.

Frydman, V.M., Gaskin, P. and MacMillan, J. (1974). Qualitative and quantitative analysis of gibberellins throughout seed maturation in Pisum sativum cv. Progress No. 9. Planta **118**, 123-132.

Frydman, V.M. and MacMillan, J. (1973). Identification of gibberellins A$_{20}$ and A$_{29}$ in seed of Pisum sativum cv. Progress No. 9 by combined gas chromatography-mass spectrometry. Planta **115**, 11-15.

Frydman, V.M. and MacMillan, J. (1975). The metabolism of gibberellins A$_9$, A$_{20}$ and A$_{29}$ in immature seeds of Pisum sativum cv. Progress No. 9. Planta **125**, 181-195.

Gaskin, P., Gilmour, S.J., MacMillan, J. and Sponsel, V.M. (1985). Gibberellins in immature seeds and dark-grown shoots of Pisum sativum. Gibberellins identified in the tall cultivar Alaska in comparison with those in the dwarf Progress No. 9. Planta **163**, 282-289.

Hedden, P. and Phinney, B.O. (1979). Comparison of ent-kaurene and ent-isokaurene synthesis in cell-free systems from etiolated shoots of normal and dwarf-5 maize seedlings. Phytochemistry 18, 1475-1479.

Hedden, P., Phinney, B.O., Heupel, R.C., Fujii, D., Cohen, H., MacMillan, J., Gaskin, P. and Graebe, J.E. (1982). Hormones of young tassels of Zea mays. Phytochemistry 21, 391-393.

Heupel, R.C., Phinney, B.O., Spray, C.R., Gaskin, P., MacMillan, J., Hedden, P. and Graebe, J.E. (1985). Native gibberellin and the metabolism of [^{14}C]gibberellin A_{53} and of [$17-^{13}$C,$17-^{3}$H$_2$]gibberellin A_{20} in tassels of Zea mays. Phytochemistry 24, 47-53.

Hoad, G.V. and Kuo, C.C. (1970). Activity of gibberellin A_{17} in 13 bioassay systems. Canadian Journal of Botany 48, 1423-1429.

Hooley, R. (1981). Protoplasts isolated from aleurone layers of wild oat (Avena fatua L.) exhibit the classical response to gibberellic acid. Planta 154, 29-40 and unpublished data.

Ingram, T.J., Reid, J.B. and MacMillan, J. (1986). The quantitative relationship between gibberellin A_1 and internode growth in Pisum sativum L. Planta 168, 414-420.

Ingram, T.J., Reid, J.B., Murfet, I.C., Gaskin, P., Willis, C.L. and MacMillan, J. (1984). Internode length in Pisum. The le-gene controls the 3β-hydroxylation of gibberellin A_{20} to gibberellin A_1. Planta 160, 455-463.

Ingram, T.J., Reid, J.B., Potts, W.C. and Murfet, I.C. (1983). Internode length in Pisum. IV. The effect of the le-gene on gibberellin metabolism. Physiologia Plantarum 59, 607-616.

Kamiya, Y. and Graebe, J.E. (1983). The biosynthesis of all major pea gibberellins in a cell-free system from Pisum sativum L. Phytochemistry 22, 681-89.

Katsumi, M., Foard, D.E. and Phinney, B.O. (1983). Evidence for the translocation of gibberellin A_3 and gibberellin-like substances in grafts between normal, dwarf-1 and dwarf-5 seedlings of Zea mays L. Plant and Cell Physiology 24, 379-388.

Katzenellenbogen, B.S. and Gorski, J. (1972). Induction of the synthesis of specific uterine protein. Journal of Biological Chemistry 247, 1299-1305.

Knox, J.P., Beale, M.H., Butcher, G.W. and MacMillan, J. (1986). Preparation and characterisation of monoclonal antibodies which recognise different gibberellin epitopes. Planta (in press).

Lawson, D.E.M., Fraser, D.R. and Kodicek, E. (1971). Identification of 1,25-dihydroxycholecalciferol, a new kidney hormone controlling calcium metabolism. Nature 230, 228-230.

Lockhart, R.G. and Grunwald, C. (1970). Grafting and gibberellin effects on the growth of tall and dwarf peas. Plant Physiology 45, 160-162.

McComb, A.J. and McComb, J.A. (1970). Growth substances and the relationship between phenotype and genotype in Pisum sativum. Planta 91, 235-245.

MacMillan, J. (1984). Analysis of plant hormones and metabolism of gibberellins. In "The Biosynthesis of Metabolism of Plant Hormones" (A. Crozier and J.R. Hillman, eds.), Society for Experimental Biology Seminar Series 23, pp 1-16. Cambridge University Press, Cambridge.

MacMillan, J. (1985a). Gibberellin metabolism: objectives and methodology. Biologia Plantarum (Praha) **27**, 172-179.

MacMillan, J. (1985b). Gibberellins: metabolism and function. In "Current Topics in Plant Biochemistry and Physiology" (D.D. Randall, D.G. Boomis, D.G. and R.L. Larson, eds.) Vol. **4**, pp. 53-66. The Interdisciplinary Plant Biochemistry and Physiology Program, University of Missouri, Columbia, Missouri, USA.

Morris, D.J., Kenyon, G.J., Latif, S.A., McDermott, M. and Goodfriend, T.L. (1983). The possible biological role of aldosterone metabolites. Hypertension, Suppl. I **5**, pp I-35 to I-40.

Norman, A.W., Myrtle, J.F., Midgett, R.J., Nouricki, H.F., Williams, V. and Popjack, G. (1971). 1,25-Dihydroxycholecalciferol. Identification of the proposed form of vitamin D_3 in the intestine. Science **173**, 51-54.

Phinney, B.O. (1984). Gibberellin A_1, dwarfism and the control of shoot elongation in higher plants. In "The Biosynthesis and Metabolism of Plant Hormones" (A. Crozier and J.R. Hillman, eds.). Society for Experimental Biology Seminar Series **23**, pp. 17-41. Cambridge University Press.

Phinney, B.O., Freeling, M., Robertson, D.S., Spray, C.R. and Silverthorne, J. (1986). Dwarf mutants of maize - the gibberellin pathway and its molecular future. In "Plant Growth Substances 1985" (M. Bopp, ed.), pp. 55-64. Springer-Verlag, Berlin.

Phinney, B.O. and Spray, C. (1982). Chemical genetics and the gibberellin pathway in Zea mays L. In "Plant Growth Substances 1982" (P.F. Wareing, ed.) pp. 101-110. Academic Press, London.

Potts, W.C. and Reid, J.B. (1983). Internode length in Pisum. III. The effect and interaction of the Na/na and Le/le gene differences on endogenous gibberellin-like substances. Physiologia Plantarum **57**, 448-454.

Potts, W.C., Reid, J.B. and Murfet, I.C. (1982). Internode length in Pisum. I. The effects of the Le/le gene difference on endogenous gibberellin-like substances. Physiologia Plantarum **55**, 323-328.

Reid, J.B. (1986). Internode length in Pisum. Three further loci, lh, ls and lk. Annals of Botany **57**, 577-592; and unpublished results.

Reid, J.B., Murfet, I.C. and Potts, W.C. (1983). Additional information on the relationship and action of loci Le, La, Cry, Na and Lm. Journal of Experimental Botany **34**, 349-364.

Reid, J.B. and Potts, W.C. (1986). Internode length in Pisum. Two further mutants, lh and ls, with reduced gibberellin synthesis, and a gibberellin insensitive mutant lk. Physiologia Plantarum (in press).

Ross, J.J. and Reid, J.B. (1987). Internode length in Pisum. A new allele at the le locus. Annals of Botany **59**, 107-109.

Sponsel, V.M. (1983). The localisation, metabolism and biological activity of gibberellins in maturing and germinating seeds of Pisum sativum cv. Progress No. 9. Planta **159**, 454-468.

Sponsel, V.M. and MacMillan, J. (1977). Further studies on the metabolism of gibberellins (GAs) A_9, A_{20} and A_{29} in immature seeds of Pisum sativum cv. Progress No. 9. Planta **135**, 129-136.

Sponsel, V.M. and MacMillan, J. (1978). Metabolism of gibberellin A_{29} in seeds of Pisum sativum cv. Progress No. 9; use of [^{2}H] and [^{3}H]GAs and the identification of a new GA catabolite. Planta **144**, 69-78.

Sponsel, V.M. and MacMillan, J. (1980). Metabolism of [$^{13}C_1$]gibberellin A_{29} to [$^{13}C_1$]gibberellin A_{29}-catabolite in maturing seeds of Pisum sativum cv. Progress No. 9. Planta **150**, 46-52.

Spray, C.R., Phinney, B.O., Gaskin, P., Gilmour, S.J. and MacMillan, J. (1984). Internode length in Zea mays L. The dwarf-1 mutation controls the 3β-hydroxylation of gibberellin A_{20} to gibberellin A_1. Planta **160**, 464-468.

Tamura, S., Takahashi, N., Murofushi, N. and Kato, J. (1966). Growth promoting activities of bamboo gibberellin. Plant and Cell Physiology **7**, 677-681.

Trewavas, A.J. (1981). How do plant growth substances work? Plant, Cell and Environment **4**, 203-228.

Trewavas, A.J. (1982). Growth substance sensitivity: the limiting factor in plant development. Physiologia Plantarum **55**, 60-72.

Trewavas, A.J. (1985). Review of "The Biosynthesis and Metabolism of Plant Hormones" (A. Crozier and J.R. Hillman, eds.) Cambridge University Press 1984. The New Phytologist **99**, 626-627.

Vanderhoef, L.N. and Kosuge, T. (1984). The molecular biology of plant hormones action: research directions for the future. Workshop Seminars-II. American Society of Plant Physiology, Rockville, U.S.A.

Yokota, T., Murofushi, N. and Takahashi, N. (1971). Biological activities of gibberellins and their glycosides in Pharbitis nil. Phytochemistry **10**, 2943-2949.

USE OF GENOTYPES DIFFERING IN ENDOGENOUS ABSCISIC ACID LEVELS IN STUDIES OF PHYSIOLOGY AND DEVELOPMENT

S.A. Quarrie

Plant Breeding Institute, Maris Lane, Trumpington, Cambridge, CB2 2LQ, England

Genotypes differing in endogenous abscisic acid (ABA) content are valuable for studying the influence of ABA on plant processes and development. ABA-deficient mutants are known in a number of monocotyledonous and dicotyledonous species and, for several cereals, varietal differences in drought-induced ABA accumulation have been identified. These differences can sometimes be magnified by crossing and selection. However, the nature of any genetic modifications resulting in differences in ABA levels needs to be established before genotypes varying in ABA content can be compared to assess unequivocally the consequences of modified ABA production. Ideally the genetic variation should be restricted to genes modifying only the level of ABA itself. Otherwise, complications will arise due to pleiotropic effects of the genes which are not related to the level of ABA or effects caused by variation in closely-linked genes.

Nevertheless, these genetic variants give good corroborative evidence that endogenous ABA affects many physiological processes, including stomatal control, dormancy and germination, vegetative and reproductive growth and development.

INTRODUCTION

Plant hormones are thought to regulate many aspects of growth and development. But how does one prove beyond all reasonable doubt that a hormone, such as abscisic acid (ABA), in its endogenous state has a role to play in regulating plant physiology and development? Our present knowledge of the role of ABA is derived from studies designed to correlate differences in ABA levels in the plant with some physiological or developmental change. There are four ways in which this can be done, by comparing:

1. Treatments in which ABA is applied to plants or isolated tissues
2. Chemical treatments which modify ABA levels
3. Environmental treatments which modify ABA levels
4. Plants which differ genetically in their ABA levels.

However, in general, none of these techniques gives unambiguous answers. Application of ABA may give misleading results because the distribution of exogenous ABA within the plant may be very different from that of endogenously produced ABA. Treatments modifying endogenous ABA levels are likely to have effects on other processes that will modify or obscure the effects of altered ABA levels. Genetic modification of ABA content constitutes the most powerful tool of the physiologist for studying the role of ABA in physiological processes and plant development and, with the right genotypes, is capable of giving unequivocal results. Nevertheless, caution needs to be exercised in the use of these genetic variants, as I shall demonstrate in the next section for mutants affecting ABA levels.

THE NATURE OF MUTATIONS AFFECTING ABA LEVELS

A mutation in a single gene may affect endogenous ABA levels in many ways. Four possibilities are illustrated in Fig. 1. The weight of evidence now favours a carotenoid (C40) pathway to ABA, such as that shown in Fig. 2 (Taylor, 1987), and not the

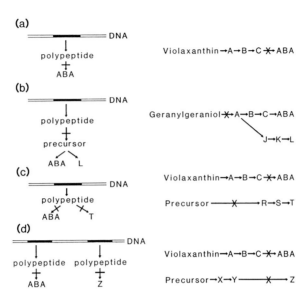

Fig. 1 **The nature of mutations affecting ABA levels.** Each of these examples would be classified by genetic analysis as a single gene mutation.

direct C15 route that was at one time in vogue (Neill et al., 1984), and the C40 xanthophyll violaxanthin is therefore given in Fig. 1 as the likely precursor of ABA.

The ideal mutation is one which occurs in a gene coding for a polypeptide uniquely responsible for a step in the synthesis of ABA itself (Fig. 1a). However, even this can cause problems if the affected step is near the end of the biosynthetic pathway to ABA and a build-up of the intermediates A–C is able to occur. One of these intermediates may itself have physiological effects.

The most effective site in the ABA biosynthetic pathway for inhibiting ABA synthesis without causing any side-effects due to a build-up of intermediates would therefore be at the start of the route to ABA, by a mutation in the gene coding for this enzyme, resulting in a significant decrease in the enzyme's Km below that of the rate-determining step. According to the biosynthetic pathway indicated in Fig. 2, the natural product cis-xanthoxin would be an intermediate on the route to ABA. Thus, a mutation reducing the efficiency of any steps from xanthoxin to ABA would be likely to reduce also the ability of the tissue to convert exogenous xanthoxin into ABA. Conversely, the conversion of xanthoxin into ABA should be unaffected by a mutation resulting in a decreased rate of synthesis of xanthoxin from violaxanthin. Recent unpublished results of Parry, Neill and Horgan (presented at an SEB meeting, 1986) with the ABA-deficient tomato mutants have shown that both flacca and sitiens convert xanthoxin into ABA much less efficiently than does the wild type and that the notabilis mutation does not affect the incorporation of exogenous xanthoxin into ABA. Also, data of Linforth (1986) (see Taylor 1987) show that levels of a C10 by-product (Fig. 2) are much higher in the flacca and sitiens mutants than they are in the notabilis mutant. These results for xanthoxin conversion and levels of the C10 by-product are all consistent with the idea that the flacca and sitiens mutations occur in steps between xanthoxin and ABA and the notabilis mutation affects a step in the biosynthetic pathway prior to xanthoxin. There is no biochemical information of this type available yet for any other of the ABA-deficient mutants.

In Figs. 1b and 1c, the reduction in ABA levels is accompanied by other unrelated

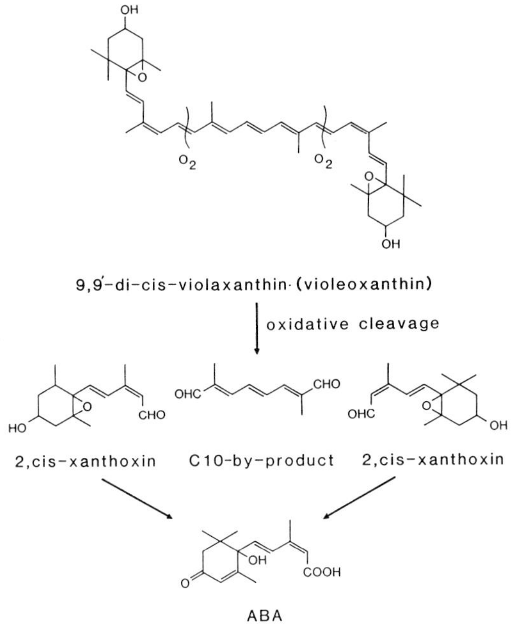

9,9′-di-cis-violaxanthin (violeoxanthin)

oxidative cleavage

2,cis-xanthoxin   C10-by-product   2,cis-xanthoxin

ABA

Fig. 2 The biosynthetic pathway to ABA proposed by Taylor (1987)

biochemical changes. In Fig. 1b, the altered polypeptide is an enzyme for a step early on in the isoprenoid pathway, which would result in other physiologically active substances, such as carotenoids or gibberellins, being affected.

Several ABA-deficient mutants would come under this category; most of them mutants of maize (Smith et al., 1978; Neill et al., 1986a) and plants expressing extreme symptoms of the albostrians mutation in barley (Quarrie and Lister, 1984). All of these mutations are characterised by albino plants which are devoid of carotenoids. In the case of the maize mutants this is because specific steps in the synthesis of carotenoids have been inhibited. In the albostrians mutant of barley, caroteno- genesis is still thought to take place, but plastid ribosome deficiency and insta- bility of the internal membrane structures leads to photooxidation of the caro- tenoids, and this results in very low carotenoid levels (Börner and Meister, 1980).

Alternatively, the affected enzyme may be relatively non-specific and therefore a component of more than one biosynthetic pathway (Fig. 1c). Several oxidative steps are required from violaxanthin to ABA (Fig. 2) and, for example, the enzyme carrying out the oxidative step from the aldehyde to carboxylic acid, a very common biochem- ical process, may also perform the same function in other physiologically important metabolic pathways.

Finally, an example is given in Fig. 1d of mutations having occurred in two closely- linked genes, as may well occur with mutation treatments that give rise to deletions; one directly affecting ABA biosynthesis and the other having an unrelated effect. The chances of being able to separate the two mutations by backcrossing to the wild type and progeny testing would depend on the number of map units separating the two genes. Even after six backcrosses, the mean length of a chromosome segment carrying the desired gene (ABA-deficiency) on a chromosome of length 100 cM would be 32 cM

(Stam and Zeven, 1981). And 1 cM is equivalent to approximately 1000 kbases (Flavell et al., 1984), enough for several hundred genes! Clearly, the amount of genetic information that may be retained through close genetic linkage during a backcrossing programme is potentially immense. In practice, of course, the mutant and wild type may carry the same alleles at many of these linked loci. It should be remembered, though, that all the differences between two near-isogenic lines need not necessarily be caused by the phenotypically-selected marker gene, but may be induced by other genes linked to this marker gene. For this reason, in any backcrossing programme to produce near isogenic lines, it is important to retain at least duplicate lines carrying the marker gene and, for comparison of the phenotypes, to recover the wild type from each backcross. In the case of the three ABA-deficient mutants of tomato, each of the mutant genes has been transferred into the variety Ailsa Craig by Darby et al. (1978) with five backcrosses for flacca and notabilis, but only three back-crosses for sitiens (I.B. Taylor, personal communication).

Each of these three tomato mutants arose originally from X-ray mutagenesis of the varieties Rheinlands Ruhm (flacca and sitiens) or Lukullus (notabilis) (Stubbe, 1957, 1958, 1959). Chromosomal abnormalities often occur with irradiation mutation treatments and it is possible that other mutations, such as deletions, were initially present adjacent to one or other of the flacca, sitiens and notabilis loci. Even with extensive backcrossing, any such closely linked chromosomal abnormalities would be difficult to spot. A mutation at the sitiens locus of tomato has recently been isolated by chemical mutagenesis (ethylmethanesulphonate, EMS) of the variety Moneymaker (Koornneef et al., 1985). Chemical mutagenesis is more likely to induce point mutations than X-ray irradiation, so it would be valuable to compare the phenotypes of the X-ray- and EMS-induced sitiens mutations.

For any apparently single gene mutation resulting in ABA-deficiency, it may be extremely difficult to distinguish between the four genotypes illustrated in Fig. 1. The only way to ensure that two genotypes differing in ABA content are strictly isogenic is to identify the genes coding for the enzymes of ABA synthesis, or genes which regulate the synthesis of ABA. This should be perfectly feasible with the techniques of molecular genetics now available, and the ABA deficient mutants of tomato would be an ideal starting point for this. Once the genes have been identified and defined modifications to the DNA completed, a readily-available transformation system for tomato (Koornneef et al., 1986) would enable the modified DNA to be incorporated into the tomato genome.

In the meantime, as far as the present ABA-deficient mutants are concerned, we have to rely upon phenotypic similarities between the mutants. If all ABA-deficient mutants, however produced, and whatever the species, had the same modified phenotype, then it would seem reasonable to assume that ABA-deficiency was the most probable common denominator to account for those phenotypic changes. In this context, the 8-point series of wild type, single, double and triple ABA-deficient mutants that have recently been produced in Taylor's laboratory (Taylor and Tarr, 1984, and unpublished results) is probably the best material now available. This series gave a 30-fold range of ABA contents from the wild type (110 ng g FW^{-1}) to the notabilis/ sitiens double mutant (3.3 ng ng FW^{-1}) (Linforth, 1986; Taylor, 1987) and it will allow the variation amongst the genotypes in physiological and developmental processes to be correlated over a wide range of genotype ABA contents.

THE ABA-DEFICIENT MUTANT PHENOTYPE

In addition to the mutants of tomato, maize and barley already mentioned, which are probably of the types shown in Fig. 1a, 1b and 1b respectively, ABA-deficiency has been identified in several other species. Koornneef et al. (1982) have produced a number of ABA-deficient mutants of Arabidopsis, but the 14 independently induced mutations were at only one or possibly two loci. Wilty mutants of both potato (droopy) and pea (wilty) were found to be associated with ABA-deficiency (Quarrie, 1982a; Wang et al., 1984). All the ABA-deficient mutants are reported to be "single" gene recessives though, strictly speaking, it is the mutant phenotype that has been identified as being recessive. Whilst the nature of the genetic lesion(s) in the mutants of Arabidopsis, potato and pea have not yet been characterised, the pheno-types of all ABA-deficient mutants have several features in common. Some of these are now discussed in detail. Other aspects of their physiology have recently been reviewed (Karssen and Laçka, 1986; Koornneef, 1986; Karssen et al., 1987) and will therefore be dealt with here only briefly.

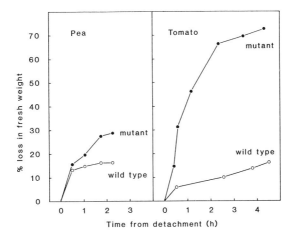

Fig. 3 Water loss in detached leaves of the wilty mutant of pea and flacca mutant of tomato and corresponding wild types. Data redrawn from Wang et al. (1984) and Neill and Horgan (1985).

Stomatal Control

All the pigmented mutants are characterised by a strong tendency to wilt (Koornneef, et al., 1982; Tal, 1966; Waggoner and Simmonds, 1966; Donkin et al., 1983) and detached leaves lose water much more rapidly than do wild type leaves. This is illustrated for the flacca mutant of tomato and the wilty mutant of pea in Fig. 3. Despite the severe water stresses that build up in the mutants, none of them seems capable of accumulating ABA in response to drought (Quarrie, 1982a; Wang et al., 1984; Neill and Horgan, 1985 and J.A.D. Zeevaart, quoted in Koornneef, 1986). Stoma-tal conductances remain high in these mutants despite the internal water stresses. In droopy potato plants (Quarrie, 1982a), after 5 days without water, the conductance of abaxial leaf surfaces remained around 0.9–1.0 cm s^{-1} even though the leaves were very flaccid. In contrast, by the time similarly flaccid leaves were present in the wild-type plants (12 days without water), abaxial conductances had reduced to 0.1–0.4 cm s^{-1}.

Although water stress has very little effect on mutant stomata, the responses of stomata of wilty pea (Donkin et al., 1983) and flacca tomato (Bradford et al., 1983) to other stimuli appear to be normal. Stomatal conductances in these mutants were reduced by increased CO_2 partial pressure, increased leaf-to-air vapour pressure gradients and decreased light intensity, though mutant stomata very rarely seemed to close completely. Stomata of the tomato mutants flacca and sitiens (but not nota-bilis) and droopy potato failed to close completely even when the guard cells of epidermal strips were plasmolysed (Tal, 1966; Quarrie, 1982a). Similarly, phenyl-mercuric acetate in the light failed to close stomata of all the tomato mutants, whereas those of the wild type shut completely (Tal, 1966). Together, these results were interpreted by Tal and Imber (1972) to indicate that guard cell wall extensibility was reduced in flacca and sitiens and a similar situation appears to exist in droopy potato (Quarrie, 1982a). Significantly, the aperture of stomata of flacca with plasmolysed guard cells could be nearly halved by prior treatment with ABA for only 3.5 h (Tal et al., 1974), suggesting that ABA may have a rapid effect on cell wall extensibility. Bradford et al. (1983) also showed that transpiration in the dark in flacca leaves could be reduced to the cuticular transpiration rate by treating plants with ABA for 4 days beforehand i.e. normal cell wall extensibility was restored by several days of ABA treatment.

Work by Rikin et al. (1980) may be relevant to this effect of ABA. They showed that ABA counteracted the effects of anti-microtubular drugs on microtubule disassembly in the plasma membrane. Stomatal guard cells have a radial array of cellulose micro-fibrils in the cell wall (Raschke, 1979), and the orientation of microfibrils in the cell wall is thought to be under microtubule control (Hepler, 1976). The absence of ABA in the mutants may therefore result in a less structured assembly of microfibrils in the guard cell walls and thus reduce the longitudinal extensibility of the ventral cell walls. The microfibrillar and microtubular structure of guard cells of the ABA-deficient mutants therefore deserves examination.

The difference between the mutants and wild type in the rate of water loss from detached leaves raises an intriguing question. Why do stomata normally close when the leaf is detached? According to Raschke (1976) most textbooks conveyed the impression "that stomata close in response to a lowered water potential because guard cells passively lose water to their neighbouring cells. Turgor declines; the guard cells shrink; the pore closes." However, on this basis the mutant stomata in de-tached leaves should close just as readily as those in detached wild-type leaves. Indeed, with higher initial conductances and therefore a greater rate of water loss they should close even more rapidly. In fact the opposite is true. Partly, this may be because of reduced guard cell wall elasticity in the mutant leaves, though it is also possible that wild-type stomata close in detached leaves because of the effect of endogenous ABA, which is absent from the mutants. Considerable controversy exists at the moment over whether changes in the content or distribution of endogenous ABA can be rapid enough to account for the rapid closure response of stomata to water stress (Henson, 1981; Dörffling et al., 1980; Raschke, 1982). However, recent re-sults from Hartung's laboratory (Behl and Hartung, 1986) on the rapid release of ABA from stomatal guard cells into the surrounding apoplast are helping to clarify the overall picture. Using an alternative approach, it would be instructive to study the rate of water loss of detached mutant leaves that have been treated on the plant for up to 4 days beforehand with ABA to ensure normal guard-cell wall elasticity. This does not appear to have been investigated yet. If these ABA-treated mutant leaves, when cut off the plant, continue to lose water at a rate greater than that of the wild type leaves, then this would be unequivocal evidence that the rapid closure of stomata in response to water stress is a "hydroactive" process mediated through ABA changes and not a "hydropassive" response to loss of turgor in the tissue.

Leaf, Shoot and Root Growth

ABA is regarded as being a growth inhibitor in many biological systems (Bornman, 1983), and plants treated with ABA often have smaller leaves and shorter stems (Sloger and Caldwell, 1970; Quarrie, 1982b). On this basis ABA deficiency should be associated with greater leaf and stem growth. However, the reality is often dif-ferent. Apart from the wilty pea mutant, for which there appear to be no data on leaf or shoot growth, the leaf size of the green ABA-deficient mutants seems to be reduced compared with the corresponding wild types (Taylor, 1987; Taylor and Tarr, 1984; Koornneef et al., 1982; Bradford, 1983; Simmonds, 1966 and Quarrie unpublished observations). This applied whether plants were grown without humidity control or under nearly saturating humidity conditions. Bradford (1983) ascribed the reduced leaf expansion in flacca plants to reduced water potentials and turgors in the leaves, even under well-watered conditions. However his plants were grown in a greenhouse without humidity control. There are no published data on leaf turgor pressures for mutant plants grown at very high relative humidity, so it is not possible to say whether the smaller leaf size of the mutants is entirely due to poorer leaf water relations (i.e. greater degree of stress on average) during expansion growth or whether the lack of ABA is also directly responsible for some of the reduction in size. Unpublished data of H.G. Jones (personal communication) suggest that under some conditions the length of leaves 1 and 2 of the three tomato mutants was little different from that of the wild type, though the later-formed leaves tended to be shorter than wild-type leaves. However, the plastochron index differs for wild type and mutant tomatoes as both Tarr, Linforth and Taylor (unpublished data presented at an SEB meeting, 1986) and H.G. Jones (unpublished data) report that leaves are produced more quickly in the mutants (Table 1). Data on rates of leaf emergence are not available for other ABA-deficient mutants.

Although Taylor's group found a progressive reduction in stem height when comparing the wild type with the single, double and triple mutants of tomato (unpublished data presented at an SEB meeting, 1986), this was almost certainly an effect of incipient wilting under the greenhouse conditions used. Koornneef et al. (1982) also found

Table 1 Number of leaves in the tomato cultivar Ailsa Craig and in the ABA-deficient near-isogenic mutants notabilis, flacca and sitiens.

Source	Age of plants (weeks)	Ailsa Craig	notabilis	flacca	sitiens
Tarr et al. (unpublished)	4	9.0	10.4	10.2	13.4
Jones (unpublished)	7	9.1	10.7	10.6	12.3

that, when comparing the wild type with two ABA-deficient mutants, the heights of Arabidopsis genotypes were proportional to their ABA contents. Under high humidity conditions the influence of ABA-deficiency on plant height is more variable. At 95% relative humidity in a controlled environment cabinet, plants of Arabidopsis wild type and the partially ABA-deficient mutant G4 were the same height and those of the severely ABA-deficient mutant A26 were only 10-12% shorter (Quarrie, unpublished observations). Internode length is always shorter in the tomato mutants (I.B. Taylor, personal communication and Linforth, 1986), though, with a greater leaf number, overall plant height is sometimes similar to that of the wild type, and unpublished data of I.B. Taylor and H.G. Jones show that the tomato single gene mutants can grow up to 50% taller than the wild type and have thinner stems. This phenotype is also characteristic of droopy potato (Simmonds, 1966), and is what would be expected by analogy with the growth inhibitory effects of applied ABA.

Root growth has been examined in ABA-deficient mutants of tomato (Bradford, 1983) and potato (Waggoner and Simmonds, 1966). In both species, root growth was inhibited more than shoot growth (Table 2), so that the shoot:root ratios in these mutants were higher than in the wild types, particularly in the case of droopy potato. It may be that the poorer development of the root systems of the mutants was the result of lower turgor pressures in the expanding zones of roots, despite the plants being well watered. However the supply of assimilates should not have been limiting for either root or shoot osmotic adjustment, as assimilation rates per unit leaf area of flacca plants were either equal to or greater than those of the wild type plants (Bradford et al., 1983). ABA probably has a direct effect on the distribution of current assimilates between the shoot and root, with the root system receiving a smaller proportion of assimilates in the absence of ABA. This conclusion is in agreement with reports showing that ABA application stimulates root growth at the expense of shoot growth (Watts et al., 1981; Biddington and Dearman, 1982).

Table 2   Shoot and root growth in wild type and ABA-deficient mutants of tomato and potato.

Reference	Species	Genotype	Shoot DW (g)	% of normal	Root DW (g)	% of normal	Ratio shoot/root
1	tomato	RR[+]	9.41		2.17		4.47
		flacca	3.61	38.2	0.58	26.7	6.29
1	tomato	RR[+]	5.10		1.07		4.87
		flacca	3.18	62.4	0.63	58.9	5.18
2	potato	normal	4.1		8.9		0.46
		droopy	2.1	51.2	1.2	13.5	1.75

[+] RR = Rhinelands Ruhm, grown with flacca in two experiments
1 Bradford, K.J. (1983). Plant Physiology 72, 251-255.
2 Waggoner, P.E. and Simmonds, N.W. (1966). Plant Physiology 41, 1268-1271.

Dormancy and Germination

The use of ABA-deficient mutants in the study of dormancy and germination has been discussed at length in several recent reviews (Karssen and Laçka, 1986; Koornneef, 1986; Karssen et al., 1987) and the subject will only briefly be mentioned here.

Apart from the albostrians mutant of barley and wilty mutant of pea, for which no data are available, all the ABA-deficient mutants identified so far show vivipary under some, if not all conditions: Arabidopsis (Koornneef et al., 1982), tomato in mutations induced at the sitiens locus by either X-rays (H.G. Jones, unpublished observations) or EMS (Koornneef et al., 1985), potato (Simmonds, 1966), and maize (Robertson, 1975). ABA therefore seems to be necessary for the induction of primary dormancy. These mutants can also germinate in conditions that prevent germination in the wild type, such as a germination medium of high osmotic potential (Koornneef et al., 1985). By studying the ABA content and germinability of seeds derived from reciprocal crosses between the wild type and ABA-deficient mutants of Arabidopsis, Karssen et al. (1983) showed that the genotype of the embryo determined whether dormancy induction took place. In addition, frequent sprays of ABA-deficient lines with ABA solution failed to induce dormancy in the mutants, showing that dormancy induction occurred entirely within the embryo (Karssen, 1982; Karssen et al., 1983). The same conclusion was reached by Robertson (1955) who studied vivipary in the albino mutants of maize which are now known to be ABA-deficient.

As current evidence favours ABA formation via the carotenoid pathway, all albino plants would be expected to contain very low ABA levels. This is so for the albino mutants of maize that have been analysed so far (Smith et al., 1978; Neill et al., 1986a) and for the albostrians mutant (Quarrie and Lister, 1984). However, not all albino mutants of maize are viviparous (Robertson, 1975). For example, isogenic lines carrying the Mumm # 1 allele of the vp5 albino mutant of maize (a mutant unable to convert phytoene into phytofluene (Moore and Smith, 1985)) give rise to seeds which are entirely non-viviparous. If ABA is necessary to induce dormancy, then it is difficult to explain the dormancy of vp5-Mumm # 1 seeds if the mutation is in a gene affecting only a step in the carotenoid pathway, which should result in ABA deficiency.

A footnote to the subject of ABA and dormancy: severe potassium deficiency is reported to result in seed vivipary in pepper plants (Harrington, 1960). It would be interesting to know whether, under those conditions, the ABA concentration of the developing embryos was much less than normal. As Harrington states: "potassium may be necessary to the formation of a germination-inhibiting compound".

Other Physiological and Developmental Processes

For some while there has been speculation that redistribution of hormones, including ABA, could mediate gravitropic responses of roots and shoots (Audus, 1983). However, the gravitropic responsiveness of primary roots of ABA-deficient mutants of maize was the same as that of wild-type roots and wild-type roots treated with fluridone, an inhibitor of ABA synthesis (Moore and Smith, 1985; Moore and Dickey, 1985). It, therefore, seems very unlikely that ABA plays a part in the gravitropic response of roots. This conclusion is reinforced by recent data of Mertens and Weiler (1983) on levels and redistribution of endogenous hormones, including ABA, in gravireacting plant organs.

ABA has for several years been thought to participate in the induction of cold hardiness. Many studies have shown that applied ABA increases cold hardiness (e.g. Rikin et al., 1975, 1980; Chen et al., 1983; Chen and Gusta, 1983) and there are reports that endogenous ABA levels increase during cold-hardening treatments (Eamus and Wilson, 1983; Lalk and Dörffling, 1985). However, cold hardening does not always lead to a rise in shoot ABA levels (Quarrie and Cloutier, paper in preparation). Despite the obvious attractiveness of ABA-deficiency as a means of studying this, until now there have been no published reports on the cold-tolerance of ABA-deficient mutants. Therefore, solute leakage from leaf discs in response to incubation at low temperatures has now been examined in notabilis and sitiens mutants of tomato and droopy potato (Quarrie, unpublished data). In all cases, ABA-deficiency was associated with greater solute leakage from discs incubated for 3 days at 2°C (Table 3).

Table 3   Leakage of electrolytes into water from leaf discs of wild type and ABA-deficient tomato and potato genotypes in response to incubation at 2°C in the dark. The conductivity of the bathing medium was measured after 3 days, and again in fresh incubation medium after leaf discs had been killed by freezing and thawing, to estimate total electrolytes remaining.

| Species | Genotype | Conductance (ohms^{-1} x 10^8) | | |
		at 2°C	after freezing	% total[+]
tomato	Ailsa Craig	615	1905	32.3
	notabilis	857	1791	47.9
	sitiens	1745	1926	90.6
potato	normal	743	2413	30.8
	droopy	1347	2299	58.6

[+] % total is the conductance of electrolytes released at 2°C expressed as a percentage of the conductance of electrolytes released after freezing and thawing the tissue.

Although these results implicate ABA in modifying the resistance of tissues to low temperature stress, the picture is not as clear-cut as the results might suggest. Considerable solute leakage also occurred from discs of the ABA-deficient mutants at room temperature (Quarrie, unpublished data). ABA-deficiency therefore has a generally deleterious effect on the permeability of membranes to electrolytes. This finding and the effects of ABA-deficiency on microtubule and microfibril development discussed above all imply an important role for ABA in regulating membrane and cell wall structure.

Other pleiotropic effects of the mutations have been reported in some species. For example, the seeds of ABA-deficient mutants of Arabidopsis (Karssen et al., 1983) and of some of the single and double mutants of tomato (Quarrie, unpublished observations) have a much reduced mucilage layer around them. Hydraulic conductance of the roots of flacca tomato was significantly less than it was for roots of the wild type Rhinelands Ruhm (Bradford, 1983). This confirms the earlier finding of Tal and Nevo (1973) that root resistance to water flow was higher in all three of the ABA-deficient tomato mutants.

Although, in the aspects of phenotype and physiology of the ABA-deficient mutants discussed so far, the different mutations have had, in general, similar effects both within and between species, this is not always so. The tomato mutants are characterised by leaf epinasty, swelling of the upper stem and frequent rooting on all parts of the stem (Tal, 1966), effects which were thought to be characteristic of auxin overproduction (Tal and Imber, 1970; Tal et al., 1979). Such effects were not observed in Arabidopsis (Koornneef, 1986) and droopy potato (Quarrie, 1982a), or were present in both mutant and wild type plants (Quarrie, 1982a). Although Tal and Imber (1970) found high levels of auxins in the tomato mutants using bioassay, Neill et al. (1986b) have recently questioned whether auxin is overproduced in the tomato mutants.

GENETIC VARIATION IN ABA CONTENT IN GENOTYPES NOT DEFICIENT IN ABA

Whereas the single gene mutants of ABA which have been isolated so far result in very low levels of ABA, genotypic variation in ABA content amongst cultivars or ecotypes within species offers a means of altering endogenous ABA concentrations within a physiologically "normal" range. Natural genetic variation in endogenous ABA levels has been identified in several species. In nearly all cases, however, the variation has been found amongst the elevated levels of ABA that are stimulated by drought stress, either in detached leaves or in drought-stressed plants. At least two-fold differences in ABA concentration have been identified in the cereals barley (Quarrie and Arachchi, unpublished data), maize (Larqué-Saavedra and Wain, 1976; Ilahi and Dörffling, 1982; Pekić and Quarrie, 1987), millet (Henson et al., 1981), rice (Henson, 1983), sorghum (Larqué-Saavedra and Wain, 1976; Durley et al., 1983) and wheat (Quarrie, 1981, 1987), and in the dicotyledonous species cotton (Ibragimov et al., 1978), potato (Evans et al., 1981 and Quarrie unpublished data) and Vitis (Scienza et al., 1981). In the cereals maize (Quarrie, 1987), millet (Henson, 1984), rice (Henson, 1983; Henson et al., 1985) and wheat (Quarrie, 1981, 1987) this genetic variation in drought-induced ABA accumulation has been introduced into common genetic backgrounds by crossing and selection, with the aim of studying the consequences for growth, development and yielding ability under drought conditions of natural variation in endogenous ABA levels. In both millet (Henson, 1984) and wheat (Quarrie, 1981), the capacity for ABA accumulation in the progeny of crosses could be increased beyond that of the high-ABA parents because transgressive segregation for ABA production occurred in the F2 populations.

Despite this extensive list of species exhibiting genotypic variation in ABA production there is, as yet, little reliable information on correlations between the ABA differences and variation in other physiological and developmental parameters. Varietal comparisons will always be unreliable because of the confounding effects caused by variation in background genes. The following details are given to illustrate this. In a comparison of about 20 wheat varieties for ABA accumulation (Quarrie, 1981), the ability to accumulate ABA was significantly positively correlated ($P < 0.001$) with the presence of the semi-dwarfing genes Rht1 and Rht2 (Quarrie, 1987). However, wheat lines nearly isogenic for the presence or absence of Rht1 and Rht2 (produced by backcrossing three times onto the tall parent) were identical in their ABA contents in both unstressed and partially dehydrated leaves (King et al., 1983).

Occasionally, the comparison of genetically similar plants and the comparison of varieties give the same results. The capacity for ABA accumulation both in wheat varieties and in F4 plants derived from a high-ABA x low-ABA cross was significantly negatively correlated with their freezing tolerance (Quarrie, unpublished data and Fig. 4), with $P < 0.001$ for about 20 varieties and $P < 0.05$ for the progeny of 18 F4

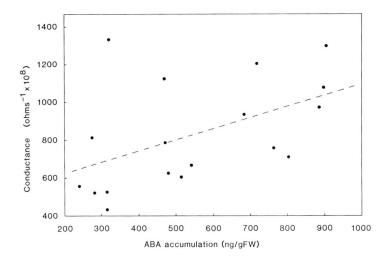

Fig. 4   Frost resistance in F5 progeny and ABA accumulation in response to drought stress in F4 selections from the wheat cross TW 269/9 x Highbury.   Frost resistance was measured as the conductivity of electrolytes released within the tissue during the low temperature treatment.

lines.   In the freezing test, seedlings were hardened for 3 weeks at 4°C and then cooled to -12°C.   Leakage of electrolytes within the leaves during the freezing test was measured by inserting electrodes into the leaves and recording the resistance between the electrodes with an Avo-meter.   This significant negative correlation could be explained by assuming that cell membranes which were more susceptible to damage by cold stress would also be more damaged by drought stress so that ABA accu-mulation would be more stimulated in these cells.

In general the comparison of wheat lines differing in ABA accumulation corroborates the results expected of ABA treatments, so that high ABA accumulation was associated with lines that had, on average, lower stomatal conductances, smaller leaves, shorter stems and fewer spikelets per ear (Quarrie, 1982b).   However, the high-ABA and low-ABA selections also differed in the number of main stem leaves (Quarrie, 1982b), and this effect could never be mimicked by ABA treatments, even when emerging seedlings, with 5-6 leaves and leaf primordia visible, were given ABA by injection into the endosperm cavity of the seed (Quarrie, unpublished data).   Because of the relatively small population size (only 160 F2 plants) from which the high- and low-ABA plants were selected, it remains a possibility, therefore, that close genetic linkage may have confounded the phenotypic differences between the high-ABA and low-ABA selec-tions.   This was the conclusion of Henson for rice (Henson, 1985), who found a highly significant negative correlation between the capacity to accumulate ABA and leaf size in F2 and F3 progeny from a cross between parents differing in both ABA accumulation and leaf size (Henson, 1983).   In the progeny from another rice cross there was, however, no correlation between leaf size and ABA accumulation (Henson, 1985).

CONCLUSIONS

Although the precise nature of the genetic lesions leading to ABA deficiency is not known for any of the ABA-deficient mutants, useful progress has been made with these mutants in studying the physiological and developmental roles of ABA.   Through the sheer consistency of effect, across species and with mutants that have arisen either naturally (potato), or by X-ray or chemical mutagenesis, it seems inconceivable that in every case the resulting phenotype would be due to the confounding influence of linked genes or a response to some other modified biochemical process, and never to just the measured ABA differences. Consequently it seems certain that, in relation to many of the aspects of physiology and development I have discussed here, the effects of applied ABA on those processes reflect the action of ABA in its natural environment. Nevertheless, there are still some areas of uncertainty, such as the role of ABA in leaf expansion, cold tolerance and membrane structure, where the use of genotypes differing in ABA content is likely in the future to play an important part in unravelling the inconsistencies.

The use of genotypes varying in ABA content over a physiologically normal range will augment the results from studies with ABA-deficient mutants, provided that these genotypes are compared in suitable genetic backgrounds (by crossing and selection), and provided that this is done on a scale large enough to overcome the confounding effects of linked genes.

ACKNOWLEDGEMENTS

I am grateful to Professor C.M. Karssen and Drs M. Koornneef, S.J. Neill and H.G. Jones for providing manuscripts and proofs of articles and unpublished data, and to colleagues at the Plant Breeding Institute for valuable discussions. In particular I would like to thank Dr I.B. Taylor for his useful comments and for providing seeds of tomato genotypes as well as unpublished manuscript and poster information.

REFERENCES

Audus, L.J. (1983). Abscisic acid in root growth and geotropism. In "Abscisic acid" (F.T. Addicott ed.), pp 421-477. Praeger Special Studies, New York.

Behl, R. and Hartung, W. (1986). Movement and compartmentation of abscisic acid in guard cells of Valerianella locusta; effects of osmotic stress, external H^+-concentration and fusicoccin. Planta 168, 360-368.

Biddington, N.L. and Dearman, A.S. (1982). The effect of abscisic acid on root and shoot growth of cauliflower plants. Plant Growth Regulation 1, 15-24.

Börner, Th. and Meister, A. (1980). Chlorophyll and carotenoid content of ribosome-deficient plastids. Photosynthetica 14, 589-593.

Bornman, C.H. (1983). Morphological, anatomical, and ultrastructural responses to abscisic acid. In "Abscisic acid" (F.T. Addicott ed.), pp 523-551. Praeger Special Studies, New York.

Bradford, K.J. (1983). Water relations and growth of the flacca tomato mutant in relation to abscisic acid. Plant Physiology 72, 251-255.

Bradford, K.J., Sharkey, T.D. and Farquhar, G.D. (1983). Gas exchange, stomatal behavior, and $\delta^{13}C$ values of the flacca tomato mutant in relation to abscisic acid. Plant Physiology 72, 245-250.

Chen, H.H. and Gusta, L.V. (1983). Abscisic acid-induced freezing resistance in cultured plant cells. Plant Physiology 73, 71-75.

Chen, H.H., Li, P.H. and Brenner, M.L. (1983). Involvement of abscisic acid in potato cold acclimation. Plant Physiology 71, 362-365.

Darby, L.A., Ritchie, D.B. and Taylor, I.B. (1978). Isogenic lines of the tomato 'Ailsa Craig'. The Glasshouse Crops Research Institute 1977 Annual Report pp 168-184.

Donkin, M.E., Wang, T.L. and Martin, E.S. (1983). An investigation into the stomatal behaviour of a wilty mutant of Pisum sativum. Journal of Experimental Botany 34, 825-834.

Dörffling, K., Tietz, D., Streich, J. and Ludewig, M. (1980). Studies on the role of abscisic acid in stomatal movements. In "Plant Growth Substances 1979" (F. Skoog ed.), pp 274-285. Springer-Verlag, Berlin.

Durley, R.C., Kannangara, T., Seetharama, N. and Simpson, G.M. (1983). Drought resistance of Sorghum bicolor. 5. Genotypic differences in the concentrations of free and conjugated abscisic, phaseic and indole-3-acetic acids in leaves of field-grown drought-stressed plants. Canadian Journal of Plant Science 63, 131-145.

Eamus, D. and Wilson, J.M. (1983). ABA levels and effects in chilled and hardened Phaseolus vulgaris. Journal of Experimental Botany 34, 1000-1006.

Evans, K., Greet, D.N., Minter, K. and Wilson, S. (1981). Tolerance by potatoes to cyst nematode attack. In "Rothamsted Experimental Station, Annual Report 1980", Part I. p 155.

Flavell, R.B., O'Dell, M., Smith, D.B. and Thompson, W.F. (1984). Chromosome architecture : the distribution of recombination sites, the structure of ribosomal DNA loci and the multiplicity of sequences containing inverted repeats. In "Molecular Form and Function of the Plant Genome" (L. van Vloten-Doting, G.S.P. Groot and T.C. Hall eds.), pp 1-14. Plenum Press, New York.

Harrington, J.F. (1960). Germination of seeds from carrot, lettuce, and pepper plants grown under severe nutrient deficiencies. Hilgardia 30, 219-235.

Henson, I.E. (1981). Changes in abscisic acid content during stomatal closure in pearl millet (Pennisetum americanum (L.) Leeke). Plant Science Letters 21, 121-127.

Henson, I.E. (1983). Abscisic acid accumulation in detached leaves of rice (Oryza sativa L.) in response to water stress : a correlation with leaf size. Annals of Botany 52, 385-398.

Henson, I.E. (1984). The heritability of abscisic acid accumulation in water-stressed leaves of pearl millet (Pennisetum americanum (L.) Leeke). Annals of Botany 53, 1-11.

Henson, I.E. (1985). Modification of leaf size in rice (Oryza sativa L.) and its effects on water stress-induced abscisic acid accumulation. Annals of Botany 56, 481-487.

Henson I.E., Loresto, G.C. and Chang, T.T. (1985). Developing closely related rice lines with different drought-induced abscisic acid (ABA) accumulation. International Rice Research Newsletter 10, 12-13.

Henson, I.E., Mahalakshmi, V., Bidinger, F.R. and Alagarswamy, G. (1981). Genotypic variation in pearl millet (Pennisetum americanum (L.) Leeke), in the ability to accumulate abscisic acid in response to water stress. Journal of Experimental Botany 32, 899-910.

Hepler, P.K. (1976). Plant microtubules. In "Plant Biochemistry, Third Edition" (J. Bonner and J.E. Varner eds.), pp 147-187. Academic Press, New York.

Ibragimov, A.P., Igamberdyeva, Z.I. and Saidova, S.A. (1978). Effect of moisture stress on level of abscisic acid in cotton leaves. Uzbekskii Biologicheskii Zhurnal 4, 11-14.

Ilahi, I. and Dörffling, K. (1982). Changes in abscisic acid and proline levels in maize varieties of different drought resistance. Physiologia Plantarum 55, 129-135.

Karssen, C.M. (1982). The role of endogenous hormones during seed development and the onset of primary dormancy. In "Plant Growth Substances 1982" (P.F. Wareing ed.), pp 623-632. Academic Press, London.

Karssen, C.M., Brinkhorst-van der Swan, D.L.C., Breekland, A.E. and Koornneef, M. (1983). Induction of dormancy during seed development by endogenous abscisic acid : studies on abscisic acid deficient genotypes of Arabidopsis thaliana (L.) Heynh. Planta 157, 158-165.

Karssen, C.M., Groot, S.P.C. and Koornneef, M. (1987). Hormone mutants and seed dormancy in Arabidopsis and tomato. In "Developmental mutants in higher plants" (H. Thomas and D. Grierson eds.), pp 119-134. SEB Seminar Series, Cambridge University Press, Cambridge.

Karssen, C.M. and Laçka, E. (1986). A revision of the hormone balance theory of seed dormancy : studies on gibberellin and/or abscisic acid-deficient mutants of Arabidopsis thaliana. In "Plant Growth Substances 1985" (M. Bopp ed.), pp 315-323. Springer-Verlag, Berlin.

King, R.W., Gale, M.D. and Quarrie, S.A. (1983). Effects of NORIN 10 and Tom Thumb dwarfing genes on morphology, physiology and abscisic acid production in wheat. Annals of Botany 51, 201-208.

Koornneef, M. (1986). Genetic aspects of abscisic acid. In "Genetic Approach to Plant Biochemistry" Plant Gene Research, Volume 3, pp 35-54, Springer, New York.

Koornneef, M., Cone, J.W., Karssen, C.M., Kendrick, R.E., van der Veen, J.H. and Zeevaart, J.A.D. (1985). Plant hormone and photoreceptor mutants in Arabidopsis and tomato. In "Plant Genetics" (M. Freeling ed.), pp 103-114. Alan R. Liss, Inc., New York.

Koornneef, M., Hanhart, C., Jongsma, M., Toma, I., Weide, R., Zabel, P. and Hille, J. (1986). Breeding of a tomato genotype readily accessible to genetic manipulation. Plant Science 45, 201-208.

Koornneef, M., Jorna, M.L., Brinkhorst-van der Swan, D.L.C. and Karssen, C.M. (1982). The isolation of abscisic acid (ABA) deficient mutants by selection of induced revertants in non-germinating gibberellin sensitive lines of Arabidopsis thaliana (L.) Heynh. Theoretical and Applied Genetics 61, 385-393.

Lalk, I. and Dörffling, K. (1985). Hardening, abscisic acid, proline and freezing resistance in two winter wheat varieties. Physiologia Plantarum 63, 287-292.

Larqué-Saavedra, A. and Wain, R.L. (1976). Studies on plant growth-regulating substances. XLII. Abscisic acid as a genetic character related to drought tolerance. Annals of applied Biology 83, 291-297.

Linforth, R.S.T. (1986). A genetic approach to the study of ABA biosynthesis. Ph.D. thesis, University of Nottingham.

Mertens, R. and Weiler, E.W. (1983). Kinetic studies on the redistribution of endogenous growth regulators in gravireacting plant organs. Planta 158, 339-348.

Moore, R. and Dickey, K. (1985). Growth and graviresponsiveness of primary roots of Zea mays seedlings deficient in abscisic acid and gibberellic acid. Journal of Experimental Botany 36, 1793-1798.

Moore, R. and Smith, J.D. (1985). Graviresponsiveness and abscisic-acid content of roots of carotenoid-deficient mutants of Zea mays L. Planta 164, 126-128.

Neill, S.J. and Horgan, R. (1985). Abscisic acid production and water relations in wilty tomato mutants subjected to water deficiency. Journal of Experimental Botany 36, 1222-1231.

Neill, S.J., Horgan, R. and Parry, A.D. (1986a). The carotenoid and abscisic acid content of viviparous kernels and seedlings of Zea mays L. Planta, 169, 87-96.

Neill, S.J., Horgan, R. and Walton, D.C. (1984). Biosynthesis of abscisic acid. In "The biosynthesis and metabolism of plant hormones" (A. Crozier and J.R. Hillman eds.), pp 43-70. SEB seminar Series, Cambridge University Press, Cambridge.

Neill, S.J., McGaw, B.A. and Horgan, R. (1986b). Ethylene and 1-aminocyclopropane-1-carboxylic acid production in flacca, a wilty mutant of tomato, subjected to water deficiency and pre-treatment with abscisic acid. Journal of Experimental Botany 37, 535-541.

Pekić, S. and Quarrie, S.A. (1987). Abscisic acid accumulation in lines of maize differing in drought resistance : a comparison of intact and detached leaves. Journal of Plant Physiology (in press).

Quarrie, S.A. (1981). Genetic variability and heritability of drought-induced abscisic acid accumulation in spring wheat. Plant, Cell and Environment 4, 147-151.

Quarrie, S.A. (1982a). Droopy : a wilty mutant of potato deficient in abscisic acid. Plant, Cell and Environment 5, 23-26.

Quarrie, S.A. (1982b). The role of abscisic acid in the control of spring wheat growth and development. In "Plant Growth Substances 1982" (P.F. Wareing ed.), pp 609-619. Academic Press, London.

Quarrie, S.A. (1987). Evaluation of the influence of a metabolic character on drought resistance exemplified by studies on abscisic acid in wheat and maize. In "Drought Resistance in Plants : Genetic and Physiological Aspects" Proceedings EEC Plant Productivity Programme Meeting, 1986, EEC, Luxembourg (in press).

Quarrie, S.A. and Lister, P.G. (1984). Evidence of plastid control of abscisic acid accumulation in barley (Hordeum vulgare L.). Zeitschrift fur Pflanzenphysiologie 114, 295-308.

Raschke, K. (1976). How stomata resolve the dilemma of opposing priorities. Philosophical Transactions of the Royal Society, London, B. 273, 551-560.

Raschke, K. (1979). Movements of stomata. In "Physiology of Movements". (A. Pirson and M.H. Zimmermann eds.). Encyclopedia of Plant Physiology, Volume 7, pp 382-441. Springer-Verlag, Berlin.

Raschke, K. (1982). Involvement of abscisic acid in the regulation of gas exchange : evidence and inconsistencies. In "Plant Growth Substances 1982" (P.F. Wareing ed.), pp 581-590. Academic Press, London.

Rikin, A.,Atsmon, D. and Gitler, C. (1980). Chilling injury in cotton (Gossypium hirsutum L.) : Effects of antimicrotubular drugs. Plant and Cell Physiology 21, 829-837.

Rikin, A., Waldman, M., Richmond, A.E. and Dovrat, A. (1975). Hormonal regulation of morphogenesis and cold-resistance I. Modifications by abscisic acid and by gibberellic acid in alfalfa (Medicago sativa L.) seedlings. Journal of Experimental Botany 26, 175-183.

Robertson, D.S. (1955). The genetics of vivipary in maize. Genetics 40, 745-760.

Robertson, D.S. (1975). Survey of the albino and white-endosperm mutants of maize: their phenotypes and gene symbols. The Journal of Heredity 66, 67-74.

Scienza, A., Fregoni, M. and Boselli, M. (1981). Influenza del portinnesto sulla resistenza stomatica, sul potenziale idrico e sul contenuto di acido abscissico di foglie di "Barbera". Vignevini 7, 39-44.

Simmonds, N.W. (1966). Linkage to the S-locus in diploid potatoes. Heredity 21, 473-479.

Sloger, C. and Caldwell, B.E. (1970). Response of cultivars of soybean to synthetic abscisic acid. Plant Physiology 46, 634-635.

Smith, J.D., McDaniel, S. and Lively, S. (1978). Regulation of embryo growth by abscisic acid in vitro. Maize Genetics Cooperation Newsletter 52, 107-108.

Stam, P. and Zeven, A.C. (1981). The theoretical proportion of the donor genome in near-isogenic lines of self-fertilizers bred by backcrossing. Euphytica 30, 227-238.

Stubbe, H. (1957). Mutanten der Kulturtomate Lycopersicon esculentum Miller I. Kulturpflanze 5, 190-220.

Stubbe, H. (1958). Mutanten der Kulturtomate Lycopersicon esculentum Miller II. Kulturpflanze 6, 89-115.

Stubbe, H. (1959). Mutanten der Kulturtomate Lycopersicon esculentum Miller III. Kulturpflanze 7, 82-112.

Tal, M. (1966). Abnormal stomatal behavior in wilty mutants of tomato. Plant Physiology 41, 1387-1391.

Tal, M. and Imber, D. (1970). Abnormal stomatal behavior and hormonal imbalance in flacca, a wilty mutant of tomato II. Auxin- and abscisic acid-like activity. Plant Physiology 46, 373-376.

Tal, M. and Imber, D. (1972). The effect of abscisic acid on stomatal behaviour in flacca, a wilty mutant of tomato, in darkness. New Phytologist 71, 81-84.

Tal, M., Imber, D., Erez, A. and Epstein, E. (1979). Abnormal stomatal behavior and hormonal imbalance in flacca, a wilty mutant of tomato V. Effect of abscisic acid on indoleacetic acid metabolism and ethylene evolution. Plant Physiology 63, 1044-1048.

Tal, M., Imber, D. and Gardi, I. (1974). Abnormal stomatal behaviour and hormonal imbalance in flacca, a wilty mutant of tomato: effect of abscisic acid and auxin on stomatal behaviour and peroxidase activity. Journal of Experimental Botany 25, 51-60.

Tal, M. and Nevo, Y. (1973). Abnormal stomatal behavior and root resistance, and hormonal imbalance in three wilty mutants of tomato. Biochemical Genetics 8, 291-300.

Taylor, I.B. (1987). ABA deficient tomato mutants. In "Developmental mutants in higher plants" (H. Thomas and D. Grierson eds.), pp 197-218. SEB Seminar Series, Cambridge University Press, Cambridge.

Taylor, I.B. and Tarr, A.R. (1984). Phenotypic interactions between abscisic acid deficient tomato mutants. Theoretical and Applied Genetics 68, 115-119.

Waggoner, P.E. and Simmonds, N.W. (1966). Stomata and transpiration of droopy potatoes. Plant Physiology 41, 1268-1271.

Wang, T.L., Donkin, M.E. and Martin, E.S. (1984). The physiology of a wilty pea : abscisic acid production under water stress. Journal of Experimental Botany 35, 1222-1232.

Watts, S., Rodriguez, J.L., Evans, S.E. and Davies, W.J. (1981). Root and shoot growth of plants treated with abscisic acid. Annals of Botany 47, 595-602.

GENETIC VARIANTS AS AIDS TO EXAMINE THE SIGNIFICANCE OF ETHYLENE IN DEVELOPMENT

J.A. Roberts, D. Grierson and G.A. Tucker

University of Nottingham, School of Agriculture, Sutton Bonington, Loughborough,

Leics., LE12 5RD, England

The contemporary approach by which to probe critically the role of a plant hormone in development is to identify and study specific mutants. Mutations of interest would affect either the biosynthetic pathway of ethylene or its mechanism of action. Few mutations in these areas have been documented which may be a reflection either of the difficulties of screening ethylene mutants or their potential deleterious properties. There are, however, several mutants available which exhibit abnormalities in those areas of development where ethylene is thought to play an important role. This review describes some ripening, abscission and senescence mutants and considers how they may be useful in elucidating the significance of ethylene in development.

INTRODUCTION

The discovery that ethylene could have a profound influence on plant development was made by the Russian Scientist Neljubov in 1901. His work demonstrated that exposure of pea seedlings to the gas could transform their direction of growth from vertical to horizontal. Some years later it was documented that inhibition of cell elongation and lateral expansion accompanied the induced horizontal growth and this 'triple response' to ethylene became accepted as the primary diagnostic test for the gas (Knight et al., 1910). Since these first observations, ethylene has become firmly established in the premier division of plant hormones, ranking alongside the auxins, gibberellins, cytokinins and abscisic acid.

In comparison to these other compounds ethylene appears to be a rather unusual candidate for the role which it has been ascribed. For instance, it has a simple structure and being volatile its translocation cannot be directly regulated. Also, endogenous levels of the gas can be rapidly altered by a wide variety of environmental conditions such as temperature and water availability. The aim of this review is to assess critically the role that ethylene plays in development and to consider whether this assessment may be accomplished more easily by studying plant genetic variants.

ETHYLENE AND PLANT DEVELOPMENT

The advent of gas chromatography as an analytical tool (Huelin and Kennett, 1959) has had a marked effect on the number of publications linking ethylene with aspects of plant development. It is now a straightforward operation to expose plant material to predetermined ethylene concentrations or measure evolution of the gas during the course of a developmental event. A list of the processes where ethylene has been reported to play an important role is shown in Table 1. This list is by no means exhaustive but makes the point that the documented effects of ethylene are wide-ranging and take place throughout the life cycle of a plant. Not all plants respond to ethylene in the same fashion nor are they equally sensitive to the gas. For example, higher concentrations of ethylene are required to inhibit stem elongation in monocotyledons than dicotyledons (Abeles, 1973) whilst exposure to the gas stimulates the growth of water plants such as Regnellidium diphyllum

Table 1 Developmental processes where a role for ethylene has been implicated.

Germination
Growth
Apical dominance   (For further
Flowering   details see
Ripening   Roberts and Tucker, 1985)
Abscission
Senescence

(Cookson and Osborne, 1978) and rice (Raskin and Kende, 1984). Similarly the response of tissues to the gas can be dictated by the concentrations to which they are exposed. Konings and Jackson (1974) reported that below 0.02 $\mu l_1 l^{-1}$ ethylene promoted root growth of tomato seedlings but above 0.1 $\mu l \; l^{-1}$ growth was inhibited.

In order to assign a role to ethylene convincingly we need to do more than just demonstrate that the gas can influence the progress of a developmental event. As a first step, some correlation between the phenomenon and a change in endogenous ethylene levels should be sought. In theory such a correlation (if present) should be easy to establish, particularly since highly sensitive means of detecting ethylene have now been designed (Bassi and Spencer, 1985). In practice, however, attempts of this type are commonly made on excised tissue segments making extrapolation of the results to an intact system difficult. Furthermore the nature of the analytical technique means that plant material is commonly enclosed in a sealed container to enable detectable quantities of ethylene to accumulate and this procedure itself may be sufficient to affect the developmental process under study.

Recent approaches to the problem have employed the utilisation of chemicals to 'specifically' block ethylene action or biosynthesis. The use of chemical antagonists such as these has inherent problems. For instance although silver ions have been reported to have a specific effect on ethylene action (Beyer, 1979) their application to plant tissue can induce the appearance of a spectrum of novel proteins (Tucker, unpublished). Norbornadiene, a structural analogue of ethylene, has also been employed to block the action of the hormone (Sisler and Yang, 1984). This antagonist is gaseous and can therefore be applied and removed readily; however, it has carcinogenic properties which limits its application. Use of biosynthetic inhibitors such as aminoethoxyvinylglycine (AVG) might be considered a preferable alternative since the progress of the compound in reducing ethylene production can be monitored and its specificity probed by the application of exogenous ethylene. This latter precaution is important since the chemical is a general inhibitor of pyridoxal phosphate linked enzymes (Rando, 1974). The drawbacks of using AVG are that it has limited mobility and a relatively short half life. Hypobaric pressure treatments have also been adopted to study the role of ethylene in processes such as ripening and abscission (Burg and Burg, 1966, Jordan et al., 1972). Hypobaric conditions are thought to reduce ethylene accumulation within the tissue and its biosynthesis (Nilsen and Hodges, 1983). To test this hypothesis, Sexton et al. (1985) added ethylene back to the incubation chamber and found that abscission under these conditions was slower and more erratic than that caused by ethylene at normal atmospheric pressure. Therefore, the primary effects of reduced pressure may not be solely restricted to its ability to lower internal ethylene levels.

In conclusion then it is clear that ethylene can exert a myriad of effects on plant development. However, a definitive role for the gas in the regulation of any one of these has yet to be proven. Furthermore it is unlikely that the evidence provided by the approaches outlined will ever be conclusive.

ETHYLENE AND MUTANTS

The logic behind the use of the chemical antagonists and inhibitors described previously is that it allows one to assess the impact of impaired ethylene biosynthesis or sensitivity on the course of plant development. A more subtle means of achieving this objective is to study the phenotype of appropriate mutant plants. This approach, which is proving to be a highly effective means of probing plant development, hinges on the recognition and classification of specific mutants.

Ethylene mutants of interest would fall into two distinct classes. The first would comprise those which have aberrant endogenous levels of the hormone. These might be over-producers or under-producers or even devoid of the gas (although the latter mutation might prove to be highly deleterious in nature). The ethylene biosynthetic pathway is catalysed by a series of enzymes (Fig. 1). Molecular modifications affecting the activity of any one of these could elevate or repress rates of ethylene production. A mutation affecting the activity of 1-aminocyclopropane-1-carboxylic acid synthase might have the most significant impact on ethylene biosynthesis since this enzyme is hypothesized to catalyse the rate limiting step in the pathway (Yang et al., 1985).

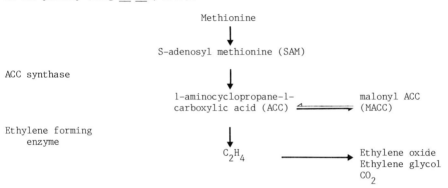

Fig. 1   Ethylene biosynthesis and metabolism.

Production of ethylene could also be affected by a change in the ability of plant cells to metabolise ACC to malonyl-ACC (MACC) or ethylene itself. The capacity of tissues to metabolise ethylene varies enormously and in some plants up to 80% of applied $^{14}C_2H_4$ is metabolised to products such as ethylene oxide and CO_2 (Beyer, 1985).

Major contributions have been made already by studying mutants with abnormal hormone levels. For instance work on gibberellin (Phinney et al., 1986) and abscisic acid (Taylor, 1987) deficient plants has enabled some of the complexities of the biosynthetic pathways of these hormones to be resolved. One plant which has been reported to show signs of ethylene deficiency is the tomato mutant diageotropica (dgt) (Zobel, 1973). The diagnostic characteristic of dgt plants is that the stems grow at an angle to gravity and that this abnormality can be 'corrected' by exposure to ethylene (Zobel, 1973). Since the mutant also exhibits a reduced capacity to produce ethylene after indole-3-acetic acid (IAA) treatment it was hypothesized that dgt was an ethylene deficient mutant and that the gas played a crucial role in shoot gravitropism. Quantification of basal ethylene emanations from mutant tissues has subsequently led to the rejection of the ethylene deficiency hypothesis (Jackson, 1979). It is clear that dgt does have a reduced capacity to produce ethylene in response to application of IAA (Fig. 2) and since IAA is thought to exert its effect on the conversion of S-adenosyl methionine to

ACC this might implicate the enzyme ACC synthase. However, since the activity of this enzyme in dgt tissue can apparently be enhanced by wounding or anaerobiosis it is most likely that the genetic lesion is associated with the perception of IAA rather than the ethylene biosynthetic pathway per se (Bradford and Yang, 1980).

A second class of ethylene mutants would be those that exhibit a modified capacity to respond to the gas. Members of this group would originate from a mutation which affects any step in the pathway of ethylene action (Fig. 3). These reactions are currently unknown but are thought to be initiated by binding of the hormone to a receptor located in a membrane (Evans et al., 1982) or solubilised within the cytoplasm. It is likely that binding initiates a sequence of events which culminates in changes in such processes as ion transport, transcription or translation. Although we have no definitive evidence for the site of action of ethylene, it is well documented that the gas can regulate gene expression (Grierson, 1985). However some of its effects may be too rapid for it to act solely at this level (Eisinger, 1983). Mutants with a reduced sensitivity to the plant hormone gibberellic acid (GA_3) have been identified in a number of species, but as yet their contribution to our understanding of the mechanism of hormone action has been minor.

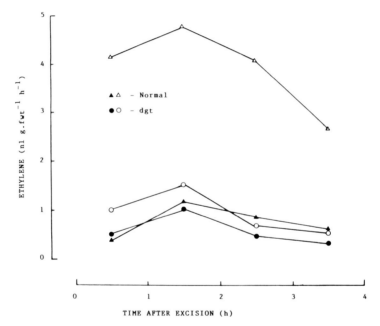

Fig. 2 <u>Time course of ethylene production by excised petiole tissue from normal or dgt plants after treatment with H_2O (closed symbols) or 10^{-4} M IAA (open symbols).</u> (From Bradford and Yang, 1980).

No ethylene action mutant has so far been characterised, although attempts have been made to identify them by screening pea mutants for an inability to exhibit the triple response when exposed to the gas (Abeles, pers. comm.). The lack of success in identifying ethylene mutants of either of the classes described above could be due to a number of reasons. Firstly, if the hormone is such a critical regulator of plant development, mutations affecting its endogenous levels or activity might prove highly deleterious to the individual concerned. Alternatively, as yet we may have no adequate means of recognising an ethylene mutant. This line of thought generates a circular argument in that an effective screen for a hormone

mutant relies on an ability to anticipate its mutant phenotype on the basis of a
predictable impact on a developmental process. In turn this relies on a knowledge
of the role of the particular plant hormone in development. This reasoning explains
why most hormone mutants identified so far have been related to the gibberellins or
abscisic acid whose role in vivo in the regulation of elongation growth and
stomatal aperture respectively has been established with some degree of confidence.
The phenotypes of such mutants can therefore be clearly recognised by their dwarf
stature or wilty appearance.

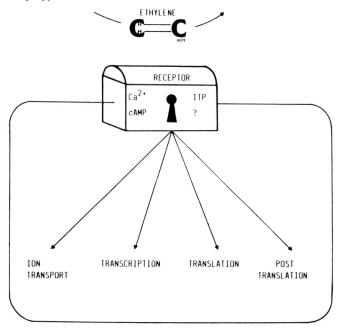

Fig. 3 Diagrammatic representation of the mechanism of action of ethylene (cAMP -
cyclic adenine monophosphate, ITP - inositol triphosphate).

A clue to the potential phenotypic appearance of an ethylene mutant may come from
an examination of the developmental events where ethylene is implicated (Table 1).
In order to screen for such plants ideally we require a characteristic early in the
life cycle of a plant. Unfortunately the events where a role for ethylene is most
convincing, for instance ripening, senescence and abscission primarily occur once
the plant has reached maturity. However, at least the nature of these mutations
make them readily apparent. Mutants of this type have been identified and studied
by a number of workers; it remains to be seen whether the lesion associated with
any one of these mutants is primarily related to ethylene.

RIPENING, SENESCENCE AND ABSCISSION MUTANTS

Mutations which affect the ability of fruit such as the tomato to ripen have been
widely reported (Grierson, 1985). Most commonly they have been identified by a
modified capacity to change colour. However, detailed studies of the fruit have
revealed that many other facets of the ripening programme may be affected (Table
2). Potential ethylene mutants, amongst the population of ripening mutants, have
been examined for their ability to produce the gas or ripen in response to it.
Adopting this screening procedure the mutants Ripening inhibitor (rin), Never ripe
(Nr), non-ripening (nor) and alcabaca (alc) are plants of interest.

The rin mutation influences ethylene production, acting to abolish the climacteric rise which accompanies ripening of normal fruit (Herner and Sink, 1973). However, this phenomenon is not associated with an inherent inability of the fruit to produce the gas. For instance, during development, green fruit from rin plants produce levels of ethylene comparable to those from normal fruit prior to ripening (Herner and Sink, 1973). Also, if rin fruit are mechanically wounded then the subsequent production of stress-induced ethylene is 'normal' (Herner and Sink, 1973, McGlasson, 1975). McMurchie et al. (1972) have suggested that at least two ethylene synthesizing systems operate in fruit tissue. They suggest that System I is responsible for the low background ethylene production during maturation and for any stress-induced ethylene; whilst System II contributes to the autocatalytic

Table 2   Characteristics of tomato ripening mutants.

Characteristic	Never ripe (Nr)	ripening inhibitor	non-ripening nor	alcabaca alc
Ethylene climacteric	Reduced	Absent	Much reduced	*Reduced
Respiratory climacteric	Reduced	Absent	Absent	*Reduced
Colour change	Orange	Yellow	Yellow	Pink
Softening	Slow	Very Slow	Very Slow	Slow

* Ethylene and respiration rates are higher than in rin and nor
  mutants but do not exhibit any clear climacteric pattern

ethylene rise observed during the ripening climacteric. Adopting this nomenclature, rin fruit might, therefore, be considered to have a functional System I but be deficient at some site in system II (McGlasson, 1985). This conclusion is supported by experiments where fruit have been exposed to propylene, a structural analogue of ethylene (Herner and Sink, 1973; McGlasson et al., 1975). In response to propylene, the ethylene production by normal fruit is elevated, presumably via the autocatalytic stimulation of ethylene production, after propylene treatment. From the work of Yang's group it is apparent that both stress-induced (Yu and Yang, 1980) and autocatalytic (climateric) (Hoffman and Yang 1980) ethylene synthesis result from the same ACC-mediated pathway (Fig. 1). The evidence presented previously indicates that the rin mutation does not affect the biosynthetic pathway directly. However, it remains to be seen whether the mutation affects a step in the biochemical pathway regulating autocatalytic ethylene production by plant tissues in general or is restricted to ripening. A comparison of the ethylene production by normal and rin leaf tissue during senescence would contribute towards answering this question.

One explanation for the inability of rin fruit to produce autocatalytic ethylene would be that they lack the capacity to perceive the plant hormone. Alas, the answer is not as simple as that. The application of ethylene to rin fruit has been shown to result in a stimulation of respiratory activity (Herner and Sink, 1973), an increased rate of decolourisation (Tigchelaar et al., 1978) and an enhanced appearance of ethylene forming enzyme (EFE) activity (Lui et al., 1985). All of these events are induced in normal fruit by exposure to ethylene. It is clear, therefore, that rin fruit perceive ethylene and that the gas does accelerate a number of the ripening associated events. However, it cannot overcome the genetic block to 'normal' ripening, i.e. fruits do not turn red, soften, or synthesise ripening specific enzymes such as poly-galacturonase and invertase.

With these results in mind, how would a study of the rin mutant aid our understanding of ethylene action during ripening? Firstly, the mutant may be useful in
elucidating the control steps associated with system II of ethylene production.
Secondly, rin fruit either lack a specific sub-class of ethylene receptor
(McGlasson, 1985) (Fig. 4), or they carry a lesion affecting the response rather
than the perception mechanism (Fig. 5). It has been claimed that attached rin fruit
can be induced to 'ripen' if exposed to ethylene at a critical developmental stage
(Mizrahi et al., 1975). This significant observation needs to be re-examined since
it could provide us with important clues to solve the question of which of the
above scenarios account for the rin mutation.

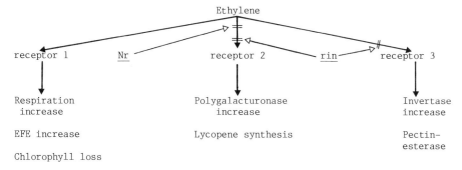

Fig. 4 'Multireceptor' mechanism for the action of the rin and Nr mutations.

The less aberrant Nr mutation is somewhat different from rin. In this mutant the
ethylene climacteric is not abolished although it may be attenuated (Tigchelaar et
al., 1978), yet subsequent ripening events are abnormal. Presumably, in this case
both Systems I and II are operative although the latter may be reduced in efficacy.
Nr fruit produce normal amounts of stress-induced ethylene but their response to
added propylene is unrecorded. Once again, fruit of the mutant must be able to
perceive ethylene since the gas stimulates their respiratory activity and induces
limited colour change. Ethylene can also stimulate the synthesis of ripening
specific enzymes such as pectinesterase (Hobson, 1967; Tucker et al., 1980) and
invertase (Tucker unpublished) in Nr fruit, while the synthesis of
polygalacturonase is attenuated (Hobson, 1967; Tucker et al., 1982). The
explanation for the Nr lesion may also reside in a deficiency in a particular
receptor type (Fig. 4), or in a ripening-control gene (Fig. 5) minor in comparison
to rin in that it affects fewer ripening events. Greater information on the types
and numbers of ethylene receptors are required to distinguish between these two
possibilities.

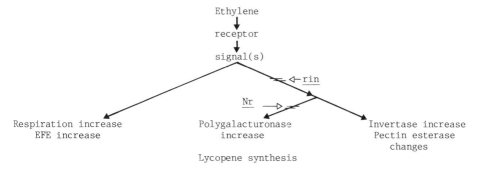

Fig. 5 'Downstream control' mechanism for the action of the rin and Nr mutations.

The ripening mutants nor and alc are superficially similar to rin or Nr respectively. Thus, the majority of what has been said about rin could equally apply to the nor mutant and Nr to the alc mutant, although in each case the genetic lesion lies at a different locus (Rick, 1980).

Our original intention in studying mutants was to probe the significance of ethylene in development. How can the ripening mutants that have been described make a contribution towards this goal? Ideally for this task we require an ethylene mutant whose phenotype could be 'corrected' by exposure to the gas. A study of this plant would then reveal those events where ethylene played a critical role. Evidently the ripening mutants rin, Nr, nor and alc are not of this type. However, if the genetic lesion associated with any one of them is restricted to a basic biochemical event normally regulated by ethylene then other events where the gas has a role might also be affected. This philosophy led Tucker et al. (1984) to examine the flower abscission response of the mutants Nr and rin. The results of this study showed that flower abscission in the former mutant is markedly delayed compared to normal plants in response to ethylene. This effect is even more pronounced for leaf abscission (Roberts, unpublished). In contrast the rates of flower (Tucker et al., 1984) and leaf (Roberts, unpublished) abscission in rin plants are unaffected by the mutation. These observations lend credence to the hypothesis that the genetic lesion giving rise to the rin phenotype resides in a ripening specific control gene and therefore it does not influence other developmental events where ethylene plays a role. It is apparent, however, that the mutation associated with the Nr genotype may affect a gene which is involved in the regulation of a number of ethylene-related processes. Further investigations utilising this mutant, of phenomena such as leaf senescence, may enable us to discern whether the mutation affects a central step in the ethylene action mechanism or is restricted to events such as ethylene-stimulated wall breakdown. If a central step is deficient, then a detailed study of the Nr phenotype could provide us with further information concerning the roles of ethylene during plant development.

Other mutations which affect the process of abscission have been identified. The most dramatic tomato mutants are those which fail to shed their flowers or fruit. These are termed jointless (j). There is no evidence that the j mutation is associated with ethylene, and the most likely explanation is that these plants have no differentiated separation zone at the 'knuckle' site (Roberts, unpublished). The sideshoot-less mutant, Lateral suppressor (ls) also fails to shed its flowers in response to ethylene. However, once again the lesion appears to lie at an anatomical level (Roberts, unpublished). In this section we have examined specific developmental mutants in an attempt to identify a genetic lesion associated with the plant hormone ethylene. Having appraised the evidence it remains highly unlikely that any of the mutants that have been discussed conforms to our definition of an ethylene mutant.

SPECIES-SPECIFIC RESPONSES

Different species of plants exhibit marked differences ⁀in their responses to ethylene during development. A further method of extracting information about the mechanism of ethylene action may be to study these genetic variants.

A classic example of this phenomenon is the two types of fruit ripening – climacteric and non-climacteric. The main criteria distinguishing these two are given in Table 3. From these characteristics, it would appear that climacteric fruit ripen in response to ethylene whilst non-climacteric fruit ripen independently of the gas. However, application of ethylene stimulates the rate of ripening of both classes of fruit (Proctor and Caygill, 1985). How can we rationalise these observations?

Firstly, ethylene could hasten the onset of the 'ripening programme' in non-climacteric fruit but, in contrast to the situation in climacteric fruit, it is not needed for the process to be initiated. The phenomenon of developmental events being regulated in different species by disparate signals is not uncommon. Alternatively, ethylene could be a vital ingredient for ripening to take place in both climacteric and non-climacteric fruit. In this case, the rise in ethylene which precedes ripening of climacterics (Grierson and Tucker, 1983), would trigger the cascade of events culminating in changes of colour, flavour, aroma and texture. Since levels of ethylene do not increase prior to ripening of non-climacteric fruit, then if the gas does act to regulate the process one would have to hypothesise that an increase in tissue sensitivity must occur to allow the basal endogenous concentration of ethylene to become stimulatory. This hypothesis does not set a physiological precedent since there is a wealth of evidence that the sensitivity of plant cells to ethylene can change during development (McGlasson 1985). However, the biochemical basis underlying this phenomenon is as yet unknown (Trewavas, 1982). An understanding of this is crucial, in order to determine whether ethylene functions as a trigger of developmental processes or merely as a coordinator of their progression. If sensitivity changes do precipitate the ripening programme of non-climacteric fruit in vivo, then a comparative investigation of the response of climacteric and non-climacteric fruits to ethylene may help us to elucidate the nature of these changes.

Table 3   Ripening characteristics of climacteric and non-climacteric fruits

Criteria	Climacteric	Non-climacteric
Ethylene production during ripening	Transient	Gradual decline
Respiratory changes during ripening	Transient increase coincident with and following ethylene	Gradual decline
Response to exogenous propylene	Increased ethylene	No increase in ethylene

CONCLUSIONS

The demonstration that ethylene can influence a developmental event is not definitive proof that the gas does regulate the process in vivo. In order to ascertain its hormonal properties we require ideally to be able to examine a plant where the gas cannot undertake its normal role. Plant mutants offer us the most elegant way of achieving this; however, at the present time few potential ethylene mutants have been identified. Some progress is being made in this direction but it may be hampered by an inability to recognise an ethylene mutant, or the deleterious nature of the mutant phenotype. A note of caution should be added at this stage concerning the conclusions reached from the studies of hormonal mutants. It should be remembered that the activities of the major hormonal groups closely interact. A good example of this is the ability of auxins to stimulate ethylene production by many plant tissues, and the capacity of ethylene to inhibit auxin transport. Therefore, a change in the activity of one hormone can rapidly affect the level of another. An instance of this situation is exhibited by the gibberellin-insensitive pea mutant lk which has internodes of greatly reduced length. It has recently been reported that shoot tissues of the mutant produce high levels of ethylene and, therefore, the phenotypic effects of the mutation may be not only the result of an insensitivity to a growth promoting compound i.e. gibberellin, but also in part due to elevated levels of a growth inhibitor i.e. ethylene (Ross and Reid, 1986). It is evident therefore that the conclusions reached as a result of studying hormonal mutants should be considered carefully.

The mutants discussed in this review will be very useful in the study of processes such as ripening and abscission, where ethylene plays a role. However, it is unlikely that they will contribute to our understanding of the wider functions of the gas in plant development. To achieve this we require genuine ethylene mutants which conform to the criteria outlined earlier. To obtain such plants we will probably have to carry out an intensive programme of mutagenesis and screening rather than scratching around in the pot of mutants that we currently have at our disposal.

REFERENCES

Abeles, F.B. (1973). "Ethylene in plant biology". Academic Press, New York.

Bassie, P.K. and Spencer, M.S. (1985). Comparative evaluation of photoionization and flame ionization detectors for ethylene analysis: technical report. Plant Cell and Environment 8, 161-6.

Beyer, E.M., Jr. (1979). Effect of silver ion carbon dioxide and oxygen on ethylene action and metabolism. Plant Physiology 63, 169-173.

Beyer, E.M., Jr. (1985). Ethylene metabolism. In "Ethylene and Plant Development" (J.A. Roberts and G.A. Tucker eds.) pp 125-137. Butterworths, London.

Bradford, K.J. and Yang, S.F. (1980). Stress-induced ethylene production in the ethylene-requiring tomato mutant diageotropica. Plant Physiology 65, 327-330.

Burg, S.P. and Burg, E.A. (1966). Fruit storage at subatmospheric pressures. Science 153, 314-5.

Cookson, C. and Osborne, D.J. (1978). The stimulation of cell extension by ethylene and auxin in aquatic plants. Planta 144, 39-47.

Eisinger, W. (1983). Regulation of pea internode expansion by ethylene. Annual Review of Plant Physiology 34, 225-240.

Evans, D.E., Bengochea, T., Cairns, A.J., Dodds, J.H. and Hall, M.A. (1982). Studies on ethylene binding by cell-free preparations from cotyledons of Phaseolus vulgaris L: Subcellular location. Plant Cell and Environment 5, 101-7.

Grierson, D. (1985). Gene expression in ripening tomato fruit. CRC Critical Reviews in Plant Science 3, 113-132.

Grierson, D. and Tucker, G.A. (1983). Timing of ethylene and polygalacturonase synthesis in relation to the control of tomato fruit ripening. Planta 157, 174-179.

Herner, R.C. and Sink, K.C. (1973). Ethylene production and respiratory behaviour of the rin tomato mutant. Plant Physiology 52, 38-42.

Hobson, G.E. (1967). The effect of alleles at the Nr locus on the ripening of tomato fruit. Phytochemistry 6, 1337-1341.

Hoffman, N.E. and Yang, S.F. (1980). Changes of 1-amino-cyclopropane-1-carboxylic acid content in ripening fruits in relation to their ethylene production rates. Journal of the American Society of Horticultural Science 105, 492-495.

Huelin, F.E. and Kennett, B.H. (1959). Nature of the olefines produced by apples. Nature **184**, 996.

Jackson, M.B. (1979). Is the diageotropic tomato ethylene deficient? Physiologia Plantarum **46**, 347-351.

Jordan, W.R., Morgan, P.W. and Davenport, T.L. (1972). Water stress enhances ethylene-mediated leaf abscission in cotton. Plant Physiology **50**, 756-8.

Knight, L.I., Rose, C.R. and Crocker, W. (1910). Effect of various gases and vapours upon etiolated seedlings of the sweet pea. Science **31**, 635-636.

Konings, H. and Jackson, M.B. (1974). Production of ethylene, and the promoting and inhibiting effects of applied ethylene on root elongation in various species. Letcombe Laboratory Annual Report pp 23-24.

Liu, Y., Hoffman, N.E. and Yang, S.F. (1985). Promotion by ethylene of the capability to convert ACC to ethylene in preclimacteric tomato and cantaloupe fruit. Plant Physiology **7**, 407-411.

McGlasson, W.B. (1975). Ethylene production and respiration in aging leaf segments and in discs of fruit tissue of normal and mutant tomatoes. Plant Physiology **56**, 547-549.

McGlasson, W.B. (1985). Ethylene and fruit ripening. HortScience **20**, 51-54.

McGlasson, W.B., Dostal, H.C. and Tigchelaar, E.C. (1975). Comparison of propylene-induced responses of immature fruit of normal and rin mutant tomatoes. Plant Physiology **55**, 218-222.

McMurchie, E.J., McGlasson, W.B. and Eaks, I.L. (1972). Treatment of fruit with propylene gives information about the biogenesis of ethylene. Nature **237**, 235-236.

Mizrahi, Y., Dostal, H.C. and Cherry, J.H. (1975). Ethylene-induced ripening in attached rin fruits, a non-ripening mutant of tomato. HortScience **10**, 414-415.

Nilsen, K.N. and Hodges, C.F. (1983). Hypobaric control of ethylene-induced leaf senescence in intact plants of Phaseolus vulgaris. Plant Physiology **71**, 96-101.

Phinney, B.O., Freeling, M., Robertson, D.S., Spray, C.R. and Silverthorne, J. (1986). Dwarf mutants in maize – the gibberellin biosynthetic pathway and its molecular future. In "Plant Growth Substances 1985" (M. Bopp ed.) pp 55-64. Springer-Verlag, Berlin.

Proctor, F.J. and Caygill, J.C. (1985). Ethylene in commercial post-harvest handling of tropical fruit. In "Ethylene and Plant Development" (J.A. Roberts and G.A. Tucker eds.), pp 317-332. Butterworths, London.

Rando, R.R. (1974). Chemistry and enzymology of K_{cat} inhibitors. Science **185**, 320-4.

Raskin, I. and Kende, H. (1984). Regulation of growth in stem sections of deep water rice. Planta **160**, 66-72.

Rick, C.M. (1980). Tomato linkage survey. Tomato Genetics Cooperative Report **30**, 2-17.

Roberts, J.A. and Tucker, G.A. (1985). "Ethylene and Plant Development" (eds.). Butterworths, London.

Ross, J.J. and Reid, J.B. (1986). Internode length in Pisum. The involvement of ethylene with the gibberellin-insensitive erectoides phenotype. Physiologia Plantarum **67,** 673-679.

Sexton, R., Lewis, L.N., Trewavas, A.J. and Kelly, P. (1985). Ethylene and abscission. In "Ethylene and Plant Development" (J.A. Roberts and G.A. Tucker eds.) pp 173-196. Butterworths, London.

Sisler, E.C. and Yang, S.I. (1984). Anti-ethylene effects of cis-2-butene and cyclic olefins. Phytochemistry **23,** 2765-2768.

Taylor, I.B. (1987). ABA deficient mutants. In "Developmental mutants in higher plants" (H. Thomas and D. Grierson eds.) In press, C.U.P., Cambridge.

Tigchelaar, E.C., McGlasson, W.B. and Buescher, R.W. (1978). Genetic regulation of tomato fruit ripening. HortScience **13,** 508-513.

Trewavas, A.J. (1982). Growth substance sensitivity: The limiting factor in plant development. Physiologia Plantarum **55,** 60-72.

Tucker, G.A., Robertson, N.G. and Grierson, D. (1980). Changes in polygalacturonase isoenzymes during ripening of normal and mutant tomato fruit. European Journal of Biochemistry **112,** 119-124.

Tucker, G.A., Robertson, N.G. and Grierson, D. (1982). Purification and changes in activities of tomato pectinesterase isoenzymes. Journal of the Science of Food and Agriculture **33,** 396-400.

Tucker, G.A., Schindler, C.B. and Roberts, J.A. (1984). Flower abscission in mutant tomato plants. Planta **160,** 164-167.

Yang, S.F., Liu, Y., Su, L., Peiser, G.D., Hoffman, N.E. and McKeon, T. (1985). Metabolism of 1-aminocyclopropane-1-carboxylic acid. In "Ethylene and Plant Development" (J.A. Roberts and G.A. Tucker eds.) pp 9-21. Butterworths, London.

Yu, Y.B. and Yang, S.F. (1980). Biosynthesis of wound ethylene. Plant Physiology **66,** 281-285.

Zobel, R.W. (1973). Some physiological characteristics of the ethylene-requiring tomato mutant diageotropica. Plant Physiology **52,** 385-389.

CYTOKININ GENES

R. Horgan

Department of Botany and Microbiology, The University College of Wales,
Aberystwyth, SY23 3DA, Wales

> This article was to have been entitled 'Cytokinin and auxin
> T-DNA genes and plant development'. However, although the
> T-DNA auxin and particularly the cytokinin oncogenes provide
> useful models for the possible nature and functioning of the
> naturally-occurring plant genes it is not possible to discuss
> cogently their functions in relation to normal plant
> development. This article therefore seeks to extend an account
> of the T-DNA genes into the incompletely understood area of the
> possible genetic control of cytokinin levels in plants via
> endogenous cytokinin and auxin biosynthetic and metabolic
> genes.

INTRODUCTION

Stepping aside from the rather sterile arguments regarding hormone action and 'tissue
sensitivity' it would seem highly likely that if auxins and cytokinins play any role
in plant growth and development mechanisms must exist for the control of their levels
in plants. Whether or not such mechanisms are utilised by the plant as primary
controls of growth and development depends on the existence of conditions under which
the availability of cytokinin and/or auxin limit these processes. Unfortunately this
is a question which cannot be answered given the current state of knowlege of
cytokinin and auxin physiology.

In the case of the gibberellins (GAs),studies on dwarf mutants of corn and pea have
provided incontrovertible evidence that these hormones are required for normal stem
elongation and have pointed to GA_1 as most probably being the key active GA (Phinney,
1984). In addition, work with GA mutants has led to the elucidation of many of the
steps of GA biosynthesis in higher plants. In the case of abscisic acid (ABA), the
existence of ABA deficient mutants of tomato (Neill and Horgan, 1985), Zea mays
(Neill et al., 1986) and Arabidopsis (Koorneef et al., 1982) has demonstrated the
requirement for ABA for normal stomatal function and normal seed development.

In spite of the above evidence, considerable argument, largely semantic, surrounds
the question as to whether or not changes in hormone level may control these
processes. This probably arises from a grossly simplistic extrapolation from the
effects of externally-applied hormones to the endogenous situation. Given the
multitude of biochemical events that may attenuate the concentration of an externally
-applied hormone before it reaches its site of action, it would seem naive to
believe that the dose-response relationships for endogenous compounds will have the
same logarithmic forms of those for externally-applied compounds. However, with
regard to cytokinins and auxins, it is more difficult to make a case for their
involvement in normal growth and development, since mutants of the sort described
above for GAs and ABA have not been detected as yet. Indeed the paucity of
knowlege of the possible roles of these compounds in the normal growth and
development of plants would make it particularly difficult to recognise such mutants.
Of course it can be argued that the requirement for cytokinins and auxin by all
normal plant cells is absolute and therefore such mutants would be lethal. In the
case of the cytokinins the only clear cytokinin mutants are the cytokinin
overproducing (OVE) mutants of the moss Phycomitrella patens (Wang et al., 1984). In
this case the mutant phenotype is easily recognised by its resemblance to the
wild-type moss which has been treated with cytokinin.

Because of the lack of suitable mutants, current evidence for the existence of mechanisms which control endogenous cytokinin levels is indirect. Such evidence has been produced mainly from studies on plant tissue cultures. The value of plant tissue and cell cultures for the study of the genetics underlying cytokinin biosynthesis and metabolism stems from the existence of the various types of cytokinin- autonomous tissue cultures and also tisssue cultures which exhibit different responses to a variety of externally-applied cytokinins. These systems provide some evidence for the existence of genes which regulate the biosynthesis and metabolism of cytokinins.

CYTOKININ BIOSYNTHESIS AND TISSUE CULTURE AUTONOMY

It is generally assumed that tissue cultures which require an external supply of cytokinin for growth do not possess the capacity to biosynthesise these compounds. Although perhaps a more realistic assumption would be that they are unable to maintain a sufficiently high level of biologically-active cytokinin. Thus metabolism, as well as biosynthesis, may be involved in this process. Likewise cytokinin-autonomous cultures are assumed to produce sûfficent of these hormones to maintain cell division and cell expansion.

Autonomus tissue cultures may be divided broadly into three types:

(1) Crown gall tissues.

(2) Tissues derived from 'genetic tumours'.

(3) Habituated tissues which either never have, or eventually lose, the requirement for cytokinin and/or auxin.

CROWN GALL TISSUES

The hormone autonomy of crown gall tissues has been explained almost completely at the genetic level. The demonstration that cytokinin and auxin autonomy is due to the presence on the T-DNA of genes directing the synthesis of $(\Delta^2$-isopentenyl)adenosine-5'-monophosphate ([9R-5'P]iP) and indole-3-acetic acid (IAA) has been an outstanding achievement of plant molecular biology. Considerable work by several groups using transposon mutageneisis revealed the presence of two loci on the T-DNA which markedly affected crown gall tumour morphology. Insertional inactivation of a locus, designated tms, gave rise to tumours consisting mainly of leafy shoots. Insertional inactivation of a locus, designated tmr, produced tumours consisting mainly of roots. The marked similarity between the morphology of these tumour tissues and the differentiation produced in normal, hormone-requiring, tobacco tissue cultures by varying the cytokinin:auxin ratio led to the suggestion that the tms and tmr loci controlled the ratio of endogenous auxin to cytokinin in crown gall tumours (Hooykaas et al., 1982). It was suggested that the tmr locus controlled the level of cytokinin and the tms locus the level of auxin. Measurement, by radioimmunoassay, of gross 'zeatin like' cytokinin levels in tms and tmr mutants of tobacco crown gall tissue revealed a very large reduction in the level of these cytokinins in tmr tissue when compared with a wild-type tumour. Tms mutant tissue on the other hand, had considerably elevated levels of 'zeatin like' cytokinins (Akiyoshi et al., 1983).

The results of these studies suggested that the tmr gene was directly involved in cytokinin biosynthesis. Cloning of the tmr region in an E. coli plasmid, designated pMON230, resulted in the direct demonstration that the tmr gene coded for a protein which catalysed the key reaction of cytokinin biosynthesis, shown in Fig. 1, between 5'-AMP and Δ^2-isopentenyl pyrophospate to give [9R-5'P]iP (Barry et al., 1984). This result, which was independently confirmed by two other groups (Akiyoshi et al., 1984; Buchman et al., 1985) uneqivocally established the function of the tmr gene.

Although insertional inactivation of the tms gene appeared to affect cytokinin levels more than auxin levels it was suggested that its primary function was to control auxin biosynthesis. It was shown that the tms region contained two genes, designated gene 1 and gene 2, which from sequence analysis probably produced protein products of

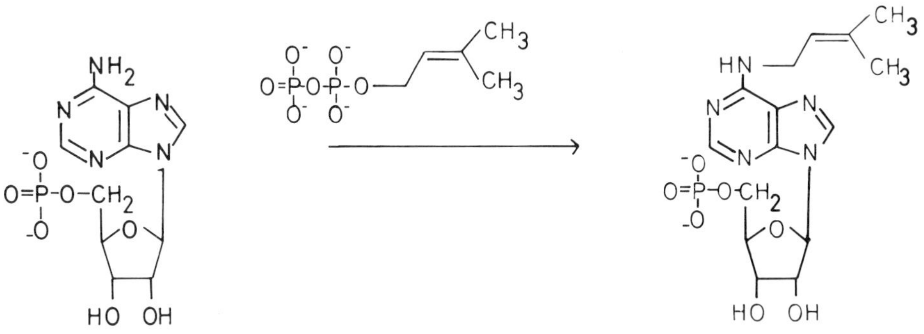

Fig. 1 Biosynthesis of [9R-5'P]iP catalysed by the tmr gene product.

83.7 kD and 49.6 kD respectively (Klee et al., 1984). It has been demonstrated (Schroder et al., 1984; Van Onckelen et al., 1985; Van Onckelen et al., 1986) that these genes function in an analagous manner to the auxin biosynthetic genes of Pseudomonas savastanoi. This organism converts tryptophan to indole-3-acetamide (IAM) via tryptophan-2-monooxygenase and IAM to IAA via an amidohydrolyase. This, as shown in Fig. 2, is a pathway which is not believed to operate in plants.

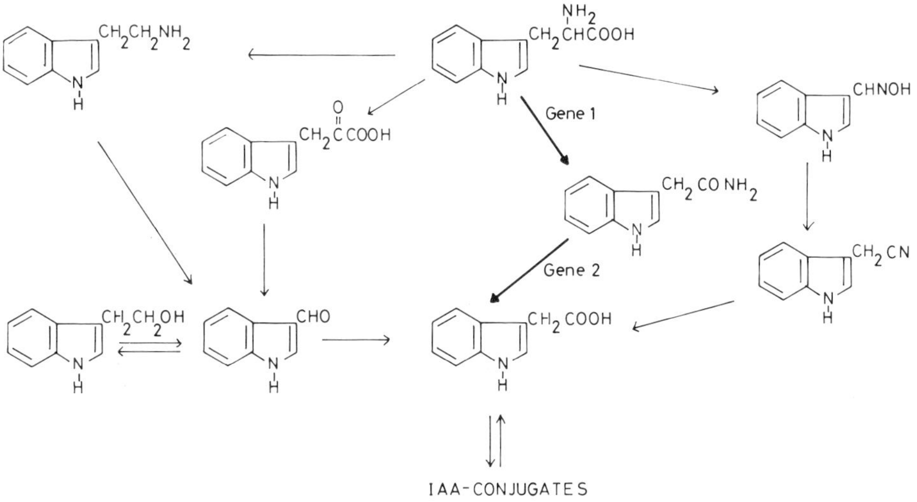

IAA-CONJUGATES

Fig. 2 Pathway of IAA biosynthesis in crown gall tissue, catalysed by gene 1 and gene 2 products. Presumed plant pathways are also shown.

It can be seen from the above brief account that hormone autonomy in crown gall tissues depends on the presence of oncogenes coding for cytokinin and auxin biosynthesis. However the exact role of these genes in controlling growth and development of crown gall tissues is still not entirely clear. Although concerned with auxin biosynthesis the tms genes markedly influence cytokinin levels which are greatly elevated in tissue in which these genes have been inactivated. The effects of tmr and tms mutations on the full cytokinin profile of crown gall tissue are shown in Table 1.

The effect of tms mutations on cytokinin levels is seen clearly, as is the fact that the qualitative and quantitative spectra of cytokinins follows closely the pattern of metabolism of externally-applied compounds. These data also suggest that the morphological changes observed in tms tissues may be caused by changes in cytokinin rather than auxin levels.

Pengelly et al. (1986) have recently shown that while tissues of N. tabacum carrying T-DNA with an insertionally-inactivated gene 2 exhibited the expected shooty phenotype and corrrespondingly low levels of IAA relative to wild-type tumours, variants arose from the mutant tissue which lacked shoots and were essentially similar to wild-type crown gall tissue. These variants still possessed a transposon in gene 2 and retained low IAA levels. Growth inhibition of the variant lines by NAA was greater than that of the parental shooty line and similar to that of wild-type tissue. These results led the authors to conclude that the change in phenotype from shooty to unorganised growth was accompanied by an increase in auxin sensitivity.

TABLE 1   Cytokinin levels in tobacco crown gall tissues carrying mutations in the tms (auxin) and/or tmr (cytokinin) genes. (McGaw, Horgan, Wullems and Schilperoort, unpublished data). Measurements were made by the method of Scott and Horgan (1984).

Cytokinin levels (ng.g^{-1} fresh wt.)

Tissue	[9R-5'P]Z	[9R]Z	Z	[7G]Z
LBA 4001 (wt)	25	17	22	10
LBA 4210 (tmr)	10	19	33	2
LBA 4060 (tms)	183	62	74	779
LBA 1501-1 (tms)	526	77	34	316
TSO 119 (tmr, tms)	10	26	35	8
SRI 4013-3	91	51	31	70
SRI (control)	10	16	7	4

Whilst studies of the crown gall system have provided invaluable information on the molecular biology of cytokinin and auxin production they also raise the important question: to what extent does the crown gall system provide a model for cytokinin and auxin production in normal plant tissues?

In the case of auxin, the crown gall genes introduce a novel pathway which is probably not relevant to the plant's own production of auxin. However the above data indicate that cytokinin levels may be markedly influenced by auxin levels, since direct interaction between genes 1 and 2, and gene 4 can be ruled out. It remains to be established if this effect occurs at the biosynthetic or metabolic level.

In the case of the cytokinins, knowledge of the nature of gene 4 and its product may provide important leads as to the mechanism of cytokinin biosynthesis in normal plant tissue. From the limited studies so far carried out it would appear that the mechanism of cytokinin biosynthesis in normal plant tissues is as shown in Fig. 1, although there are differences in molecular size between the plant enzyme and the T-DNA gene 4 product. Nevertheless there may be sufficient homology between plant and T-DNA genes to allow the use of cDNA probes derived from gene 4 to detect plant cytokinin-biosynthetic genes. It is clear, however, that a major difference between cytokinin biosynthesis in crown galls and normal plant tissues is the apparent lack of any regulation of the biosynthetic gene in the crown gall system. Thus the levels of cytokinins produced in crown galls are greatly in excess of those needed for growth of normal callus tissue. In normal plant tissues cytokinin levels need to be controlled carefully if unorganised growth is not to occur. If cytokinins do perform endogenous regulatory functions then it is highly likely that their biosynthetic genes will be regulated precisely . Studies on the other autonomous tissue culture systems tend to confirm this possibility.

Also, it should be pointed out that the Ti plasmid carries an additional cytokinin-biosynthetic gene in the vir region. This is not incorporated into the plant genome but is activated when the bacterium comes into contact with wounded plant tissue. Stachel et al. (1985) have shown that the vir group of genes can be activated by acetosyringone and α-hydroxyacetosyringone which are released from wounded plant cells. Activation of the plant's own cytokinin-biosynthetic genes may explain the cytokinin activity of dihydroconiferyl alcohol (Lee et al., 1981), which is structurally dissimilar to N-6 substituted purines but has close structural similaritiy to the syringones.

GENETIC TUMOURS

Genetic tumours, e.g. in tobacco, are produced by the combination of genetically distant genomes and characterised by growth in tissue culture without the addition of cytokinin and auxin. Naf (1958) has placed the parental species of tobacco crosses leading to genetic tumours into two groups called 'plus' and 'minus'. It has been suggested that members of the 'plus' group carry genes for a factor (factor 1) which regulates tumour induction whereas members of the 'minus' group carry genes for a factor (factor ee) which controls the degree of tumour expression (Ahuja, 1968). Hybrids of members in the same group are not tumorous whereas inter-group hybrids produce tumours. Unfortunately the molecular nature of these factors is unknown, although it has been suggested that in combination they produce some form of biochemical and/or physiological imbalance which leads to tumour formation. One component of this 'imbalance' is presumably an increase in auxin and cytokinin production to a level necessary to sustain autonomous growth. Unfortunately there is little reliable information on cytokinin levels in genetic tumour tissues. Palni et al. (1985) have analysed the cytokinin content of genetic tumours from N. glauca x N. langsdorffii. The major cytokinin present was [9R]Z with small amounts of Z, (diH)Z, [9R-5'P] and [9R-5'P](diH)Z being detected by a stable isotope dilution technique. Although the precise levels of the cytokinins were not reported it is clear that they were considerably lower than those found in crown gall tissues. Preliminary attempts to detect the incorporation of [^{3}H]adenine into cytokinins in this tissue were unsuccessful. This contrasts markedly with the situation in crown gall tissue where incoporation of radioactively labelled adenine into a variety of cytokinins has been demonstrated (Palni et al.,1983, Palni et al., 1985).

HABITUATED TISSUES

The term 'habituation' refers to the loss of a requirement for externally supplied auxin and/or cytokinin by plant tissues and cells in culture. Meins and his co-workers have made extensive studies of cytokinin habituation in tissue cultures of the tobacco variety 'Havana 425' (Meins, 1982; Meins and Foster, 1985). Cortical cells of this variety are cytokinin autonomous when initially isolated whereas pith tissues appear to contain two cell types. One cell type which becomes cytokinin autonomous when exposed to kinetin or incubated at 35°C, is classified as 'inducible'. The other cell type which does not respond to these treatments is said to be 'non-inducible'. 'Non-inducible' cells can change into 'inducible' cells at rates greater than 5×10^{-3} per cell generation which is 100 to 1000 times faster than the reported rates of somatic mutations in tobacco. Since this process is also reversible Meins has argued that it involves 'epigenetic' changes. It is presumed that 'epigenetic' in this context refers to relatively stable yet reversible changes in gene expression brought about by some as yet uncharacterised mechanism.

A second form of habituation in Havana 425, which involves stable and heritable genetic change, has also been described by Meins et al. (1983). Plants regenerated from cloned leaf and cortex cells of one particular plant differed in their cytokinin habituation. Leaf tissues from leaf-cell derived plants were non-habituated whereas leaf tissues from cortical-cell derived plants were habituated. A preliminary genetic analysis indicated that in this system cytokinin autonomy is controlled by a single Mendelian gene exhibiting incomplete dominance.

Mok et al. (1980) have studied the cytokinin requirement of hypocotyl-tissue cultures of plants derived from crosses between a genotype of P. vulgaris (P.I.200960), which exhibits cytokinin dependence in tissue culture, and two cytokinin-independent genotypes (G 50 and P.I. 286303). Hypocotyl-tissue cultures from F1 plants exhibited an intermediate degree of cytokinin autonomy. The F2 generation contained both parental and intermediate phenotypes. The frequency distribution of cytokinin-requiring progeny in F2 and backcross populations suggested, as for the tobacco system described above, the presence of a single set of alleles controlling cytokinin autonomy.

CYTOKININ METABOLISM IN TISSUE CULTURES

The response of tissue cultures to externally supplied cytokinin is clearly a complex function of several biochemical processs. These include uptake and transport, metabolic deactivation and possibly metabolism to an active form, interaction of the active form of the cytokinin with a putative receptor and finally the trandsduction of this interaction into some biochemical process or processes involved with cell division.

Principally as a result of work by Laloue and his coworkers there is considerable detailed information on the uptake and metabolism of cytokinins by tobacco cell-suspension cultures. In tobacco cells, cytokinins are accumulated as the 5'nucleotide and 7-glucoside. The 7-glucoside appears to be an inactive end product but the nucleotide regulates the level of free base, which is considered to be the active form of the cytokinin. The level of free base is always low as it can diffuse freely through the cell membrane whereas the membrane is impermeable to nucleotides (Laloue and Pethe, 1982).

From the physiological viewpoint cytokinin metabolism may be classified under three headings:

(1) Irreversible loss of the N-6 side chain leading to loss of biological activity.

(2) Irreversible conjugation with sugars or amino acids leading to loss of, or reduced, biological activity.

(3) Reversible conjugation leading to compounds which may in themselves posess biological activity or function as storage forms, i.e. are potential sources of active cytokinins.

With regard to the biological activity of externally applied cytokinins in tissue culture systems, side chain cleavage is a key reaction since it leads directly to loss of cytokinin activity. The enzyme responsible for this step, 'cytokinin oxidase' has been isolated and partially purified from several plant sources. Cytokinin oxidase acts only on cytokinins possessing a - double bond in the side chain as shown in Fig 3. The substrate specificty of cytokinin oxidase for a wide variety of cytokinins has been studied (McGaw and Horgan, 1983). The synthetic

124

cytokinins most frequently used in tissue culture applications, benzyladenine and kinetin, are resistant to cytokinin oxidase although long term metabolic studies reveal that these compounds do eventually lose the N-6 side chain by as yet uncharacterised enzymatic reactions.

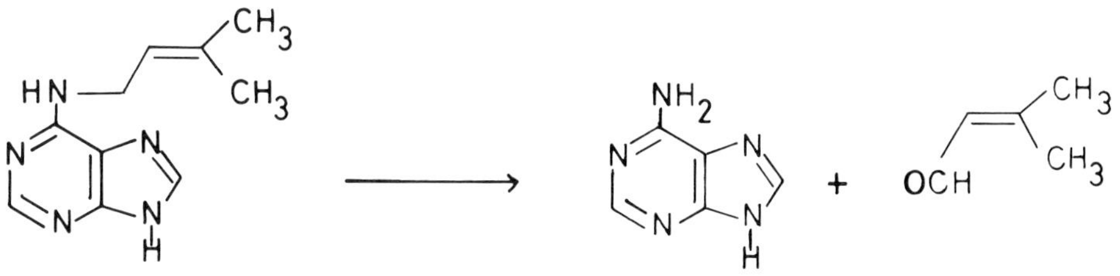

Fig. 3 Side chain cleavage of Δ^2-isopentenyl adenine by cytokinin oxidase.

Naturally-occurring cytokinins such as zeatin and isopentenyladenine are excellent substrates for cytokinin oxidase and yet are often more active in promoting cell division in tissue cultures than synthetic cytokinins. Since side chain cleavage certainly attenuates the activity of externally applied natural cytokinins one may speculate that the real activity of these compounds, i.e. the response elicited at the putative receptor, may be relatively much greater than that of their synthetic counterparts as judged by simple dose-response relationships.

The growth of two cell supension cultures derived from the same batch of soybean cotyledon callus tissue is shown in Fig. 4. A mid log-phase culture, produced as a result of 12 subcultures from the original culture, was divided into 18 subcultures using benzyladenine at 0.45 μM as the cytokinin source. These cultures all showed the growth characteristics typified by Z005 in Fig. 4. However, the subculture of mid log-phase aliquots of the 18 cultures into a medium containg zeatin at 0.45 μM resulted in somewhat reduced growth of all subcultures, eg. Z005 in Fig. 4. However, one subculture designated B023 (Fig. 2.) exhibited greatly reduced growth on zeatin. When mid log-phase zeatin grown cells were recultured on benzyladenine normal growth was restored. A comparative study of zeatin metabolism in B023 and Z005 revealed a greater rate of zeatin inactivation, by side chain cleavage, in the poor zeatin responder B023, than in the good zeatin responder Z005. Fig. 5 shows the qualitative and quantitative pattern of ^{14}C-zeatin metabolism in these cultures.

These differences in growth were not apparent in callus cultures re-isolated from the cell suspension cultures. In addition, in the callus cultures from all sources, zeatin was more active than benzyladenine in promoting growth.

The physiological and biochemical differences between Z005 and B023 were not stable. After several subcultures B023 began to grow on zeatin to the same extent as the other cultures. Since none of the material used in these experiments was cloned, this may have occurred simply as a result of a change in balance from cells with a high capacity to degrade zeatin in favour of more zeatin-responsive cells. However an alternative explanation of this phenomenon could be a reversible change in the activity of cytokinin oxidase brought about by a change in the degree of expression of the gene coding for this enzyme. If cytokinin oxidase modulates endogenous cytokinin levels, a reduction in its activity could lead to the elevated levels of cytokinins often associated with 'habituated' tissues.

The results described above demonstrate that degradative metabolism can be a very important factor in determining the response of cell cultures to applied cytokinin. In this case the differences in response were not observable in callus tissue grown on solid medium. This is almost certainly due to differences in metabolism caused by different rates of supply of cytokinin to the growing cells. In cell suspension cultures all cells receive a uniform dose of cytokinin and uptake is rapid. In solid

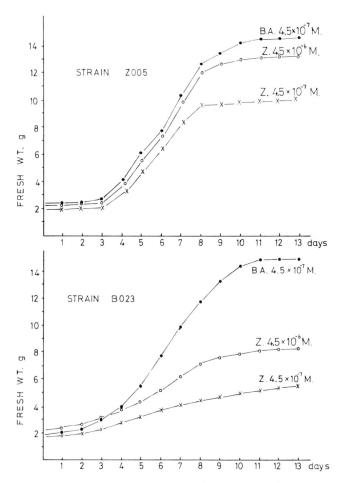

Fig. 4 Growth of two strains of soybean cells (Z005 and B023) in liquid culture on benzyladenine and zeatin.

grown cultures the cells in intimate contact with the medium receive a high initial dose of cytokinin, but this is considerably attenuated across the tissue. We have shown that in contrast to cell suspension cultures, where zeatin is predominantly degraded to adenine and related compounds, soybean callus cultures show less degradative metabolism and more conversion of zeatin to the 0-glucoside and lupinic acid, when zeatin is supplied through the agar. This provides an explanation for the different growth patterns of cell suspension cultures and callus tissues described above. It also highlights some of the pitfalls likely to be encountered in ascribing a physical meaning to so-called 'tissue sensitivity'.

Similar correlations between cytokinin degradation and biological activity have been observed in callus tissues derived from two different geneotypes of Phaseolus vulgaris. Mok et al. (1978) have shown that callus cultures derived from P. vulgaris

126

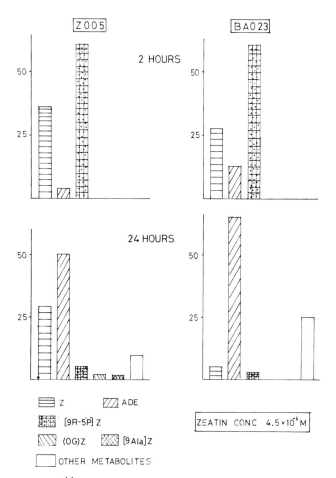

Fig.5 Metabolism of 8-^{14}C zeatin by a zeatin responsive (Z005) and a zeatin non
-responsive (BA023) strain of soybean cells grown in liquid culture.

grow better on dihydrozeatin, which lacks a Δ^2-double bond in the side chain, and its
riboside than on zeatin and zeatin riboside.   The reverse was found to be true for
callus cultures derived from P. lunatus.   They were able to show an increased rate of
breakdown of Δ^2-isopentenyl cytokinins by P. vulgaris callus (Mok et al., 1982).   This
presumably involved cytokinin oxidase to which dihydrozeatin and its riboside are
resistant.   Callus tissue from a P. vulgaris x P. lunatus hybrid exhibited
intermediate responses to the two classes of cytokinin and a metabolism
characteristic of both parents.

From the above account of cytokinin biosynthesis and metabolism it would appear that
there are at least two genes which may be involved in the control of cytokinin levels
in plants namely the gene for the enzyme responsible for the synthesis of [9R-5'P]iP

and the gene for cytokinin oxidase. In addition the possibilty exists for the control of the level of biologically-active cytokinin (presumably the free base) by enzymes involved in the interconversions of the various forms of cytokinins.

In seeking to draw an analogy between cytokinin biosynthesis in crown gall tissues and other forms of cytokinin autonomous tissue cultures one major point emerges. Namely that crown gall tissues produce vastly more cytokinin than is required to maintain the tumorous state and the other forms of autonomous tissues produce extremely small amounts of cytokinin. Using bioassays Nakajima et al. (1979) estimated the [9R]Z content of tobacco crown gall cells to be 40-80 ng kinetin equivalents per g.f.wt. and that of habituated cells to be less than 0.1 ng kinetin equivalents per g.f.wt. Using mass spectrometry and stable isotope dilution Scott and Horgan (1984) found levels of several zeatin-related cytokinins in tobacco crown gall callus tissue to be in the region of 100 ng per g.f.wt., whereas in an autonomous, non-crown gall tissue they were at least 100 fold lower and barely detectable by the method used. Hansen et al. (1985) were unable to detect, using HPLC and immunoassay, the presence of any cytokinins in a cytokinin-autonomous tobacco cell line.

Assuming that the pathway of biosynthesis is the same in crown gall and normal plant tissue then, as argued previously, expression of the plant biosynthetic gene must be very precisely controlled. Given the extreme efficacy of cytokinins as promoters of cell division this could be deduced by applying 'physiological common sense'. A major requirement for an understanding of cytokinin production in plants must be knowledge of the nature of this control at the molecular level. It is to be hoped that this will eventually emerge by adoption of the type of approach already discussed. As stated previously it is extremely important to ascertain if the plant gene(s) can be detected using suitable probes derived from the T-DNA and Ti plasmid vir genes. If there is sufficient homolgy between the plant and bacterial genes for this to be successful then there is good reason to be optimistic regarding the eventual elucidation of the mechanism(s) which regulate cytokinin biosynthesis in plants.

The role of cytokinin oxidase in regulating cytokinin levels is still unclear. The enzyme appears to be highly specific towards naturally-occuring cytokinins with Δ^2-isopentenyl side chains. M. Laloue (personal communication) has shown that diphenylurea derivatives, which are active as cytokinins in tissue culture systems, are potent inhibitors of a cytokinin oxidase isolated from wheat germ. It may be hypothesised that a reduction in cytokinin oxidase activity could result in an increase in endogenous cytokinin level sufficient to cause growth. Paradoxically however, high cytokinin oxidase activity may be found in tissues with high endogenous cytokinin levels, e.g. Zea mays kernels and Vinca rosea crown gall tissue. Clearly it will be necessary to eluciate the inter- and intracellular distribution of this enzyme, preferably by immunological methods, to assist in clarifying its physiological function. As with the biosynthetic gene, it is to be hoped that application of the techniques of molecular biology will lead eventually to cloning of the gene for cytokinin oxidase and elucidation of the mechanism whereby its expression is regulated.

REFERENCES

Ahuja, M.R. (1968). An hypothesis and evidence concerning the genetic components controlling tumor formation in Nicotiana. Molecular and General Genetics 103, 176-184.

Akiyoshi, D.E., Morris, R.O., Hinz, R., Mischke, B.S, Kosuge, T., Garfinkle, D.J., Gordon, M.P. and Nester, E.W. (1983). Cytokinin auxin balance in crown gall tumors is regulated by specific loci in the T-DNA. Proceedings of the National Academy of Sciences, USA 80, 407-411.

Akiyoshi, D.E., Klee, H., Amasino, R.M., Nester, E.W. and Gordon, M.P. (1984). T-DNA of Agrobacterium tumefaciens encodes an enzyme of cytokinin biosynthesis. Proceedings of the National Academy of Sciences, USA 81, 5994-5998.

Barry, G.F., Rogers, S.G., Fraley, R.T. and Brand, L. (1984). Identification of a cloned cytokinin biosynthetic gene. Proceedings of the National Academy of Sciences, USA 81, 4776-4780.

Buchmann, I., Marner, F.J., Schroder, G., Waffenschmidt, S., and Schroder, J. (1985). tumour genes in plants: T-DNA encoded cytokinin biosynthesis. European Molecular Biology Organisation Journal 48, 53-859.

Hansen, C.E., Meins, F. Jr. and Milani, A. (1985). Clonal and physiological variation in the cytokinin content of tobacco-cell lines differing in cytokinin requirement and capacity for neoplastic growth. Differentiation 29, 1-6.

Hooykaas, P.J.J., Ooms, G. and Schilperoort, R.A. (1982). Tumors induced by different strains of Agrobacterium tumefaciens. In "Molecular Biology of Plant tumors" (G. Kahl and J.S.Schell eds.), pp 373-390. Academic Press, New York.

Klee, H., Montoya, A., Horodyski, F., Lichtenstein, C., Garfinkle,D., Fuller, S., Flores, C., Peschon, J., Nester, E.W. and Gordon M., (1984). Nucleotide sequence of the tms genes of the pTiA6NC octopine Ti plasmid: Two gene products involved in plant tumorigenisis. Proceedings of the National Academy of Sciences, USA 81, 1728-1732.

Koorneef, M., Journa, M.L., Brinkhorst-van der Swan, D.L.C. and Karssen, C.M. (1982). The isolation of abscisic acid (ABA) deficient mutants by selection of induced revertants in non-germinating gibberellin sensitive lines of Arabidopsis thaliana (L.) Heynh. Theoretical and Applied Genetics 61, 385-393.

Laloue, M. and Pethe, C. (1982). Dynamics of cytokinin metabolism in tobacco cells. In "Plant Growth Substances 1982" (P.F. Wareing ed.), pp 185-195. Academic Press, London.

Lee, T.S., Purse, J.G., Pryce, R.J., Horgan, R. and Wareing, P.F.(1981). Dihydroconiferyl alcohol-A cell division factor from Acer species. Planta 152, 571-577.

McGaw, B.A. and Horgan, R. (1983). Cytokinin oxidase from Zea mays kernels and Vinca rosea crown gall tissue. Planta 159, 30-37.

Meins, F.Jr. (1982). Habituation of cultured plant cells. In "Molecular Biology of Plant tumors" (G.Kahl and J.S. Schell eds.), pp 3-31. Academic Press, New York.

Meins, F.Jr. and Foster, R. (1985). Reversible, cell-heritable changes during the development of tobacco pith tissues. Developmental Biology 108, 1-5.

Meins, F.Jr., Foster, R. and Lutz, J.D. (1983). Evidence for a Mendelian factor controlling the cytokinin requirement of cultured tobacco cells. Developmental Genetics 4, 129-141.

Mok, M.C., Mok, D.W.S. and Armstrong, D.J. (1978). Differential cytokinin structure activity relationships in Phaseolus. Plant Physiology 61, 72-75.

Mok, M.C., Mok, D.W.S., Armstrong, D.J., Rabakoarihanata, A. and Kim, S-G. (1980). Cytokinin autonomy in tissue cultures of Phaseolus: A genotype-specific and heritable trait. Genetics 94, 675-686.

Mok, M.C., Mok, D.W.S., Dixon, S.C., Armstrong, D.J. and Shaw, G. (1982). Cytokinin structure activity relationships and the metabolism of N^6 -(Δ^2-isopentenyl)adenosine-8-^{14}C in Phaseolus callus tissues. Plant Physiology 70, 173-178.

Naf, U. (1958). Studies in tumour formation in Nicotiana hybrids.I. The classification of parents into two etiologically significant groups. Growth 22, 167-180.

Nakajima, H., Yokota, T., Matsumoto, T., Noguchi, M. and Takahashi, N.(1979). Relationships between hormone content and autonomy in various autonomus tobacco cells cultured in suspension. Plant and Cell Physiology 29, 1489-1499.

Neill, S.J., Horgan, R. and Parry, A.D. (1986). The carotenoid and abscisic acid content of viviparous kernels and seedlings of Zea mays L. Planta 169, 87-96.

Neill, S.J. and Horgan, R. (1985). Abscisic acid production and water relations in wilty tomato mutants subjected to water deficiency. Journal of Experimental Botany 36, 1222-1231.

Palni, L.M.S., Horgan, R., Darral, N.M., Stutchbury, T. and Wareing, P.F. (1983). Cytokinin biosynthesis in crown gall tissue of Vinca rosea: the significance of nucleotides. Planta 159, 178-181.

Palni, L.M.S., Tay, S.A.B., Nandi, S.K., Pianca, D.J., de Klerk, G.J.M., Wong, O.C., Letham, D.S. and Macleod, J.K. (1985). Cytokinin biosynthesis in plant tumour tissues. Biologia Plantarum (Praha) 27, 195-203.

Pengelly, W.L., Vijayaraghavan, S.J., and Sciaky, D. (1986). Neoplastic progression in crown gall in tobacco without elevated auxin levels. Planta 169, 454-461.

Phinney, B.O. (1984). Gibberellin A_1, dwarfism and control of shoot elongation in higher plants. In " The Biosynthesis and Metabolism of Plant Hormones" (A. Crozier and J.R. Hillman eds.), pp 17-41. Cambridge University Press, Cambridge.

Schroder, G., Waffenschmidt, S., Weiler, E.W., Schroder, J. (1984). The T-region of Ti plasmids codes for an enzyme synthesising indole-3-acetic acid. European Journal of Biochemistry 138, 387-391.

Scott, I.M. and Horgan, R. (1984). Mass spectrometric quantification of cytokinin nucleotides and glycosides in tobacco crown gall tissues. Planta 161, 345-354.

Stachel, S.E., Messens, E., Van Montagu, M., Zambryski, P. (1985). Identification of the signal molecules produced by wounded plant cells that activate T-DNA transfer in Agrobacterium tumefaciens. Nature 318 624-629.

Van Onckelen, H., Rudelsheim, P., Inze, D., Follin, A., Messens, E., Horemans, S., Schell, J., Van Montagu, M. and De Greef, J. (1985). Tobacco plants transformed with the Agrobacterium T-DNA gene 1 contain high amounts of indole-3-acetamide. Federation of European Biochemical Societies Letters 181, 373-376.

Van Onckelen, H., Prisen, E., Inze, D., Rudelsheim, P., Van Lijsebettens, M., Follin, A., Schell, J., Van Montagu. M., and De Greef, J. (1986). Agrobacterium T-DNA gene 1 codes for tryptophan 2-monooxygenase activity in tobacco crown gall cells. Federation of European Biochemical Societies Letters 198, 357-360.

Wang, T.L., Futers, T.S., McGeary, F. and Cove, D.J. (1984). Moss mutants and the analysis of cytokinin metabolism. In "The Biosynthesis and Metabolism of Plant Hormones" (A. Crozier and J.R.Hillman eds.), pp 135-164. Cambridge University Press, Cambridge.

SECTION III

CHEMICAL AND ENVIRONMENTAL PROBES IN STUDIES OF HORMONES

THE USE OF INHIBITORS OF GIBBERELLIN AND STEROL BIOSYNTHESIS TO PROBE HORMONE ACTION

K. Lürssen,

Bayer AG, Pflanzenschutz Anwendungstechnik, Biologische Forschung,
D-5090 Leverkusen, Federal Republic of Germany

The generally accepted mode of action of triazole plant growth regulators (PGRs) is the inhibition of gibberellin biosynthesis at the metabolic steps from ent-kaurene to ent-kaurenoic acid. Specific inhibitors of gibberellin biosynthesis would offer themselves as useful tools to probe gibberellin action. However, the manifold effects of triazole PGRs upon plant growth and metabolism led to more intensive investigations into their mode of action. It is already known that the enantiomers of uniconazol, paclobutrazol and triapenthenol selectively act as PGRs or fungicides. It is shown for triapenthenol that the two enantiomers selectively inhibit gibberellin biosynthesis or interfere with sterol metabolism. However, these enantiomers are not specific inhibitors of the two pathways. From physiological experiments a third mode of action, not directly related to gibberellin or sterol biosynthesis, must be assumed. According to these results the distinction between a growth regulatory and a fungicidal enantiomer is not valid. It is concluded that triazole PGRs are not suitable tools to probe physiological effects of either gibberellins or sterols because interferences with other targets cannot be excluded.

INTRODUCTION

There may be several approaches to investigate plant hormone action: the use of mutants with a block in the biosynthetic pathway; the application of the plant hormone itself to whole plants or plant parts, the analysis of plant hormone content in the plant and its correlation to plant reactions or development, the application of antagonists of hormone action and the application of biosynthetic inhibitors. All these methods have advantages and disadvantages. A well defined mutant may be a fine probe for such investigations, but a mutant may be 'leaky'. The application of a plant hormone may lead to reactions that are not caused by the hormone in vivo or the plant may fail to react. This could be, for example, a question of dose, uptake and/or compartmentation. A correlation between hormone content and certain developmental aspects of plant growth is extremely difficult to establish as it is hard to ascertain whether a certain plant reaction is caused by the hormone or whether the hormone level is adjusted after a reaction to other factors has taken place. Furthermore, compartmentation of the hormone within the plant must be considered. An antagonist should inhibit hormone action, but the mode of action of antagonists is often not well defined and, therefore, specificity may be questionable. At first sight an inhibitor of hormone biosynthesis seems to be an ideal tool to probe hormone action by adjusting hormone levels within the plant. But are specific inhibitors readily available for this purpose? In this paper I shall deal with triazoles and their interference with plant metabolism to investigate whether these compounds really are suitable tools to probe hormone action.

TRIAZOLES AS FUNGICIDES AND PLANT GROWTH REGULATORS

Azoles were first introduced as fungicides and antimycotics (for a review see Krämer, 1986). Their mode of action is an inhibition of sterol biosynthesis (Buchenauer, 1976; Leroux and Gredt, 1976). To some extent the fungicidal triazoles also exhibit plant growth regulator properties especially at higher concentrations. A reduction of gibberellin content has been demonstrated (Buchenauer and Röhner, 1981). Several PGRs from this chemical group are currently marketed or in development (Fig. 1).

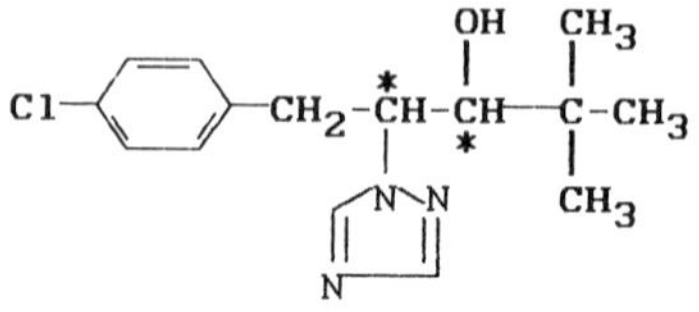

Paclobutrazol
PP 333
ICI

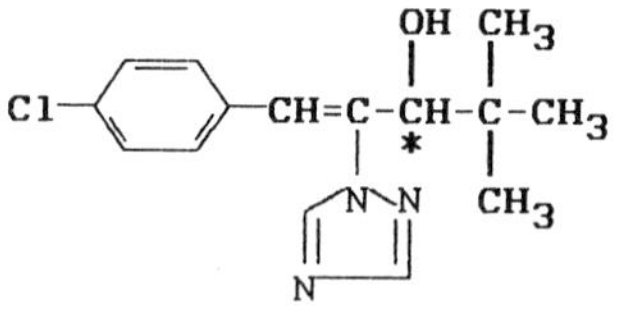

Uniconazol
S 3307
Sumitomo

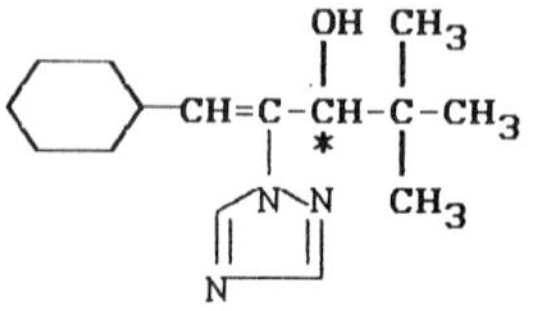

Triapenthenol
RSW 0411
Bayer

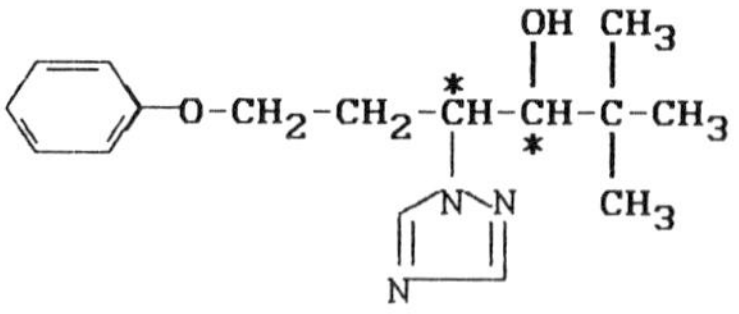

BAS 111..W
BASF

Fig. 1 Triazole Plant Growth Regulators. Asymmetric C-atoms are marked by *.

Triazole PGRs may be used for different purposes. The growth inhibition observed make them useful, for example, to prevent lodging in rape, grass-seed production, cereal crops, and for growth inhibition in orchards, ornamental plants and lawns (Lembrich et al., 1984; Hack and Lembrich, 1985; Luib et al., 1986; Lever et al., 1982). However, besides these aspects of growth inhibition, triazole PGRs show additional effects in laboratory experiments as well as in field trials. They can enhance photosynthesis, modify the water status of plants, reduce transpiration, induce resistance to drought and chilling, exhibit fungicidal effects, stimulate generative growth, and enhance yield. How are all these effects related to plant hormones and metabolism?

GROWTH INHIBITION AND THE INTERFERENCE OF GIBBERELLIN AND STEROL BIOSYNTHESIS BY TRIAZOLES

Growth inhibition of a wide spectrum of plant species by triazoles suggested an influence upon gibberellin biosynthesis, gibberellins being the plant hormones that mainly contribute to elongation growth. Indeed, the interference with gibberellin biosynthesis by triazoles could be demonstrated experimentally and the targets in the biosynthetic pathway could be identified as the oxidation steps from ent-kaurene to ent-kaurenoic acid (Rademacher et al., 1983; Izumi et al., 1984; Hedden and Graebe, 1985).

When we studied the mode of action of triapenthenol, we had a closer look at the main effect - growth inhibition - and its relation to gibberellins. Like other triazoles, a clear inhibition of gibberellin biosynthesis between ent-kaurene and ent-kaurenoic acid could be shown (Graebe, personal communication). The amount of gibberellins present in treated and untreated plants was correlated with growth (Weiler, personal communication). As all the data fit together well, it could be assumed that the only mode of action of triapenthenol is the inhibition of gibberellin biosynthesis.

However, we made further experiments, using a technique published by Lockhart (1962). This technique was developed to analyse the interference of growth inhibitors with plant hormones. When increasing amounts of gibberellin are applied to untreated plants and those treated with a growth inhibitor, the growth response curves should merge if only gibberellin effects were involved in the growth inhibition. Lockhart produced such growth curves for 2-chloroethyl-trimethyl ammonium chloride (CCC) and 2,4-dichlorobenzyl-tributylphosphonium chloride (Phosphon-D) with Phaseolus vulgaris. If factors other than an interference with gibberellins are involved, the two curves should not meet at higher concentrations of gibberellin but run in parallel to each other. This type of curve was achieved with maleic hydrazide. Thus to establish definitely an interaction with gibberellins it is not sufficient to obtain the growth height of untreated plants by adding gibberellins to inhibitor-treated plants. One must compare plants treated with inhibitor plus gibberellin with gibberellin-treated plants. This basic requirement is sometimes not realised.

Using this technique, we found that triapenthenol-induced growth inhibition is not fully compensated by gibberellin (Lürssen and Reiser, 1985; Lürssen and Reiser, in press). This type of interaction could be shown, for example, in rice, barley (Fig. 2) and soybean (Fig. 3). Thus even in the case of growth inhibition, which normally would be attributed just to the inhibition of gibberellin biosynthesis, a second target is involved. Our interpretation of these results is that growth inhibition by triapenthenol is primarily caused by an inhibition of gibberellin biosynthesis, but depending on the concentration used, there is a second site of action for triapenthenol which additionally contributes more, or less, to growth inhibition.

As triapenthenol clearly has fungicidal effects too, as it is chemically closely related to triazole fungicides and, since it is reported in the literature that these fungicides interfere with both gibberellin and sterol biosynthesis (Buchenauer and Röhner, 1981), it may be speculated that sterol biosynthesis is the second target for triapenthenol. Indeed, we found a concentration-dependent reduction in the contents of the main plant sterols - sitosterol, campesterol and stigmasterol - in triapenthenol-treated rice plants, a species in which growth inhibition could not be fully compensated by gibberellic acid (Berg and Lürssen, unpublished) (Fig. 4). As sterols are not readily taken up by plants, compensation experiments did not seem to be suitable to investigate further the question whether the inhibition of sterol biosynthesis is really the second target causing growth inhibition.

Are there compounds that specifically inhibit gibberellin biosynthesis without affecting sterols and vice versa to resolve this question? A closer look at the structure of triazoles reveals that these compounds exist in two or four enantiomeric forms, depending on the presence or absence of a double bond in the molecule.

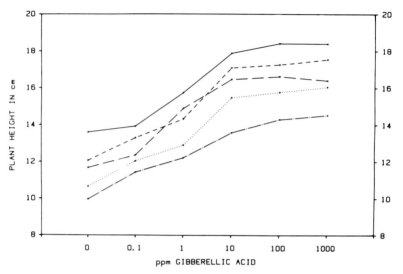

Fig. 2 <u>Interaction of triapenthenol and gibberellic acid on the growth of barley seedlings</u>. 8 plants were grown in each 5 x 5 x 7 cm pot in the greenhouse with vermiculite/water as substrate. 25 ml of a solution of gibberellic acid and the inhibitor, at the stated concentration, were added to each pot. (0 ppm ————; 2 ppm - - - -; 4 ppm — — —; 8 ppm ....; 16 ppm triapenthenol-.-.-.-.).

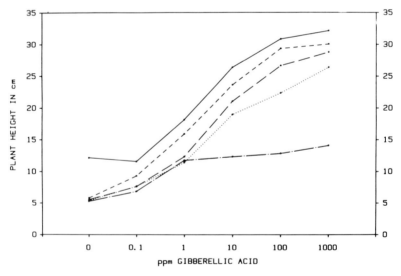

Fig. 3. <u>Interaction of triapenthenol and gibberellic acid on the growth of young soybean plants</u>. The method used and the concentrations applied are shown in the legend to Fig. 2; only 1 plant was grown in each pot.

According to their structure, uniconazol and triapenthenol are racemates of two enantiomers. Paclobutrazol, having two chiral centres consists of 4 enantiomers. However, the common name, paclobutrazol, applies only to the 2RS,3RS diastereoisomer which is the major component of the synthetic compound (Sugavanam, 1984). This diastereoisomer has been resolved into its 2S,3S (-) and 2R,3R (+) enantiomers. It was shown for uniconazole (Funaki et al., 1984), triapenthenol (Kraatz et al., 1984a; Kraatz et al., 1984b) and paclobutrazol (Sugavanam, 1984) that the effectiveness of the compounds is stereoselective. For all three compounds the plant growth regulatory effect - or rather the growth inhibitory effect - and the fungicidal effect could be attributed to different enantiomers. Uniconazole and triapenthenol have the advantage for basic research that they exist only in two enantiomeric forms. We studied the effect of the growth inhibitory (-)-enantiomer and the fungicidal (+)-enantiomer of triapenthenol separately. It could be shown that the (-)-enantiomer specifically inhibit gibberellin biosynthesis. To achieve a similar inhibition of gibberellin biosynthesis by the (+)-enantiomer, about ten times the amount is needed (Graebe, personal communication). Conversely, the (+)-enantiomer specifically interferes with sterol biosynthesis. As with the racemate, a concentration-dependent reduction of campesterol, stigmasterol and sitosterol was observed. The (-)-enantiomer also caused a more or less pronounced drop in sterol content, but there was no concentration dependency, indicating perhaps a more indirect effect (Berg and Lürssen, unpublished) (Fig. 5). With these enantiomers we have now the tools to look at growth inhibition and how it relates to gibberellin and sterol biosynthesis.

Again we made compensation experiments using the technique of Lockhart (1962). The results of our experiments clearly showed that the growth inhibition caused by the (-)- or (S)-enantiomer can be fully compensated by gibberellin. This enantiomer is identical with the gibberellin biosynthesis inhibiting one. In contrast, the growth inhibition caused by the (+)- or (R)-enantiomer cannot be fully compensated by gibberellin (Fig. 6). This enantiomer is identical to the one interfering with sterol metabolism. These results agree with field trials in rape. There we observed that the (S)-enantiomer causes a strong growth inhibition, darker green colouration of the leaves, and a yield increase. However, the plots treated with the (S)-enantiomer were not as uniformly inhibited as those treated with double the amount of the racemate. Growth inhibition and leaf colour were about equal to that achieved with the racemate, but the yield increase was only 2/3 that of the racemate. No fungicidal activity could be detected with the (S)-enantiomer. The (R)-enantiomer caused only a very slight growth inhibition and a very slight increase in the colouration of the leaves, but a yield increase of about 1/3 that of the racemate was observed. The (R)-enantiomer showed good fungicidal efficacy. Regarding practical application of triapenthenol, it should be noted that both enantiomers contribute to the yield increase and general appearance of the crop.

We have shown in our experiments to date that one enantiomer of triapenthenol causes growth inhibition by inhibition of gibberellin biosynthesis only, while the racemate, due to the other enantiomer, interferes also with sterol metabolism, which may be the cause of a slight additional effect on growth. Taking this into account, what can we say about the other effects of triazole PGRs mentioned above? Are they related to the inhibition of gibberellin biosynthesis, to the inhibition of sterol biosynthesis, or even to another effect upon plant metabolism?

ARE PLANT REACTIONS TO TRIAZOLES OTHER THAN GROWTH INHIBITION RELATED TO AN INHIBITION OF GIBBERELLIN OR STEROL BIOSYNTHESIS?

One of the effects frequently observed with triazoles is the reduction of water consumption of treated plants (Fletcher and Nath, 1984; Lürssen and Reiser, 1985; Lürssen and Reiser, in press). We compared the effects of different triazole and pyrimidine PGRs and fungicides on plant growth and water consumption in barley - pyrimidines also interfere with gibberellin biosynthesis (Shive and Sisler, 1976). All compounds were applied at 1500 g a.i./ha. No correlation between growth inhibition and a reduction of water consumption could be detected in this experiment

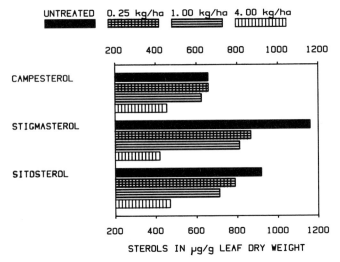

Fig. 4 Sterol content of young rice plants treated with triapenthenol.

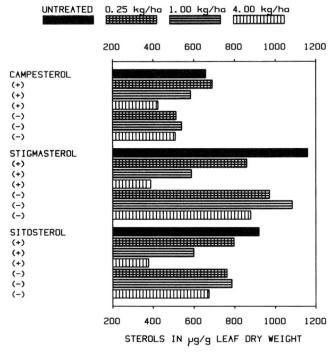

Fig. 5 Sterol content of young rice plants treated with the enantiomers of triapenthenol. (+) indicates treatment with the (+)-enantiomer, (-) indicates treatment with the (-)-enantiomer.

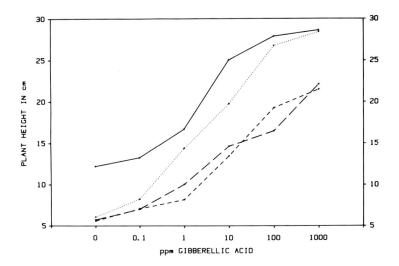

Fig. 6 Interaction of triapenthenol (+/-), its (+)- and (-)-enantiomers, and gibberellic acid on the growth of young soybean plants. The method is described in the legend to Fig. 3. Treatments: 0 ppm ————; 16 ppm (+/-)- - - -; 8 ppm (+)— — —; 8 ppm (-)........

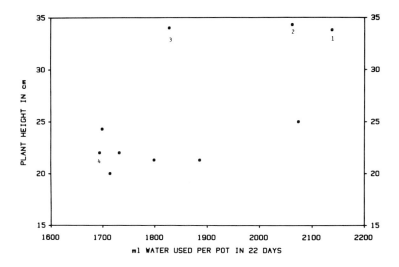

Fig. 7 Water consumption and height of barley plants treated with 1.5 kg/ha of different triazoles and pyrimidines in the greenhouse. Pots were watered daily to the initial weight. The numbers indicate the following treatments: 1 untreated; 2 triadimefon; 3 triademenol; 4 triapenthenol; unnumbered points refer to trial compounds.

Fig. 7). Small plants may have a relatively high water consumption and large plants may have a low water consumption. Treated plants having the same height as untreated ones still may show a marked reduction in water consumption (e.g. triadimenol-treated plants). If we assume that growth inhibition in barley, in response to the amounts of the compounds used, is mainly caused by an inhibition of gibberellin biosynthesis, it is obvious that this interference with gibberellins cannot be the cause of a reduction in water consumption. Is sterol biosynthesis the target responsible for this influence? At first sight this seems possible, as sterols, being constituents of membranes, may well have an effect on permeability. However, this question can only be answered by experimental evidence.

We looked at the water consumption of rape plants treated with triapenthenol in comparison to plants treated with its enantiomers. Pots with plants were watered daily for 3 weeks to 60% of their maximum soil water capacity at the beginning of the experiment. The amount of water used daily for each treatment was recorded. The results are shown in Fig. 8. Obviously a strong initial reduction in water consumption is achieved with the racemate. The effect of the (S)-enantiomer which inhibits gibberellin biosynthesis, is slightly less pronounced, while the (R)-enantiomer is only slightly effective. The reason for this reduction of water consumption is probably a closure of stomata, observed with the racemate starting one day after treatment. However, these experiments were only carried out with <u>Vicia faba</u> (Konze, personal communication). An immediate reduction of transpiration, within one hour after treatment, could not be detected in a number of plant species including <u>Vicia faba</u>. Therefore, we exclude a direct influence of the compounds on stomatal movement.

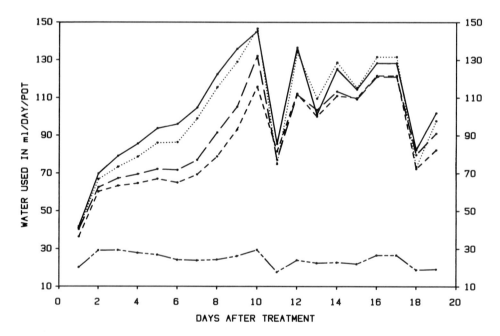

Fig. 8. <u>Water consumption of greenhouse-grown rape plants treated at the 5 leaf stage</u> <u>with triapenthenol (+/-) and its (+)- and (-)-enantiomers.</u> Treatments: without plants — -- —; untreated plants ——; 1 kg/ha (+/-) — — —; 0.5 kg/ha (-)— — — — ; 0.5 kg/ha (+) ....

The results of the experiments with the enantiomers of triapenthenol, regarding water consumption, reveal that this effect is mainly associated with the enantiomer inhibiting gibberellin biosynthesis and less with the enantiomer interfering with sterol metabolism. However, the result of the experiment with different azoles and pyrimidines (Fig. 7) showed no correlation between growth inhibition - mainly caused by an inhibition of gibberellin biosynthesis - and reduction of water consumption. Thus we must conclude that, apart from the inhibition of gibberellin biosynthesis and the interference with sterol metabolism, a further metabolic pathway is involved, resulting in a closure of stomata and a reduction of water consumption.

The fact that triapenthenol reduces water consumption of plants and leads to a closure of stomata may point to an effect upon abscisic acid metabolism. Recently it was reported that paclobutrazol, ancymidol and decylimidazol, all three compounds being inhibitors of gibberellin biosynthesis, also inhibit abscisic acid biosynthesis in the fungus Cercospora rosicola (Norman et al., 1986). However, the effects we found with triapenthenol would rather suggest the opposite action upon abscisic acid metabolism, taking into account the physiological action of this hormone. Of course an influence upon metabolism of a fungus may not necessarily be the same as in a higher plant. Further experiments should clarify this discrepancy.

In another experiment we investigated the influence of triapenthenol and its enantiomers on carbon dioxide fixation by rape plants. An infra-red gas analyser was used in an open-flow system for the measurements on whole plants in the greenhouse. The results of this experiment are given in Fig. 9. The initial drop in carbon dioxide fixation observed may also be explained by the closure of the stomata. Here again, the strongest effect is caused by the racemate, followed by the (S)- and (R)-enantiomer. While the (R)-enantiomer later in the experiment causes only a slight increase in carbon dioxide fixation compared to the untreated plants, the racemate and the (S)-enantiomer both cause a 20% increase in carbon dioxide fixation. The metabolic background of this effect is not known.

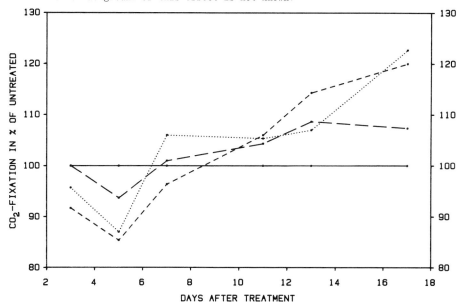

Fig. 9   Carbon dioxide fixation of greenhouse-grown rape plants at the 5 leaf stage treated with triapenthenol (+/-) and its (+)- and (-)-enantiomers.   Treatments: Control ———; 1.0 kg/ha (+/-) --------; 0.5 kg/ha (+) — — — — —; 0.5 kg/ha (-) ....

Looking at other effects of triapenthenol and its enantiomers upon growth of rape we obtained, generally, similar results with the racemate and the (S)-enantiomer compared to the (R)-enantiomer (Fig. 10). The number of leaves was slightly increased with the racemate and the (S)-enantiomer while it was unchanged or perhaps slightly reduced with the (R)-enantiomer. Plant height was strongly reduced by the racemate and the (S)-enantiomer, the (R)-enantiomer having only a weak influence as mentioned already above. Leaf area, fresh weight and dry weight were reduced only by the racemate and the (S)-enantiomer. It is difficult to say how these effects relate to the influence of inhibition of gibberellin biosynthesis, sterol biosynthesis or even a further effect upon plant metabolism.

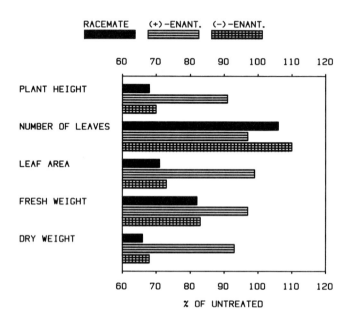

Fig. 10 Growth parameters of rape plants treated at the 5 leaf stage for 3 weeks with triapenthenol (1 kg/ha) and its enantiomers (0.5 kg/ha) in the greenhouse.

CONCLUSIONS

It was shown that triapenthenol, originally believed to inhibit only gibberellin biosynthesis and causing only an inhibition of growth of plants, is not a specific inhibitor. Rather it influences sterol biosynthesis too and acts upon a further metabolic pathway in plants possibly related to abscisic acid. It could be shown that the two enantiomers of triapenthenol selectively inhibit gibberellin biosynthesis or interfere with sterol metabolism. However, the enantiomers are not specific inhibitors, and a third mode of action is implicated both to explain the action upon water consumption and stomatal movement of the plants.

It is obvious that probing hormone action with inhibitors requires compounds which act highly specifically. At least triapenthenol and most probably also the other triazole plant growth regulators are not at all highly specific. Whatever plant reactions we achieve with these compounds, we cannot be sure about what target in the plant is involved. Thus I maintain that these compounds are not useful tools to probe hormone action. Furthermore, I regard this study as an example of what may happen when metabolic inhibitors are used. A careful study of their mode of action, at the very least, is necessary before any conclusions can be drawn about how they influence plant constituents. To probe hormone action in plants we obviously cannot rely on just one method. All the available methods mentioned before should be used and the results compared to clarify hormone action.

REFERENCES

Buchenauer, H. (1976). Hemmung der Ergosterinbiosynthese in Ustilago avenae durch Triadimefon and Fluotrimazol. Zeitschrift für Pflanzenkrankheiten Pflanzenschutz **83**, 363-367.

Buchenauer, H. and Röhner, E. (1981). Effect of Triadimefon and Triadimenol on growth of various plant species as well as on gibberellin content and sterol metabolism in shoots of barley seedlings. Pesticide Biochemistry and Physiology **15**, 58-70.

Fletcher, R.A. and Nath, V. (1984). Triadimefon reduces transpiration and increases yield in water-stressed plants. Physiologia Plantarum **62**, 422-426.

Funaki, Y., Yoneyochi, Y., Ishiguri, Y. and Izumi, K. (1984). Optical isomers of triazolylpentenols, and their production and use as fungicide, herbicide and/or plant growth regulant. United States Patent No. 4, 435,203.

Hack, H. and Lembrich, H. (1985). The use of RSW 0411 as a growth regulator in different crops under different conditions. Proceedings 1985 British Crop protection Conference - Weeds, 113-120.

Hedden, P. and Graebe, J.E. (1985). Inhibition of gibberellin biosynthesis by paclobutrazol in cell-free homogenates of Cucurbita maxima endosperm and Malus pumila embryos. Journal of Plant Growth Regulation **4**, 111-122.

Izumi, K., Yamaguchi, I., Wada, A., Oshio, H., Takahashi, N. (1984). Effects of a new plant growth Retardant (E)-1-(4-chlorophenyl)-4,4-dimethyl-2-(1,2,4-triazol-1-yl) -1-penten-3-ol (S-3307) on the growth and gibberellin content of rice plants. Plant & Cell Physiology **25**, 611-617.

Kraatz, U., Reiser, W., Büchel, K.-H. and Lürssen, K. (1984a). (-)-Antipode des (E)-1-Cyclohexyl-4,4-dimethyl-3-hydroxy-2-(1,2,4   triazol-1-yl)-pent-1-ens. Europäische Patentanmeldung 0114609.

Kraatz, U., Reiser, W., Büchel, K.-H., Brandes, W,. and Reinecke, P. (1984b). (-)-Antipode des (E)-1-Cyclohexyl-4,4-dimethyl-3-hydroxy-2-(1,2,4 triazol-1-yl)-pent -1-ens. Europäische Patentanmeldung 0114608.

Krämer, W. (1986). Chemistry of sterol-biosynthesis inhibiting fungicides.   In "Chemistry of Plant Protection" (G. Haug and N. Hoffmann eds), pp. 25-64. Springer-Verlag, Berlin.

Lembrich, H., Dengel, H.-J., Lürssen, K. and Reiser, W. (1984). RSW 0411, ein Wachstumsregulator zur Verbesserung der Standfestigkeit im Winterraps sowie im Grasvermehrungsbau. Mitteil. Biol. Bundesanstalt, Berlin-Dahlem **223**, Oktober 1984, 315-316.

Leroux, P. and Gredt, M. (1976). Comparaisons des modes d'action fongitoxique du Triadimefon (Meb 6447), du Triarimol et de la Triforine. Phytopathologische Zeitschrift **86**, 276-279.

Lever, B.G., Shearing, S.J. and Batch, J.J. (1982). PP333 - a new broad spectrum growth retardant. Proceedings 1982 British Crop Protection Conference - Weeds, 3-10.

Lockhart, J.A. (1962). Kinetic studies of certain anti-gibberellins. Plant Physiology **37**, 759-764.

Luib, M., Jung, J. and Rademacher, W. (1986). BAS 111..W - ein neuer Bioregulator für Raps. XXXVIII. International Symposium on Crop Protection, Rijksuniversiteit Gent, Faculteit van de Landbouwwetenschappen (in press).

Lürssen, K. and Reiser, W. (1985). Chemistry and physiological properties of the new plant growth regulator RSW 0411. Proceedings 1985 British Crop Protection Conference - Weeds, 121-128.

Lürssen, K. and Reiser, W. (1986). Triapenthenol - a new plant growth regulator. Pesticide Science (in press).

Norman, S.M., Bennett, R.D., Poling, S.M., Maier, V.P. and Nelson, M.D. (1986). Paclobutrazol inhibits abscisic acid biosynthesis in Cercospora rosicola. Plant Physiology **80**, 122-125.

Rademacher, W., Jung, J., Hildebrandt, Graebe, J.E. (1983). Zum Wirkungsmechanismus einiger neuentwickelter Wachstumsretardantien. In "Regulation des Phytohormongehaltes und seine Beeinflussung durch synthetische Wachstumsregulatoren" (F. Bangerth, ed.), pp. 132-144. Ulmer Verlag, Stuttgart.

Shive, J.B. and Sisler, H.D. (1976). Effects of ancymidol (a growth retardant) and triarimol (a fungicide) on the growth, sterols, and gibberellins of Phaseolus vulgaris (L.). Plant Physiology **57**, 640-644.

Sugavanam, B. (1984). Diastereoisomers and enantiomers of paclobutrazol: their preparation and biological activity. Pesticide Science **15**, 296-302.

GIBBERELLIN INSENSITIVITY AND DEPLETION IN WHEAT - CONSEQUENCES FOR DEVELOPMENT

J.R. Lenton,[1] P. Hedden,[1] and M.D. Gale[2]

1 University of Bristol, Department of Agricultural Sciences, Long Ashton Research Station, Long Ashton, Bristol, BS18 9AF, England
2 Cytogenetics Department, Plant Breeding Institute, Maris Lane, Trumpington, Cambridge, CB2 2LQ, England

Near-isogenic lines of wheat containing the semi-dwarfing (Rht1) and dwarfing (Rht3) genes are reduced in height by 18% and 56% respectively, compared with the tall (rht) parent, Maris Huntsman. Variation in stem height in these lines is due to differences in rates of elongation of individual stem internodes. By contrast, the Rht genes do not affect rachis internode elongation in the developing ear. The differential effect of Rht genes on growth of stem and ear internodes results in a greater survival of florets in ears of Rht genotypes at anthesis. Associated with the reduction in stem height in Rht genotypes is an insensitivity of vegetative tissues to applied GA and an increase in the concentration of endogenous GA_1.
The relative effectiveness of chlormequat chloride and paclobutrazol as growth retardants and inhibitors of GA biosynthesis is examined in wheat seedlings. Low concentrations of 2S,3S paclobutrazol are shown to inhibit the accumulation of GA_1 in the GA-insensitive, Rht3 genotype without affecting shoot growth. This inhibitor is used to explore the relationship between GA_1 concentration in the expansion zone and final length of leaves in the GA-responsive, rht genotype. The merit of a combined genetical and chemical approach to examining the relative importance of GA concentration and tissue sensitivity in the development of wheat is discussed critically.

INTRODUCTION

In the past few years there has been considerable controversy over the relative importance of growth substance concentration and tissue sensitivity in the control of plant development (Trewavas 1981, 1982). Although it has been realised for a long time that tissue sensitivity is a prerequisite for a growth response to occur, there is no doubt that the underlying philosophy of much plant hormone research has been that changes in the concentrations of growth substances control the magnitude of the response. Trewavas has argued against this tacit assumption that growth substances are limiting, and that changes in their concentration regulate development of intact plants. He claims that plants are well buffered against changes in endogenous hormone concentration and that tissue sensitivity is regulated rather by changes in hormone receptor concentration. More recently, Firn (1986) has suggested that the concept of tissue sensitivity would benefit from a more detailed analysis in terms of numbers of receptors, their affinity for growth substances and the response capacity of the subsequent chain of events. Most importantly he points out that, in most instances, a control system dependent on changes in sensitivity may also be responsive to changes in growth substance concentration. Thus, there are good reasons for taking an integrated approach to the involvement of growth substance concentration and sensitivity in plant development. However, what is required is a sound conceptual framework in which to assess the role(s) of growth substances within the hierachical organisation of plants (Barlow, this volume).

Developmental mutants that have much reduced concentrations of gibberellins (MacMillan, this volume) and abscisic acid (Quarrie, this volume) have shown, beyond any doubt, that these growth substances are essential for normal growth and development, although it is still not clear to what extent they are the limiting factors regulating these processes in the wild-types. We are investigating the role of gibberellins (GAs) in the development of wheat by perturbing the normal GA concentration-response system. In the first approach we are examining the effect of the reduced height (Rht) genes, which confer insensitivity to applied GA. As an alternative, in the absence of GA-deficient mutants in wheat, we are using inhibitors of GA biosynthesis to reduce endogenous GA concentration. We hope that a combination of these approaches will provide some insight into the relative importance of GA concentration and sensitivity throughout development and, in the long term, a rational basis for studying the action of GA at the molecular level.

Fig. 1   Winter wheat, Maris Huntsman, near-isogenic pairs containing tall (rht1) and semi-dwarf (Rht1) alleles (left) and tall (rht3) and dwarf (Rht3) alleles (right).

REDUCED-HEIGHT DWARFING GENES AND THE DEVELOPMENT OF WHEAT

The formal genetics of the control of stem height in hexaploid bread wheat (Triticum aestivum) (2x = 6n = 42) has been difficult to characterise, both because of the quantitative nature of the trait and the buffering capacity of similar functional alleles in the three component diploid genomes (see Gale and Youssefian, 1985 for review). Certain dwarf wheat cultivars, such as Norin 10 and Tom Thumb, do not show an increase in shoot height in response to applied gibberellin (GA) although they do produce more tillers (Gale and Marshall, 1973). This is in contrast to tall wheat varieties which grow taller and produce fewer tillers in response to applied GA. The association of these dwarfing genes with an insensitivity of vegetative tissue to applied GA has allowed both their characterisation and manipulation in genetic and breeding experiments. The GA-insensitivity genes have been introduced into different background cultivars as 'near-isogenic pairs' (Fig. 1) and their effects on development and yield have been described (Gale and Youssefian, 1985).

The semi-dwarfing genes, Rht1 and Rht2, from Norin 10 are located on chromosomes 4A and 4D respectively whereas the more potent dwarfing gene, Rht3, from Tom Thumb is an alternative allele at the same locus as Rht1, on chromosome 4A (McVittie et al., 1978). The general symbol for wheat dwarfing genes, Rht (reduced height), is not intended to denote dominance but simply the allele confering reduced height relative to the tall (rht) allele at the same locus. There is good genetic evidence that the Rht alleles are 'active' and encode a product which is responsible for the reduced height phenotype (Gale and Marshall, 1975). However, it is also probable that this 'product' is limiting, even with the strongest allele, since combinations of Rht2 plus Rht3 genes produce an even shorter phenotype (M.D. Gale, unpublished). Interestingly, the non-responsiveness of Rht wheat lines to applied GA does not extend to other classes of plant hormones. The Rht genes are expressed in coleoptiles (Gale et al., 1975) and GA-insensitive genotypes still show the sequential response to cytokinins and auxins (Wright, 1961), although auxin does not inhibit cell extension in young excised coleoptiles of Rht3 lines as it does in tall (rht) lines (Flintham, 1981). Thus, there is indirect evidence that some aspects of auxin metabolism or action might be associated with the GA-insensitivity genes. Whatever the case, these genes might be expected to have pleiotropic effects on all developmental processes dependent on GAs. In the following discussion we shall consider the effects of the Rht1 and Rht3 alleles on the development of the medium-height (rht) winter wheat cultivar, Maris Huntsman, from seedling emergence to anthesis (Fig. 1).

Shoot Development

The Rht1 allele reduces final stem height by about 18% and is incompletely recessive whereas the Rht3 allele reduces stem height by about 56% and shows no dominance (Youssefian, 1986). The responsiveness to applied GA of the second leaf sheath of the near-isogenic pairs containing the semi-dwarfing (Rht1) and dwarfing (Rht3) alleles is shown in Fig. 2.

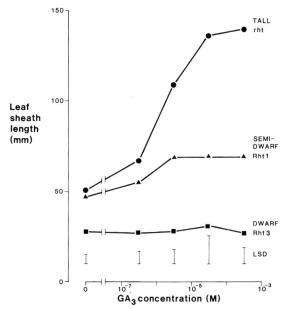

Fig. 2 Responsiveness to applied GA_3 of the second leaf of Maris Huntsman near-isogenic lines containing tall (rht), semi-dwarf (Rht1) and dwarf (Rht3) alleles. (21-day old seedlings watered with 150 ml GA_3 solution).

The tall (rht) lines (mean of each isogenic pair) are sensitive to low concentrations of gibberellic acid (GA$_3$) but the overall response (about 170% increase over control) saturates at high GA$_3$ concentrations. The line containing the Rht1 allele shows a partial response (about 40% increase over control), but saturates at low GA$_3$ concentrations. By contrast, the line containing the more potent Rht3 allele is quite unresponsive to applied GA$_3$ (Fig. 2).

Stem elongation in wheat starts before the terminal spikelet stage of development and continues until after anthesis. More distal internodes have progressively faster rates of elongation and maximum growth rate occurs in the peduncle around the time of anthesis. The reduction in stem height of Rht genotypes is not the result of fewer internodes being produced nor is it due to differences in the timing of their initiation and duration of elongation (Youssefian, 1986). Rather, the Rht genes reduce the rate of elongation of individual internodes and this effect is established early in development. The Rht alleles cause similar relative length reductions at each internode position although the later-formed, distal internodes contribute more to final stem height, particularly in Rht3 genotypes (Fig. 3).

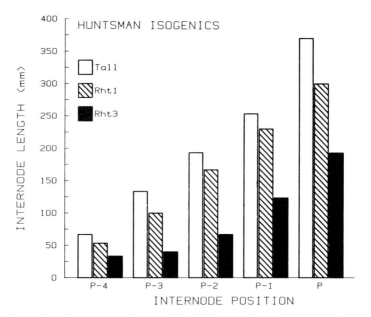

Fig. 3   Final length of individual internodes of Maris Huntsman near-isogenic lines containing tall (rht), semi-dwarf (Rht1) and dwarf (Rht3) alleles, after Youssefian (1986). (P = peduncle, P-1 = internode below peduncle etc.).

The cellular basis for such differences in internode length depends on the activity of the basal intercalary meristem. The greater length of successively higher internodes of several wheat varieties is associated with an increase in the numbers of parenchyma and epidermal cells (Nilson et al., 1957). Preliminary examination of the near-isogenic lines for Rht1 and Rht3 in Maris Huntsman shows that the reduction in length of leaves and peduncles, caused by the genes, is associated mainly with reduced epidermal cell length, although there is also some reduction in cell numbers in Rht3 lines (Gale et al., 1986). Earlier varietal comparisons have shown similarly that the internodes of Norin 10, which carries both Rht1 and Rht2, contain shorter parenchyma cells than the corresponding internodes of seven other varieties (Nilson et al., 1957).

In the P-1 internode of Avena sativa, cell division occurs with concomitant cell enlargement in epidermal cells until the internode reaches one-third final length (Kaufman et al., 1965). The region of simultaneous cell division and elongation then becomes restricted to the base of the internode. Growth during the latter two-thirds of linear extension of the internode is by cell elongation alone, with up to a 16-fold increase in length of epidermal cells (Kaufman et al., 1965). Applied GAs increase growth of excised intercalary meristem segments of Avena P-1 internodes in both light and dark by shortening the period of mitotic activity and stimulating cell elongation (Kaufman, 1965,1967). These effects of GA on the intercalary meristem activity of Avena are, however, very different from those on the sub-apical meristem of dicotyledons (Loy, 1977).

Ear Development

Besides the main effects of the Rht alleles on stem height (Fig. 1), there are additional effects on grain numbers which originate in subtle differences in early ear and stem development. The transition from vegetative growth to the initiation of a floral apex in wheat is first manifested in an elongation of the shoot apex, arrested outgrowth of the lower foliar primordial ridges and the development of the upper cauline ridges which form the spikelets of the ear. The spikelet primordia are initiated at the shoot apex faster than leaf primordia (Kirby, 1974). The last few primordia initiated at the apex give rise to the glume and floret primordia of the terminal spikelet. A series of 6 - 10 florets are initiated within each spikelet and each floret is a potential grain site. All these events occur when the apex is less than 5 mm long and still below ground level. There is no effect of the Rht alleles on the rates of initiation of leaf, spikelet or floret primordia, or on the final numbers of leaves and spikelets produced. This is an interesting and important observation since applied GAs and long days have been reported to affect the numbers of leaf and spikelet primordia produced in wheat (Hutley-Bull and Schwabe, 1982) and barley (Cottrell et al., 1982). If long days increase endogenous GAs and have the same effect on apical development in both rht and Rht genotypes, then we must assume that the 'trigger' or 'threshold' GA concentration is sufficient for apices of Rht genotypes to be able to respond to their endogenous GAs. In other words, if GAs have a role in the transition from a vegetative to floral apex, then Rht genotypes must be as responsive as rht genotypes.

The first phase of ear growth is associated with the production of spikelets. It begins before the double-ridge stage of apex development and continues until after the formation of the terminal spikelet. A second phase of rapid ear growth is associated with the expansion of the internodes of the ear to form the rachis. This begins about 200 degree-days after terminal spikelet formation when maximal primordia numbers have been established, and continues until just before ear emergence. This period of rapid ear growth coincides with the expansion of the peduncle and P-1, P-2 and P-3 stem internodes (Fig. 3). Lines containing Rht alleles show no differences in relative rates or durations of rachis elongation so final ear lengths are the same in both rht and Rht genotypes (Youssefian, 1986). Thus stem and ear internodes differ markedly in the extent to which they are influenced by the Rht alleles even though both are growing at the same time.

In barley, where the cellular basis of apical growth has been studied (Nichols and May, 1964), there is no net increase in cell number in the central pith region during the initial phase of spikelet production but cell numbers increase during the rapid phase of rachis internode growth. Mean cell length remains relatively constant throughout both phases of ear growth . Although large changes in the concentration of biologically-active GAs were found to be associated with differences in ear growth rate and development, these GA measurements require confirmation by physical techniques. Rachis internodes, however, do not appear to respond to GA by marked increases in cell elongation unlike vegetative stem internodes. The positional arrangement of meristematic nodal cells and potential internode cells of the rachis of barley (Kirby and Rymer, 1974) is different from the intercalary meristem of the stem. In addition, the rachis has many lateral appendages which may physically restrict the expansion of pith cells. There is also the possibility that the rachis does not initiate cell types which elongate in response to GA. Support for this idea comes from recent work on internode formation in the vegetative stem and flowers of Silene (Lyndon, 1987). These inflorescences do not initiate the necessary cell layers that would become an internode. By analogy, the rachis of cereals may represent an intermediate stage between vegetative stem and flower (spikelet) proper and may not initiate cell files that elongate in response to GA.

An alternative explanation for the apparent non-responsiveness of rachis internodes to GA, and the lack of effect of Rht genes on extension growth of the rachis, is that these tissues are rich sources of auxin which is known to suppress GA-promoted cell elongation in intercalary meristem segments of Avena (Kaufman, 1967). Similarly, high concentrations of abscisic acid might overcome potential GA-stimulated growth of rachis internodes. The transport pathways between stem and rachis internodes require examination as does a direct assessment of the GA-sensitivity of the two tissue types. Although floral initiation usually precedes stem elongation in cereals this sequence of events is not obligatory. It has been proposed that GAs produced in the floral apex stimulate stem elongation in barley (Nichols and May, 1964) and oats (Koning et al., 1977) but other evidence suggests there are separate mechanisms controlling internode elongation in stem and rachis (Kirby and Faris, 1970).

Assimilate Distribution and Floret Survival

The introduction of the Norin 10 semi-dwarfing genes has led to dramatic increases in wheat production during the past two decades (Gale and Youssefian, 1985). The main yield component affected is an increase in grain number per ear and the increased harvest index results from a more favourable partitioning of available assimilate to the developing ear rather than the growing stem. Dry matter accumulation in both stems and ears lags slightly behind the increases in length. Main stem dry matter accumulation starts to accelerate at the terminal spikelet stage and continues until just after anthesis. In the Maris Huntsman near-isogenic pairs, final stem dry matter is reduced by 12% for Rht1, and 53% for Rht3 compared with tall (rht) genotypes (Youssefian, 1986). The rapid linear phase of dry matter accumulation in ears starts about 250-300 degree-days after the terminal spikelet stage and continues until after anthesis. Thereafter ear dry matter continues to accumulate faster as a result of grain growth. In comparisons of near-isogenic lines there is a tendency for dry matter to accumulate faster in the Rht genotypes (Rht3>Rht1>rht) with the result that they have heavier ears at anthesis (Youssefian, 1986). The consequences of the differential effects of the Rht alleles on growth and dry matter accumulation in stems and ears is that relatively more dry matter is partitioned to ears of Rht genotypes (Fig. 4).

These differences in assimilate partitioning are established early in development and amplified during ontogeny. Thus relatively more assimilates are available for growth of ears of Rht3 and Rht1 genotypes than for tall, rht genotypes (Fig. 4). It is generally assumed that the increased availability of assimilates of Rht genotypes accounts for their greater number of fertile florets after anthesis.

It is difficult to measure maximum floret number and to determine floret death accurately. Nevertheless, it has been established that death of distal florets begins at the start of elongation of the P-1 internode and continues until after anthesis when the peduncle has ceased growth. Only a relatively small proportion of the total number of florets produced remain viable at anthesis. It appears that a greater number of florets are produced in Rht compared with rht genotypes and the period of floret death, particularly after the onset of anthesis, is correspondingly shorter (Youssefian, 1986). Although the Rht genes have no direct effect on ear growth, the greater survival of florets in Rht genotypes is probably an indirect consequence of the increased proportion of assimilate available to developing ears (Fig. 4). We assume that the direct effect of the Rht alleles is to reduce stem internode growth thus lowering demand for assimilates and making more available

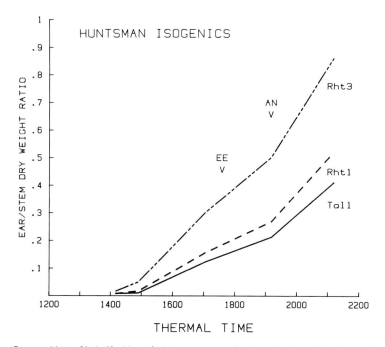

Fig. 4 Dry matter distribution between ear and stem during development of Maris
Huntsman near-isogenic lines containing tall (rht), semi-dwarf (Rht1) and dwarf
(Rht3) alleles, after Youssefian (1986). (EE = ear emergence, AN = anthesis, thermal
time in degree-days above a base temperature of $2^{\circ}C$).

to support floret survival. Similar conclusions were reached by Brooking and Kirby
(1981), although more information on assimilate levels and resistance to transport in
developing ears is required to substantiate this hypothesis. Alternative
hormonally-based hypotheses have also been advanced to explain the pattern of floret
survival. For example, it has been suggested that early formed florets may exert
some correlative-inhibitory effect on the development of more distal florets (Evans
et al., 1972; Radley, 1982).

REDUCED-HEIGHT DWARFING GENES AND ENDOGENOUS GIBBERELLINS

Increased amounts of biologically-active GAs are found in seedlings of wheat
varieties containing Rht dwarfing genes when compared with tall cultivars (Radley,
1970). More recently it has been shown by radioimmunoassay that the pool size of GA_1
is increased 12 to 15-fold in immature leaves of an Rht3 line relative to a tall
(rht) control and there are no differences in the rate of metabolism of GA_1 in leaves
of either genotype (Stoddart, 1984). Thus, in addition to reduced stem height and
insensitivity to applied GA, the Rht allele is associated with elevated levels of
endogenous GAs.

Several C_{20} and C_{19} GAs have been identified from vegetative tissues of Rht3 wheat by
comparing their mass spectra with those of authentic compounds (Table 1). Most of
these GAs are members of the early 13-hydroxylation pathway which operates in shoot
tissues of a range of species, including wheat (Ingram et al., 1987). From work on

151

Table 1 Gibberellins identified by combined GC-MS in internodes of wheat. (Maris Huntsman, dwarf (Rht3) genotype).

C_{20} GAs	C_{19} GAs
A_{17}, A_{19}, A_{44}	A_1, 3epi-A_1, A_3, A_8, A_9, A_{20}, A_{29}

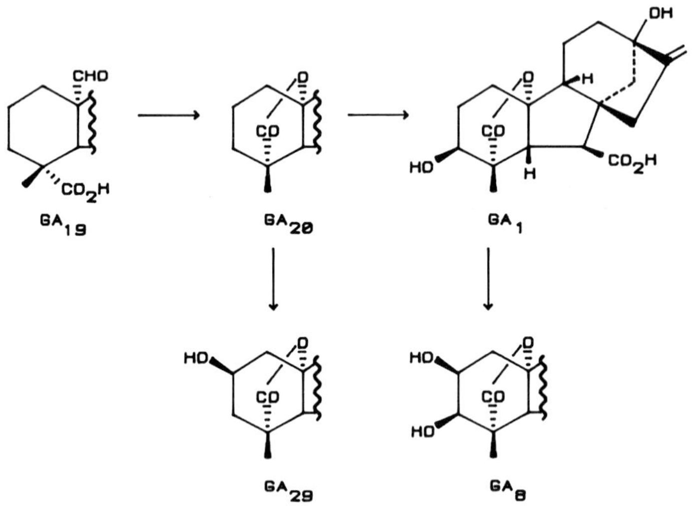

Fig. 5 Final stages in the GA biosynthetic pathway in plants.

GA-deficient mutants of maize and pea it is known that GA_1 is the active compound involved in shoot elongation and that GA_{20} is its immediate precursor (MacMillan, this volume). Both GA_{20} and GA_1 are rendered biologically-inactive by 2β-hydroxylation to GA_{29} and GA_8 respectively (Fig. 5). We have used deuterated internal standards and selected ion monitoring to quantify GA_{20} and GA_1 in stem internodes and ears of wheat containing different rht and Rht alleles (Table 2). GAs were determined in upper expanding internodes when stems were about one-third final height and in adjacent elongating ears when they were about one-half final length. The pool size of GA_1 increases 4.5-fold and 25-fold in expanding stem internodes containing Rht1 and Rht3 alleles, whereas the corresponding increases in GA_{20} are only 1.4-fold and 2.7-fold respectively compared with tall (rht) lines (Table 2). Thus, wheat stem internodes of Rht dwarf genotypes are not GA-deficient but accumulate biologically-active GA_1 in amounts directly related to the potency of the dwarfing gene. At this stage of development, the pool size of GA_1 in ears containing the rht allele is one-half that of stem internodes and increases by only 1.6-fold and 2.5-fold in ears of Rht1 and Rht3 genotypes respectively. The level of GA_{20} is similar to that of GA_1 in rht ears and shows a similar slight increase in the Rht genotypes (Table 2). Thus, ear tissues of dwarf plants do not show the dramatic increase in GA_1 concentration that is evident in adjacent stem internode tissues. There are 2-fold, 6-fold and 20-fold differences in GA_1 concentrations between stem internode and ear tissues containing rht, Rht1, and Rht3 alleles respectively. The non-accumulation of GA_1 in ears of Rht genotypes may reflect a lack of expression of the Rht gene in this tissue. Conversely, the increase in GA_1 in stem internodes may not be a direct effect of expression of the Rht genes, but may be an indirect effect resulting from reduced internode growth.

Table 2 Concentrations of GA_{20} and GA_1 (ng g^{-1} FW) determined by combined GC-MS in developing internodes and ears of wheat. (Maris Huntsman, near-isogenic pairs).

Genotype	Internode		Ear	
	GA_{20}	GA_1	GA_{20}	GA_1
rht	0.98	0.65	0.34	0.32
Rht1	1.39	2.93	0.38	0.52
Rht3	2.68	16.21	0.60	0.81

The evidence outlined above suggests an association between GA insensitivity and an accumulation of GA_1 in tissues in which the Rht gene is expressed. Shoots of Rht3 genotypes respond poorly to their own increased levels of GA_1 and are completely unresponsive to applied GA (Fig. 2). One method of comparing the relative GA-responsiveness of the rht and Rht genotypes is to examine the shapes of the dose-response curves to determine if hormone receptivity, affinity or response capacity are affected (Firn, 1986). However, such response-curves should be constructed using the measured endogenous concentration of GA in the responding tissue; they should not rely on the applied dose. The lack of response of Rht genotypes to applied GA may be exaggerated by their already high endogenous GA_1 concentrations (Table 2).

GROWTH RETARDANTS, ENDOGENOUS GIBBERELLINS AND SHOOT GROWTH

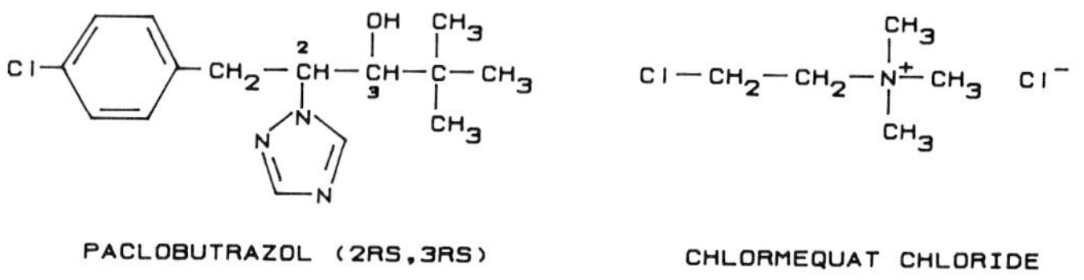

PACLOBUTRAZOL (2RS,3RS)   CHLORMEQUAT CHLORIDE

Fig. 6 Structures of paclobutrazol and chlormequat chloride.

In addition to supplementing endogenous GA_1, an alternative approach is to apply specific inhibitors of GA biosynthesis to reduce GA concentration and relate this to decreased growth. Chlormequat chloride (CCC) (Fig. 6) was the first growth retardant used commercially to reduce shoot height and prevent stem 'lodging' in tall wheat cultivars. In addition, CCC may also increase the number of grains per ear. The latter response is observed only when care is taken to prevent lodging in both control and treated plants. The reduction in shoot growth and increase in grain number is similar to that obtained with varieties containing the Norin 10 dwarfing genes. The suggestion (Gale and Hanson, 1982) that this growth retardant can mimic the effect of the dwarfing genes has been confirmed with near-isogenic lines (Gale and Youssefian, 1983). For example, significantly greater reduction in stem height in response to applied CCC is observed in the tall (rht) line compared with the semi-dwarf (Rht1) line in the Maris Huntsman near-isogenic pairs (Table 3).

Table 3 Effect of CCC treatment on Maris Huntsman tall (rht) and semi-dwarf (Rht1) near-isogenic lines, from Gale and Youssefian (1983).

	Stem height (cm)		Grain number per ear	
	rht	Rht1	rht	Rht1
Untreated	109.8	84.8	45.8	55.2
CCC treated at Zadoks 3.0-3.1	102.3	82.1	50.3	57.4
Zadoks 3.2-3.3	98.2	82.7	52.0	55.9
LSD (95%)	1.81		4.05	

Experimental: Sown as spaced plants (175 m^{-2}) on 5th October 1981. Spring application of nitrogen (40 kg ha^{-1}). 5C Cycocel (BASF) applied at 1431g (active ingredient) ha^{-1} on 14th April (Zadoks 3.0-3.1) and 10th May (Zadoks 3.2-3.3). All plants supported with mesh nets to prevent lodging.

Associated with the reduction in stem height in the rht line is an increase in grain number per ear following CCC application. These responses are obtained in the absence of stem lodging in either control or treated plants. This confirms that application of CCC to the rht line does indeed mimic the effect of the Rht1 allele and that plants containing this gene are relatively insensitive to applied CCC (Table 3). Although it is generally assumed that CCC inhibits GA biosynthesis in plants the evidence is far from conclusive (Graebe and Ropers, 1978), and its mechanism of action remains in doubt (Dicks, 1980).

By contrast, paclobutrazol (Fig. 6) is a recently introduced broad-spectrum growth retardant with some fungicidal properties making it a potentially useful anti-lodging compound for cereals (Froggatt et al., 1982). Along with other potent growth retardants, such as ancymidol and tetcyclacis, the primary mode of action of paclobutrazol is thought to be inhibition of GA biosynthesis (Dalziel and Lawrence, 1984). Paclobutrazol inhibits the sequential oxidation of ent-kaurene to ent-kaurenoic acid on the pathway to GAs (Hedden and Graebe, 1985). The commercial compound is a racemic mixture which has been resolved into its 2S,3S and 2R,3R enantiomers (Sugavanam, 1984). The 2S,3S enantiomer has high growth retardant activity and is a potent inhibitor of ent-kaurene oxidase (Hedden and Graebe, 1985) whereas the 2R,3R enantiomer has fungicidal activity and inhibits sterol C-14 demethylation in fungi (Baldwin and Wiggins, 1984).

Paclobutrazol is considerably more effective than CCC in reducing leaf growth in the Maris Huntsman (rht) tall line (Fig. 7). There is a linear reduction in leaf length with $\log_{10}$ increase in paclobutrazol concentration over the range 3×10^{-7} to 1×10^{-4}M and a 25% reduction in leaf length is obtained with 2 μM paclobutrazol. By contrast, 14 mM CCC is required for a 25% reduction in leaf length (Fig. 7) and at higher concentrations some phytotoxicity is observed.

The 2S,3S, enantiomer of paclobutrazol accounts for all the inhibition of leaf growth up to 10 μM, but higher concentrations of the 2R,3R enantiomer can also inhibit shoot growth (J.R. Lenton, unpublished). The inhibition of leaf growth caused by 2.5 mM CCC is completely reversed by applied GA and that of 2.5 μM paclobutrazol nearly so, providing indirect evidence that low effective concentrations of these retardants may inhibit GA biosynthesis.

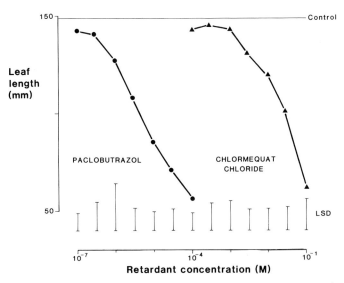

Fig. 7 Inhibition of growth of first leaf of Maris Huntsman tall (rht) wheat by paclobutrazol and chlormequat chloride. (12-day old seedlings watered with 50 ml solutions of retardants on days 1 and 2).

Direct evidence that the retardants are inhibiting GA production comes from measurements of GA_1 by selected ion monitoring in shoots and grains of control and retardant-treated wheat seedlings containing the Rht3 dwarfing gene (Table 4).

Table 4 The effects of chlormequat chloride (3 mM) and paclobutrazol (1 uM) on GA_1 levels in shoots and grains of 6-day old dwarf (Rht$_3$) wheat seedlings.

	GA_1 (ng g^{-1} FW)		Leaf length
	Shoot	Grain	(% control)
Untreated*	5.8	11.1	100
3 mM chlormequat chloride	0.2	1.1	98
1 µM 2S,3S paclobutrazol	1.7	1.6	97
1 µM 2R,3R paclobutrazol	7.1	10.5	98

* Mean of three separate experiments

Chlormequat chloride at 3 mM reduces GA_1 concentration by 90 - 95% without a reduction in leaf length. Similarly, 1 µM 2S,3S paclobutrazol reduces GA_1 concentration by 70 - 85% without inhibiting leaf growth, whereas the 2R,3R enantiomer is ineffective (Table 4). Thus, concentrations of both CCC and 2S, 3S paclobutrazol that inhibit growth of tall (rht) lines (Fig. 7) cause considerable reduction in GA_1 levels in GA-insensitive dwarf (Rht3) lines without reducing leaf growth. These observations suggest that the primary effect of the retardants is an inhibition of GA production and that the reduced GA concentration is not a consequence of reduced leaf growth.

Because of its high potency and known mode of action, 2S,3S, paclobutrazol was used to explore the relationship between GA_1 concentration and leaf growth in GA-responsive tall (rht) wheat. Seedlings were grown in concentrations of 2S,3S paclobutrazol up to 1 µM and the GA_1 concentration of lower leaf segments, containing the zone of cell expansion, was measured during the linear phase of leaf growth. The pool size of GA_1 in these GA-responsive segments was then related to final leaf length (Fig. 8). There is a linear reduction in leaf length with log_{10} decrease in

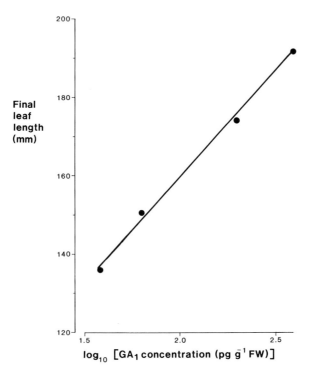

Fig. 8 Relationship between endogenous GA_1 concentration and final length of the first leaf of Maris Huntsman tall (rht) wheat.

GA_1 concentration in the zone of expansion of the leaf. A 10-fold reduction in GA_1 concentration causes a 30% reduction in final leaf length (Fig. 8). Recently, a similar log-linear relationship has been shown for the conversion of GA_{20} into the GA_1 metabolite, GA_8 and promotion of shoot growth of GA-deficient dwarf pea (Ingram et al., 1986). The linear growth response to log_{10} change in endogenous GA_1 concentration in wheat results in relatively small differences in GA_1 at low endogenous concentrations having greater effects on leaf growth than the same differences in GA_1 at high endogenous concentrations. Thus, in the absence of paclobutrazol, it seems unlikely that changes in GA_1 concentration provide sensitive regulation of leaf growth in rht wheat even though it is still responsive to applied GA (Fig. 2). In other words the response system might be relatively well buffered against changes in endogenous GA_1 concentration, as Trewavas (1982, 1986) has hypothesised. Much depends on whether or not environmental factors, such as temperature and photoperiod, can induce sufficiently large changes in GA_1 concentration in responsive target tissues without corresponding changes in the capacity of the response system.

It has been shown recently that there are only small differences in the growth rates of rht and Rht3 genotypes when seedlings grown at 20°C are cooled to temperatures below 15°C. In addition, the rht genotype is equally responsive to applied GA at both low and high temperatures, whereas the Rht3 genotype is unresponsive at all temperatures (Stoddart and Lloyd, 1986). This may indicate that endogenous GA levels are reduced to critical levels below 15°C in rht wheat but that the response capacity remains the same thus making GA a 'regulator' of leaf growth under these conditions. Whatever the case, there is a clear requirement for additional direct estimates of GA_1 levels in responsive target tissues and more precise measurements of tissue growth rates after application of GA and growth retardants under a range of environmental conditions. Only then can the relative importance of hormone concentration and tissue sensitivity be assessed objectively.

CONCLUSIONS

The two approaches that we have taken to investigate the role of GA in the development of wheat have provided useful information but still leave many questions unanswered.

The presence of the Rht allele has three main effects on vegetative growth and development; reduced stem length, reduced sensitivity of shoot tissue to applied GA and an accumulation of GA_1 in leaves and internodes. The first effect is a consequence of the second, but the accumulation of GA_1 cannot yet be explained. Although we feel that it might be giving us important clues about the nature of the normal GA response system, the accumulation of GA_1 may also be an indirect effect due to the decreased growth rate. There is no apparent direct effect of the Rht allele on apical development, but whether this is due to the lack of expression of the gene in these tissues or to these tissues being insensitive to GA even in the wild-type remains to be determined. A more detailed histological examination of the initiation and development of potentially GA-responsive cell types in both stem and ear internodes is required, preferably before attempts are made to determine the molecular basis of GA action during internode elongation.

Use of the GA biosynthesis inhibitor, paclobutrazol, has enabled us to obtain a GA response curve for leaf elongation in rht seedlings based on the concentration of endogenous GA_1 in the target tissue. In principle it should allow us to examine GA involvement in other developmental processes. However, we need to determine the specificity of the retardant, not only because of possible effects on sterol metabolism (Dalziel and Lawrence, 1984; Lürssen, this volume), but especially in the light of recent reports of an increase in ABA levels after treatment with this type of inhibitor (Asare-Boamah et al., 1986; Grossmann et al., 1986). Although a useful criterion for specificity is the reversal of symptoms with applied GA, it is important to ascertain that the growth pattern obtained is identical to that of untreated plants. If specificity can be established, then retardants provide a valuable method, together with application of GA, of manipulating endogenous GA levels in responsive tissue. We feel it is important that such measurements of GA_1 concentrations within the tissue be coupled with precise growth measurements under a range of environmental conditions. We may then be able to assess more objectively the importance of hormone concentration and tissue responsiveness in the regulation of plant growth.

ACKNOWLEDGEMENTS
   It is a pleasure to thank the following for their contributions to this work: Shohab Youssefian and Andy Salter at PBI, Cambridge for the developmental analyses; Nigel Appleford, Kay Temple-Smith and Steve Croker at LARS for the GA measurements and growth retardant studies and Christine Willis and Jake MacMillan at the Chemistry Department, University of Bristol for the generous gifts of deuterated GA_{20} and GA_1. Long Ashton Research Station and the Plant Breeding Institute are financed through the Agricultural and Food Research Council.

REFERENCES

Asare-Boamah, N.K., Hofstra, G., Fletcher, R.A. and Dumbroff, E.B. (1986). Triadimefon protects bean plants from water stress through its effects on abscisic acid. Plant and Cell Physiology **27**, 383-390.

Baldwin, B.C. and Wiggins, T.E. (1984). Action of fungicidal triazoles of the diclobutrazol series on Ustilago maydis. Pesticide Science **15**, 156-166.

Brooking, I.R. and Kirby, E.J.M. (1981). Inter-relationships between stem and ear development in winter wheat: the effects of a Norin 10 dwarfing gene, Gai/Rht2. Journal of Agricultural Science, Cambridge **97**, 373-381.

Cottrell, J.E., Dale, J.E. and Jeffcoat, B. (1982). The effects of daylength and treatment with gibberellic acid on spikelet initiation and development in Clipper barley. Annals of Botany **50**, 57-68.

Dalziel, J. and Lawrence, D.K. (1984). Biochemical and biological effects of kaurene oxidase inhibitors, such as paclobutrazol. In "Biochemical Aspects of Synthetic and Naturally Occurring Plant Growth Regulators" (R. Menhenett and D.K. Lawrence eds.), pp 43-57. Monograph 11, British Plant Growth Regulator Group, Wantage.

Dicks, J.W. (1980). Mode of action of plant growth retardants. In "Recent Developments in the Use of Plant Growth Retardants" (D.R. Clifford and J.R. Lenton eds.), pp 1-14. Monograph 4, British Plant Growth Regulator Group, Wantage.

Evans, L.T., Bingham, J. and Roskams, M.A. (1972). The pattern of grain set within ears of wheat. Australian Journal of Biological Sciences **25**, 1-8.

Firn, R.D. (1986). Growth substance sensitivity: The need for clearer ideas, precise terms and purposeful experiments. Physiologia Plantarum **67**, 267-272.

Flintham, J.E. (1981). The physiological role and plant breeding potential of the Tom Thumb dwarfing gene in wheat. PhD thesis, University of Cambridge.

Froggatt, P.J., Thomas, W.D. and Batch, J.J. (1982). The value of lodging control in winter wheat as exemplified by the growth regulator PP333. In "Opportunities for Manipulation of Cereal Productivity" (A.F. Hawkins and B. Jeffcoat eds.), pp 71-87. Monograph 7, British Plant Growth Regulator Group, Wantage.

Gale, M.D. and Hanson, P.R. (1982). The plant breeding potential of genetic variation in cereal phytohormone systems. In "Chemical Manipulation of Crop Growth and Development" (J.S. McLaren ed.), pp 425-449. Butterworths, London.

Gale, M.D., Hoogendoorn, J. and Salter, A.M. (1986). The effects of dwarfing genes of wheat on cell size and cell numbers. Annual Report for 1985, Plant Breeding Institute, Cambridge, p 69.

Gale, M.D., Law, C.N., Marshall, G.A. and Worland, A.J. (1975). The genetic control of gibberellic acid insensitivity and coleoptile length in a "dwarf" wheat. Heredity **34**, 393-399.

Gale, M.D. and Marshall, G.A. (1973). Insensitivity to gibberellin in dwarf wheats. Annals of Botany **37**, 729-735.

Gale, M.D. and Marshall, G.A. (1975). The nature and genetic control of gibberellin insensitivity in dwarf wheat grain. Heredity **35**, 55-65.

Gale, M.D. and Youssefian, S. (1983). Pleiotropic effects of the Norin 10 dwarfing genes, Rht1 and Rht2 and interactions in response to chlormequat. Proceedings of the Sixth International Wheat Genetics Symposium, Kyoto, Japan. pp 271-277.

Gale, M.D. and Youssefian, S. (1985). Dwarfing genes in wheat. In "Progress in Plant Breeding" (G.E. Russell ed.), pp 1-35. Butterworths, London.

Graebe, J.E. and Ropers, H.J. (1978). Gibberellins. In "Phytohormones and Related Compounds: A Comprehensive Treatise" Vol. 1. (D.S. Letham, P.B. Goodwin and T.J.V. Higgins eds.), pp 107-203. Elsevier, North Holland.

Grossmann, K., Schmidt, H.O. and Jung, J. (1986). Changes in membrane permeability and mineral, phytohormone and polypeptide composition in rice suspension cultures during growth and under the influence of the growth retardant tetcyclacis. Plant Cell Reports 5, 315-318.

Hedden, P. and Graebe, J.E. (1985). Inhibition of gibberellin biosynthesis by paclobutrazol in cell-free homogenates of Cucurbita maxima endosperm and Malus pumila embryos. Journal of Plant Growth Regulation 4, 111-122.

Hutley-Bull, P.D. and Schwabe, W.W. (1982). Morphogensis in the wheat apex as influenced by environment and plant growth regulators. In "Opportunities for Manipulation of Cereal Productivity". (A.F. Hawkins and B.Jeffcoat eds.), pp 150-166. Monograph 7, British Plant Growth Regulator Group, Wantage.

Ingram, T.J., MacMillan, J. and Sponsel, V.M. (1987). Gibberellin distribution and metabolism: a comparison between seeds, shoots and roots. Acta Universitatis Agriculturae, Brno (in press).

Ingram, T.J., Reid, J.B. and MacMillan, J. (1986). The quantitative relationship between gibberellin A$_1$ and internode growth in Pisum sativum L. Planta 168, 414-420.

Kaufman, P.B. (1965). The effects of growth substances on intercalary growth and cellular differentiation in developing internodes of Avena sativa. 2. The effects of gibberellic acid. Physiologia Plantarum 18, 703-724.

Kaufman, P.B. (1967). Role of gibberellins in the control of intercalary growth and cellular differentiation in developing Avena internodes. Annals of the New York Academy of Sciences 144, 191-203.

Kaufman, P.B., Cassell, S.J. and Adams, P.A. (1965). On nature of intercalary growth and cellular differentiation in internodes of Avena sativa. Botanical Gazette 126, 1-13.

Kirby, E.J.M. (1974). Ear development in spring wheat. Journal of Agricultural Science, Cambridge 82, 437-447.

Kirby, E.J.M. and Faris, D.G. (1970). Plant population induced growth correlations in the barley plant main shoot and possible hormonal mechanisms. Journal of Experimental Botany 21, 787-798.

Kirby, E.J.M. and Rymer, J.L. (1974). Development of the vascular system in the ear of barley. Annals of Botany 38, 565-573.

Koning, R., Tkaczyk, A., Kaufman, P.B., Pharis, P. and Morf, W. (1977). Regulation of internodal extension in Avena shoots by inflorescence, nodes, leaves and intercalary meristem. Physiologia Plantarum 40, 119-124.

Loy, J.B. (1977). Hormonal regulation of cell division in the primary elongating meristems of shoots. In "Mechanisms and Control of Cell Division" (T.L. Rost and E.M. Gifford eds.), pp 92-110. Dowden, Hutchinson and Ross, Strondsburg, Pennsylvania.

Lyndon, R.F. (1987). Initiation and growth of internodes and stem and flower frusta in Silene coeli-rosa. In "Manipulation of Flowering" (J.G. Atherton ed.) pp 301-314. Butterworths, London.

McVittie, J.A., Gale, M.D., Marshall, G.A. and Westcott, B. (1978). The intra-chromosomal mapping of the Norin 10 and Tom Thumb dwarfing genes. Heredity 40, 67-70.

Nicholls, P.B. and May, L.H. (1964). Studies on the growth of the barley apex. 2. On the inititation of internode elongation in the inflorescence. Australian Journal of Biological Sciences 17, 619-630.

Nilson, E.B., Johnson, V.A. and Gardner, C.O. (1957). Parenchyma and epidermal cell length in relation to plant height and culm internode length in winter wheat. Botanical Gazette 119, 38-43.

Radley, M.E. (1970). Comparison of endogenous gibberellins and response to applied gibberellin of some dwarf and tall wheat cultivars. Planta 92, 292-300.

Radley, M.E. (1982). Some factors affecting grain set in wheat. In "Opportunities for Manipulation of Cereal Productivity" (A.F. Hawkins and B. Jeffcoat eds.), pp 140-149. Monograph 7, British Plant Growth Regulator Group, Wantage.

Stoddart, J.L. (1984). Growth and gibberellin A_1 metabolism in normal and gibberellin-insensitive (Rht3) wheat (Triticum aestivum L.) seedlings. Planta 161, 432-438.

Stoddart, J.L. and Lloyd, E.J. (1986). Modification by gibberellin of the growth-temperature relationship in mutant and normal genotypes of several cereals. Planta 167, 364-368.

Sugavanam, B. (1984). Diastereoisomers and enantiomers of paclobutrazol: their preparation and biological activity. Pesticide Science 15, 296-302.

Trewavas, A.J. (1981). How do plant growth substances work? Plant Cell and Environment 4, 203-228.

Trewavas, A.J. (1982). Growth substance sensitivity: The limiting factor in plant development. Physiologia Plantarum 55, 60-72.

Trewavas, A.J. (1986). Resource allocation under poor growth conditions. A major role for growth substances in developmental plasticity. In "Plasticity in Plants" (D.H. Jennings and A.J. Trewavas eds.), pp 31-76. Society for Experimental Biology Symposium XXXX, Company of Biologists, Cambridge.

Wright, S.T.C. (1961). Sequential growth response to gibberellic acid, kinetin and indolyl-3-acetic acid in the wheat coleoptile (Triticum vulgare L.). Nature 190, 699-700.

Youssefian, S. (1986). The development and pleiotropic effects of GA-insensitive dwarfing genes in wheat. PhD thesis, University of Cambridge.

MANIPULATION OF HORMONE TRANSPORT IN PHYSIOLOGICAL AND DEVELOPMENTAL STUDIES

P.H. Rubery

Biochemistry Department, Cambridge University, Cambridge, England

The elements of hormone transport are analysed in terms of transport carrier activity, level and distribution; of availability of substrate; and of driving forces for transport. These elements are then considered as actual or potential targets for manipulation in developmental and physiological studies. The biological effects, mode of action and receptors of compounds such as TIBA, phytotropins, morphactins and fluoresceins which are known to inhibit polar auxin transport are discussed together with the extent to which their use can or cannot shed light on the control mechanisms involved in tropisms and apical dominance. Evidence for the existence of endogenous transport inhibitors is summarised. The importance of auxin substrate supply is discussed in relation to experiments on the maintenance and channelling of polar transport with particular reference to the control of vascular differentiation. The effects of other hormones on polar auxin transport are considered. ABA transport is more briefly covered, and the possibilities for manipulating ABA distribution between cells by altering pH gradients and by use of specific inhibitors of carrier-mediated ABA uptake (methyl jasmonate, methyl ABA and – and –ionone) are discussed.

INTRODUCTION

It is indisputable that plant hormones influence development. The availability of hormones, from metabolic networks and transport, to transducing receptor/effector systems is clearly essential – irrespective of whether they act as "chemical triggers, quantitative regulators or enabling substances" – to quote Dr Trewavas' Chapter title. In this article I shall consider the various elements of auxin and abscisic acid transport that have been, or could become, subjects for manipulation in particular developmental and physiological investigations, together with the corresponding biochemical and biophysical manipulative tools.

ELEMENTS OF HORMONE TRANSPORT

Transmembrane transport is fundamental to the distribution of hormones between intracellular compartments, between symplast and apoplast for intercellular transport, and for loading and unloading of the vascular conduits. Other than ethene, both endogenous and applied hormones can move in xylem and phloem. Polar transport has only been firmly established for auxin, where it is particularly relevant to development and has been linked to polar developmental and correlative growth phenomena such as vascular differentiation, apical dominance and tropisms. Although these events are undoubtedly more complex in their control than many text-book treatments have suggested, they have continued to motivate polar auxin transport research for 50-60 years.

The weakly acidic hormones can cross membranes by simple unmediated diffusion of their hydrophobic neutral species and can accumulate in more alkaline compartments which act as traps for their relatively impermeant anions. The experimentally established order of such passive permeation is $IAAH > ABAH > GAH_1 = GAH_3$ (Rubery, 1980; Nour and Rubery, 1984). Saturable high affinity uptake carriers for these three hormones have also been described in tissue segments and cultured cells, and in endomembrane vesicles for IAA (Hertel et al., 1983). Their K_m values suggest that the carriers could dominate penetration at the low concentrations at which hormones act (Nour and Rubery, 1984; Astle and Rubery, 1985a). For auxin, in vitro experiments with vesicles show that the uptake carrier is more accumulative than the simple IAAH diffusion/anion trap mechanism and may involve electro-impelled co-transport of IAA$^-$ with more than one H$^+$ (Lomax et al., 1985). The mechanism of the ABA carriers has not yet been studied in vitro, where there are no compartmentation complications and transport driving forces can be manipulated by ionophores and monitored by probes. The available evidence is consistent with an electroneutral 1:1 H$^+$/ABA anion symport (Astle and Rubery, 1983). For auxin, but not detectable for ABA and GA, there is also a carrier for the anion, probably also electro-impelled (Rubery, 1979; Astle and Rubery, 1983; Sabater and Rubery, in preparation), which catalyses IAA$^-$ efflux down the electrochemical gradient set up by the accumulative uptake mechanism. This efflux carrier is strongly antagonised by substances such as NPA which inhibit polar auxin transport.

The central proposal of the chemiosmotic theory of polar auxin transport is as follows. The asymmetry giving rise to polarity in, for example, longitudinal basipetal transport, is that at cellular junctions the plasma membrane at the basal end of the "upper" cell has a higher IAA$^-$ permeability relative to IAAH than does the apical end of the "lower cell": provided that the energising transmembrane electrical and pH gradients are metabolically maintained, polar transport will occur — with movement from cell-to-cell via the cell wall because of the high intrinsic membrane permeability of IAAH (Rubery and Sheldrake, 1974; Rubery, 1980). The postulated asymmetry could be achieved in various ways: preferential basal distribution of the efflux carrier or apical distribution of the influx carrier in individual cells (Rubery, 1980); or for short range transport, by carrier density being uniform in each cell but decreasing in a regular way down a file of cells (Milborrow and Rubery, 1985). The action of efflux carrier inhibitors and preliminary immunohistochemical evidence (Jacobs and Gilbert, 1983; Jacobs and Short, 1986) favour the first possibility, but in any event it is clear that the direction of polar transport is determined by the distribution of catalysts rather than by gross driving force gradients (Rubery, 1986). When Mitchison's mathematical analysis of the chemiosmotic hypothesis (Mitchison, 1980b) is used to compare simulation with observation (Table 1), it predicts the apical/basal polarity ratio of individual cells to be about 5-10, with an average carrier density sufficient to give auxin anion permeability coefficients of the same order as the observed velocity of polar transport (1 cm h^{-1}; 3 x 10^{-4} cm s^{-1}).

Table 1   Simulation of IAA Polar Transport Velocity.

| | Velocity (cm h^{-1}) | | | |
	P_A-(base/apex)=10		P_A-(base/apex)=5	
pH(wall)	E=-60mV	E=-120mV	E=-60mV	E=-120mV
6.0	0.77	2.09	0.55	1.39
5.5	1.34	2.41	0.84	1.55
5.0	1.74	2.53	1.05	1.61
4.5	1.92	2.57	1.13	1.63
4.0	1.99	2.58	1.16	1.64

Parameters: pH$_{inside}$=7.0; cell length = 0.01cm; temp = 298K;
Peremability coefficient of netural IAAH = 10^{-3} cm s^{-1};
Permeability coefficient of IAA$^-$ at cell apex (P_A-) = 10^{-4} cm s^{-1};
Diffusion coefficient of IAA in solution = 6.7 x 10^{-6} cm^2 s^{-1}.
Equations used for simulation from Mitchison (1980b).

This contrasts with the small polarity ratio which emerged from Leopold and Hall's, (1966) earlier and less specific analysis (of the polar secretion hypothesis) but is broadly consistent with the labelling patterns observed by Jacobs.

ASSESSMENT OF TARGETS FOR MANIPULATION

This brief account of auxin transport enables a systematic list of targets for manipulation to be compiled and assessed. ABA transport will be considered in the final section.

1. Transport catalysts:
    (a) activity;
    (b) capacity or level;
    (c) distribution in the plasma membrane.

2. Availability of auxin as substrate.

3. Driving forces for transport:
    (a) pH gradients;
    (b) electrical gradients;
    (c) temperature.

Equations are available which permit computer simulation of the effects of these variables on the steady state accumulation ratio (Rubery, 1980; Goldsmith and Goldsmith, 1981) and polar transport velocity of auxin (Mitchison, 1980b). Of the targets listed, catalyst activity is in principle most susceptible to relatively specific manipulation and will be considered first and in some detail.

1(a) Transport Catalyst Activity – Auxin Transport Inhibitors

Substances which inhibit the auxin efflux carrier are some of the longest-known and potentially most useful and specific chemical probes available for developmental studies. The first recognised inhibitor of polar auxin transport was 2,3,5-triiodobenzoic acid (TIBA) (Niedergang-Kamien and Skoog, 1956), although fluorescein inhibition of seedling gravitropism may be the earliest documented effect of such inhibitors (Boas and Merkenschlagen, 1925).

A large number of variously well-characterised auxin transport inhibitors is now known, with their effects realisable in whole plants (Morris et al., 1973), plant segments (Depta and Rubery, 1984), cultured cells (Rubery and Sheldrake, 1974) and plasma membrane-enriched vesicles (Hertel et al., 1983). Katekar has analysed their structure-activity relations and coined the term "phytotropin" (Katekar and Geissler, 1980) to refer to compounds which (a) interfere with tropic response; (b) have a 2- carboxyphenyl group separated from a second aromatic ring by a conjugated system; (c) inhibit polar auxin transport; (d) interfere with apical dominance. On this definition, NPA is a phytotropin but morphactins (based on fluorene-9-carboxylates) and TIBA are not, since criterion (b) is not met. For convenience, polar auxin transport inhibitors will be collectively abbreviated to PATIS. Morphactins were named as morphologically active substances (Schneider, 1970) and have a wider range of morphogenetic effects than NPA, for example. TIBA does not compete well for the NPA receptor (Sussman and Gardner, 1980), and unlike NPA, is itself weakly polarly transported and only abolishes root gravitropism at strongly growth-inhibitory concentrations (Katekar and Geissler, 1980). Nevertheless, morphactins compete for the NPA receptor (Thompson and Leopold, 1974; Sussman and Goldsmith, 1981) as do fluorescein and its brominated derivative eosin (Sussman and Goldsmith, 1981) which inhibit polar auxin transport as well as tropisms. Thus phytotropins, morphactin and fluorescein share a common binding site and possibly a common mode of action in their inhibition of auxin transport. Auxins themselves are poor competitors for this phytotropin receptor in its native membrane-bound state, although they have increased affinity for the solubilised protein (Sussman and Gardner, 1980). Also NPA (and TIBA) are non-competitive inhibitors of polar auxin transport (Depta et al., 1983). It therefore seems likely that these transport inhibitors bind to a regulatory site different from the substrate site and which could reside on a separate regulatory subunit, either permanently associated with the catalytic subunit of the efflux carrier or capable of interacting with it if the proteins are mobile in the membrane. A two-site model (Depta and Rubery, 1984) has been proposed to resolve the apparent paradox of TIBA being a noncompetitive inhibitor and yet a substrate of the polar transport system.

PATIS have found some commercial applications. For instance, they modify branching patterns in fruit trees and act as growth retardants (Schneider, 1970). Indeed TIBA was categorised as a growth retardant rather than a herbicide in a chemical warfare programme during World War II (Kraus and Mitchell, 1947). TIBA also promotes abscission, most effectively of all the possible 2,3,5 halogenated (Cl, Br, I) benzoic acids (Weintraub et al., 1952), but plants can recover from TIBA spraying and produce fruit. Applied auxin showed its usual opposition to abscission and antagonised the TIBA effect (Weintraub et al., 1952), which later work suggests is due to inhibition of auxin transport from the leaf to its abscission zone. Many of the effects of PATIS could reflect auxin starvation by transport inhibition although alteration of metabolism may also contribute to observed reduced auxin levels (e.g. Audus and Thresh, 1956). Morphactins in particular seem to have effects independent of auxin transport inhibition (eg Bridges and Wilkins, 1973a) and side effects of TIBA have been reported (Jacobson and Jacobson, 1981). The effects of auxin being so pleiomorphic, it is difficult to establish a clear causal chain between local hormone deprivation and the possibly far-reaching consequences of PATIS application. For example, TIBA caused changes in the growth pattern of tomato apices which resulted in formation of hollow stems with a double vascular system (Wardlaw, 1953). However, apparently curious effects of PATIS may reflect unexpected patterns of auxin transport. Thus morphactins inhibit lateral root development in pea seedlings, stimulating pericycle cell division but preventing outgrowth (Schneider, 1970), while auxin applied to the shoot tip accumulates in lateral root primordia and does not proceed to the primary root apex (Rowntree and Morris, 1979) (nor apparently to "dominated" lateral buds [Hall and Hillman, 1975] or shoots [Morris, 1977]).

The effects of PATIS to interfere with tropisms (Katekar and Geissler, 1980) and apical dominance (e.g. Panigrahi and Audus, 1966) are sometimes used as evidence for a dominant role of auxin and auxin transport in these processes. This approach has attracted criticism (e.g. Firn and Tamimi, 1986; Hillman, 1986) and deserves further comment.

Effects of PATIS on tropisms
Decapitated hypocotyls are graviresponsive (Firn et al., 1981), as are longitudinally bisected hypocotyls whose half-cylinders grow faster when their epidermis is downward oriented (Copeland, 1900; Firn and Digby, 1977). Such observations straddle the promulgation of the "Cholodny-Went Theory" and warn against allowing apical dominance of our thinking although, as Hart and MacDonald (1984) argue, some role for the shoot apex in generation of a basipetally mobile signal is difficult completely to dismiss. The half-cylinder experiments imply that wholesale lateral redistribution of auxin is as unnecessary to hypocotyl gravitropism as it is to that of grass nodes (Bridges and Wilkins, 1973b; Osborne and Wright, 1977). The relevance of the real but small trans-organ auxin gradients that can sometimes (but not always) be observed to follow gravistimulation (Mertens and Weiler, 1983; Migliaccio and Rayle, 1984) has often been doubted because of expectations of larger changes aroused by the shapes of dose-response curves: the usual riposte is "compartmentation", argued to give larger local concentration changes in the vicinity of receptors than the bulk changes observed (see Table 2 below).

It has been stated that inhibition of gravitropism by PATIS does not prove that polar auxin transport is directly linked to tropisms (Firn and Tamimi, 1986). One

164

Table 2   Calculated IAA Redistribution After Wall Acidification

IAA concentration (µM)			
pH(wall)	[IAA](cytop)	[IAA](wall)	[IAA](vacuole)
6.0	81.3	8.5	1.26
5.8	83.8	5.7	1.30
5.4	86.6	2.7	1.34
5.0	87.7	1.4	1.40

Parameters: Total [IAA] = 10µM;
respective volume fractions of cytoplasm (pH7), vacuole (pH5),
and wall are 0.1, 0.8, and 0.1.
Calculation from equation giving IAA partition between two
compartments, assuming anion impermeability (Rubery, 1980).

general argument against polar transport delivering a growth regulatory auxin supply is that application of PATIS just below the apical hook of intact seedlings had little effect on hypocotyl elongation unless growth was first stimulated by applying exogenous NAA to the apex (Tamimi and Firn, 1985; Firn and Tamimi, 1986). However, it was not established whether the apical tissue above the block was a major source of endogenous IAA - the stem and root tissue below the block contain differentiating xylem and are presumably therefore sources of IAA (Sheldrake, 1973) which would ascend in the transpiration stream with possible lateral transfer to phloem and the basipetal polar auxin transport pathway. Another argument is that morphactin inhibits grass node gravicurvature, where trans-organ lateral auxin transport is clearly excluded by experiment (Bridges and Wilkins, 1973b; Osborne and Wright, 1977) and where metabolic increases in auxin content occur in the lower half of the node (Osborne and Wright, 1977).

However auxin need not undergo classical polar transport for changes in its distribution to figure in models of tropic responses. Local auxin concentration changes could result if light and gravity differentially alter transport driving forces (pH and electrical gradients) or the distribution of regulators like Ca^{2+} or of endogenous phytotropins. There are good theoretical and experimental grounds for believing that PATIS will alter auxin compartmentation by virtue of disturbing the transport steady state via inhibition of the efflux carrier. The stimulation of net auxin uptake by PATIS is long-established (e.g. Rubery and Sheldrake, 1974). In a tissue, those cells which contain the plasma membrane efflux carrier (not necessarily asymmetrically distributed) would increase the IAA sink capacity of their cytoplasmic compartment in response to PATIS and a fixed amount of auxin would redistribute to take account of this. Cell wall concentrations around the responding cells (probably the vascular parenchyma (Wangermann, 1977) would decrease most sharply (compare Table 2) because of the wall's low relative volume and pH (Rubery, 1984).

This local draining of the wall could in turn draw in IAA from neighbouring cells, including the graviresponsive epidermis, because of its high membrane permeability. Such diffusive transport can be fast over the short distances involved. Also if the auxin receptors responsible for stimulation of proton extrusion face outward as Löbler and Klämbts, (1985) work with antibodies implies, then the differential wall acidification which may determine dicot tropic curvatures (Migliaccio and Rayle, 1984; Mulkey and Evans, 1981) could be smoothed out by the combined effects of

PATIS and decreased external pH to deplete the wall of auxin (Table 2). It is usually observed that PATIS have little effect on straight elongation growth.

Clearly, in the unlikely event that auxins have nothing to do with tropic responses, the anti-tropic effects of the many different PATIS (Katekar and Geissler, 1980) would have to result from various side effects, or from modulation of a yet-undiscovered process common to auxin transport and tropisms (Firn and Tamimi, 1986).

Effects of PATIS on apical dominance

Since the "direct" theory of auxin inhibition of lateral buds was proposed, more recent work (summarised by Hillman, 1984, 1986) has shown the role of auxin in the maintenance and release of apical dominance to be more complex and probably less central and direct than earlier envisaged. The "nutritional" class of theory is now leading to a greater emphasis on possible hormonal control of transport flows and distribution patterns of metabolites, ions, and water. The stimulation of lateral bud outgrowth by PATIS is correspondingly more difficult to interpret than when axillary bud activity was regarded as closely controlled by auxin supply. However treatment of the stem with PATIS is not just a chemical version of apex surgery, which does not remove all sources of endogenous auxin transportable through the stem (e.g. IAA made by differentiating xylem - Sheldrake, 1973), and the accelerated elongation of new side shoots brought about by PATIS is often followed by their abscission (e.g. White and Hillman, 1972). The reason for this is unknown, but the depletion of auxin in the stem together with the new production of auxin from the expanding bud could perhaps favour abscission. In possibly similar circumstances, Rubinstein and Leopold (1963) found that the effect of applying NAA to debladed beans petioles depended on for how long the stem/petiole explants had been removed from the parent plant - after 12 hours, inhibition of abscission had given way to acceleration.

Are there natural phytotropins?

The morphine/endorphin precedent has often been optimistically invoked, but there are currently only indirect hints that endogenous PATIS exist. Leopold and Guernsey (1953) found that application of flowering Coleus apices, or extracts therefrom, to decapitated vegetative Coleus stems could alter their strong basipetal polar auxin transport to the weaker polarity characteristic of flowering stems and suggested that an endogenous inhibitor was responsible.

Tomato seedlings whose phenolic content had been elevated by root-feeding with the non-toxic precursor quinic acid were morphologically dwarfed and had a many-fold higher auxin content than controls. This was attributed (Marigo and Boudet, 1977; Marigo, 1979) to the ability of phenolic compounds to inhibit both IAA polar transport to the roots and oxidative IAA destruction (for which roots have the major capacity). These data, and the work of Stenlid (1976) who found both stimulatory and inhibitory effects of phenolics on polar auxin transport, suggest that phenylpropanoid and flavonoid derivatives are worth further investigation as potential endogenous transport regulators. The herbicide glyphosate (N-phosphono-methylglycine) and β-aminooxyphenylpropionic acid which are potent inhibitors of entry to the phenylpropanoid pathways (respective targets: 5-enoylpyruvoylshikimic acid-3-phosphate synthetase and phenylalanine ammonia lyase) could be useful tools in such a study. Indeed, glyphosate has been reported to inhibit polar auxin transport in corn and cotton (Baur, 1979).

1(b) Manipulation of Transport Catalyst Capacity or Level

Effects of plant hormones on polar auxin transport

The effect of auxin itself to maintain and induce polar auxin transport will be dealt with separately in (2) below. Of the major hormones, the inhibitory effect of ethene has been most extensively studied, originally in the context of ethene-auxin antagonism in abscission (perspective given by Sexton et al., 1985). Not only can ethene pretreatment severely inhibit polar auxin transport (e.g. Morgan et al., 1968), but its acceleration of abscission is synergised by PATIS (Morgan and Durham, 1972). Species differ greatly in their sensitivity to ethene (Morgan et al., 1968) but some hours of pretreatment of whole plants (Burg and Burg, 1967) or excised segments (Osborne and Mullins, 1968) appears obligatory for polar auxin transport to be inhibited. Auxin transport slowly recovers after ethene removal (Beyer, 1973). This type of behaviour suggests that ethene may be acting to reduce the level of auxin carriers in the plasma membrane, perhaps by regulating gene expression or intracellular protein traffic. The ethene inhibition can be reversed by its antagonist 2,5-norbornadiene (Sisler et al., 1985).

Only fragmentary data are available for other hormones. GA pretreatment has been reported to increase the velocity of auxin transport (Pilet, 1965; Palmer and Halsall, 1969) whereas ABA (Pilet 1971; Naqvi and Engvild 1974) and 6-benzylamino-purine (Harrison, 1982) can inhibit.

This is potentially an important area where further investigations, including use of in vitro vesicle transport and ligand or antibody binding could be invaluable.

Effects of gene expression inhibitors
Inhibition of protein synthesis is obviously a blunt instrument, but could result in proteins with a relatively rapid turnover rate being differentially decreased in level. As an example of this approach, Morris and Rubery (1985) found that a 2-3 hour exposure of zucchini hypocotyl segments to cycloheximide or MDMP could reduce the sensitivity of auxin anion efflux to NPA inhibition without apparently altering the activity of the efflux carrier itself. Further experimentation is needed to determine whether this behaviour, which is also observed in vesicles prepared from treated tissue (M. Sabater and P.H. Rubery, unpublished), reflects selective loss of a discrete NPA receptor or whether some less direct perturbation is responsible.

1(c) Transport Catalyst Distribution in the Plasma Membrane

We expect the polarity of established auxin transport to reflect asymmetric carrier distribution (see ELEMENTS section). However, we do not understand how polarity arises developmentally and we are still too ignorant of plant cell membrane dynamics to enable us to identify specific target processes whose manipulation could abolish or redirect transport polarity by carrier redistribution. Membrane electrophoresis in response to a voltage gradient would require lateral protein mobility in the plasma membrane – which should not be taken for granted because of possible restrictions by the cell wall or the cytoskeleton. (There is no direct evidence bearing on this point for turgid, wall cells as opposed to protoplasts). We need a much greater knowledge of the insertion, mobility, and removal of plasma membrane proteins – for instance is there any contribution of endocytosis? The effects of drugs which interfere with membrane protein traffic, such as tunicamycin and monensin, could usefully be explored.

2 Manipulation of Substrate Supply

Auxin can oppose the decline in polar transport capacity that occurs in decapitated stems (Leopold and Lam, 1962) or isolated sections (Rayle et al., 1969). The mechanism is unknown. The stimulation of electrogenic H^+ excretion by auxin is potentially autocatalytic for transport, but may not share the same tissue distribution. Effects on the level or distribution of transport proteins or regulators could be involved, especially in longer term studies (Leopold and Lam, 1962).

One of the main processes in higher plant development is the ability of auxin, not simply to maintain existing polar transport, but to induce new routes, leaving freshly differentiated vascular tissue in its wake. Auxin supply was found to be the limiting factor in vascular regeneration in wounded Coleus stems (e.g. W.P. Jacobs, 1952), and this approach was extended by Sachs in an elegantly simple series of investigations combining particular wounding patterns with localised

167

auxin applications (e.g. Sachs, 1975). A hypothesis was formulated whereby auxin is a signal for vascular differentiation which is transported polarly by a pathway whose capacity for transport increases with use, so canalising signal flow and subsequent differentiation (Sachs, 1978). Mitchison (1980a) analysed this flow facilitation concept mathematically by allowing the diffusion constant of the signal to increase with its flux through cell interfaces, the chemiosmotic polar diffusion theory (Rubery and Sheldrake, 1974; Rubery, 1980) providing a suitable mechanistic framework. The model successfully simulates the natural and experimentally-induced patterns of leaf vein formation, including discrete stands, branches, and closed loops.

Disruption of polar transport by TIBA also leads to alterations in xylogenesis which reflect damming of the auxin supply. For example, Morey and Cronshaw (1968) found that Acer rubrum seedlings ringed with TIBA showed enhanced tracheary element differentiation above the blockage whereas distally, cambial division and tracheary element initiation were reduced together with the formation of a ring of tension wood and activation of axillary buds at the node. TIBA was also found to alter in vitro xylogenesis by isolated suspension cultured mesophyll cells of Zinnia elegans: cell wall thickening was inhibited and the cells adopted a polar growth pattern, developing bulbous tips (Burgess and Linstead, 1984). It was suggested that the stimulus for differentiation could be a TIBA-sensitive self-generated flux of auxin through the individual cells.

3(a,b) Manipulation of pH and Electrical Gradients

An intuition that polar transport velocity would increase with pH and electrical gradients across the plasma membrane is reinforced by simulation of Mitchison's (1980b) equations. Some examples are given in Table 1 above, where a trade off in velocity sensitivity between external pH and membrane potential may be noted. Lack of specificity and difficulties of measuring putative pH and voltage changes in the polar transport pathway makes experimental testing of those predictions difficult, and only rather crude approaches have so far been possible. Scott and Batra (1973) found that pH 4.0 buffer promoted polar IAA transport by maize roots. Hasenstein and Rayle (1984) measured basal auxin movement through 5 mm (t=0) coleoptile sections after exposure for 2 hours to pH 4 and pH 8 buffers. The velocity was slow (5 mm/h in water controls) but decreased from 4.6 to 3.9 mm/h when the pH was raised. Neither acropetal transport nor IAA metabolism were studied. Fusicoccin decreased velocity to 4 mm/h, perhaps unexpectedly in view of its stimulation of electrogenic H^+ efflux. However interpretation is complicated by the substantial increase in segment length (36% compared to 20% for pH 4 buffer) since polar transport rate is predicted (Mitchison, 1980b) and observed (Wangermann and Mitchison, 1981) to vary inversely with cell length.

Morris (1980) found that basipetal transport of auxin applied to the apex of intact pea plants could be completely blocked in a 50 mm length of the stem by a 9.0 V electrical potential (current = 15 to 20 μA). The blockage was reversible and without apparent damage to the plants, even after 3 days, but was independent of electrical polarity. Changes in extracellular pH and membrane depolarisation were suggested as contributory mechanisms but no measurements were attempted. This experiment raises more questions than it answers, but in the context of this Chapter it would be interesting to study the effect of such treatment on apical dominance and tropisms.

A striking recent observation concerns the morphogenetic effects of weak currents (1 μA for 21 d) to increase the growth of solid tobacco callus tissue, provided IAA was present in the agar medium which had to be electrically positive with respect to the callus. TIBA abolished the effect, suggesting that IAA from the medium was polarly moved into the tissue using a transport pathway somehow aligned by the electrical gradient (Goldsworthy and Rathore, 1985).

3(c) Temperature Manipulation

Since molecular motion is driven by heat, cellular processes will be temperature sensitive. However, as with the other nonspecific treatments discussed, there may be some scope for manipulative exploitation of differential effects. For example, Morris (1979) constructed Arrhenius plots of reciprocal temperature versus log auxin transport rate and found discontinuities for chill-sensitive cotton and sunflower plants, but not for chill-tolerant alaska peas. Membrane composition is the most likely physical basis for the difference.

MANIPULATION OF ABA TRANSPORT

Polar transport of ABA has not been clearly established, but could operate over shorter distances than is the case for IAA (Astle and Rubery, 1980; Milborrow and Rubery, 1985). Its uptake by ABAH diffusion, or by the carrier present in the elongating zone of roots and in cultured runner bean cells, is pH gradient driven. There appears to be no significant electrically responsive transport component (Astle and Rubery, 1983, 1985a). A physiological role for the carrier is not yet established, but its tissue location suggests that it could facilitate and channel ABA access to the cells responsible for the extent and direction of root growth (Milborrow and Rubery, 1985).

A number of substances can inhibit the ABA carrier, which is specific for (S)ABA (Milborrow and Rubery, 1985; Astle and Rubery, 1986). These include methyl jasmonate (Astle and Rubery, 1985b), methyl and phenyl ABA esters, and α- and β-ionone (Astle and Rubery, 1986). Methyl jasmonate is a partial inhibitor (but not a substrate) of the carrier which may bind to a regulatory site at the outer face of the plasma membrane. The methyl ester reversibly and completely inhibits, again externally, and is suggested to form an abortive complex at the active site which is incapable of translocation. β-Ionone is a particularly potent inhibitor, exerting half-maximal inhibition well below the carrier's K_m (Astle and Rubery, 1986).

Use of these substances as tools has not yet been explored, although the occurrence of any physiological effects independent of ABA transport inhibition (which is probably the case for methyljasmonate) would complicate interpretation. Although carrier participation has not been explored, the regulation of stomatal aperture is an attractive target for manipulation of ABA transport since ABA movement between cytoplasm and wall may be linked to pH changes, and there is evidence for a high affinity ABA binding site in the stomatal complex, which, unlike the carrier, is not inhibited by (S)methyl ABA (Hornberg and Weiler, 1984).

REFERENCES

Astle, M.C. and Rubery, P.H. (1980). A study of abscisic acid uptake by proximal and distal root segments of Phaseolus coccineus L. Planta 150, 312-320.

Astle, M.C. and Rubery, P.H. (1983). Carriers for abscisic acid and indole-3-acetic acid in primary roots: their regional localisation and thermodynamic driving forces. Planta 157, 53-63.

Astle, M.C. and Rubery, P.H. (1985a). Uptake of ABA by suspension-cultured Phaseolus coccineus L. cells: evidence for carrier participation. Journal of Experimental Botany 36, 469-484.

Astle, M.C. and Rubery, P.H. (1985b). Modulation of carrier-mediated uptake of abscisic acid by methyl jasmonate in Phaseolus coccineus L. Planta 166, 252-258.

Astle, M.C. and Rubery, P.H. (1986). Carrier-mediate ABA uptake by suspension-cultured Phaseolus coccineus L. cells: stereospecificity and inhibition by ionones and ABA esters. Journal of Experimental Botany, In Press.

Audus, L.J. and Thresh, R. (1956). The effects of synthetic growth regulator treatments on the levels of free endogenous growth-substances in plants. Annals of Botany (New Series) 20, 439-459.

Baur, J.R. (1979). Effect of glyphosate on auxin transport in corn and cotton tissues. Plant Physiology 63, 882-886.

Beyer, E.M. Jr. (1973). Support for a rôle of ethylene modification of auxin transport. Plant Physiology 52, 1-5.

Boas, F. and Merkenschlagen, F. (1925). Reizverlust, hervorgerufen durch Eosin. Berichte der Deutschen Botanischen Gessellschaft 43, 381-390.

Bridges, I.G. and Wilkins, M.B. (1973a). Effects of morphactin on IAA transport, growth and geotropic response in cereal coleoptiles. Journal of Experimental Botany 24, 711-723.

Bridges, I.G. and Wilkins, M.B. (1973b). Growth initiation in the geotropic response of the wheat node. Planta 112, 191-200.

Burg, S.P. and Burg, E.A. (1967). Inhibition of polar auxin transport by ethylene. Plant Physiology 42, 1224-1228.

Burgess, J. and Linstead, P. (1984). In vitro tracheary element formation: structural studies and the effect of tri-iodobenzoic acid. Planta 160, 481-489.

Copeland, E.B. (1900). Studies on the geotropism of stems. Botanical Gazette 29, 185-196.

Depta, H., Eisele, K.H., and Hertel, R. (1983). Specific inhibition of auxin transport: action on tissue segments and in vitro binding to membranes from maize coleoptiles. Plant Science Letters 31, 181-192.

Depta, H. and Rubery, P.H. (1984). A comparative study of carrier participation in the transport of 2,3,5-triiodobenzoic acid, indole-3-acetic acid, and 2,4-dichlorophenoxyacetic acid by Cucurbita pepo L. hypocotyl segments. Journal of Plant Physiology 115, 371-387.

Firn, R.D. and Digby, J. (1977). The role of the peripheral cell layers in the geotropic curvature of sunflower hypocotyls: A new model of shoot geotropism. Australian Journal of Plant Physiology 4, 337-347.

Firn, R.D., Digby, J., and Hall, A. (1981). The rôle of the shoot apex in geotropism. Plant, Cell and Environment 4, 125-129.

Firn, R. and Tamimi, S. (1986). Auxin transport and shoot tropisms: the need for precise models. In "Plant Growth Substances 1985" (M. Bopp ed.), pp 236-240. Springer, Heidelberg.

Goldsmith, M.H.M. and Goldsmith, T.H. (1981). Quantitative predictions for the chemiosmotic uptake of auxin. Planta 153, 25-33.

Goldsworthy, A. and Rathore, K.S. (1985). The electrical control of growth in plant tissue cultures: the polar transport of auxin. Journal of Experimental Botany 36, 1134-1141.

170

Hall, S.M. and Hillman, J.R. (1975). Correlative inhibition of lateral bud growth in Phaseolus vulgaris L. Timing of bud growth following decapitation. Planta 123, 137-143.

Harrison, M. (1982). The role of cytokinin and auxin transport in apical dominance. Plant Physiology 69, supplement, abstract 206.

Hart, J.W. and MacDonald, I.R. (1984). Is there a rôle for the apex in shoot geotropism? Plant Physiology 74, 272-277.

Hasenstein, K.-H. and Rayle, D.L. (1984) Cell wall pH and auxin transport velocity. Plant Physiology 76, 65-67.

Hertel, R., Lomax, T.L., and Briggs, W.R. (1983). Auxin transport in membrane vesicles from Cucurbita pepo L. Planta 157, 193-201.

Hillman, J.R. (1984). Apical Dominance. In "Advanced Plant Physiology" (M.B. Wilkins ed.), pp 127-148. Pitman, London.

Hillman, J.R. (1986) Apical dominance and correlations by hormones. In "Plant Growth Substances 1985" (M. Bopp ed.), pp 341-349. Springer, Heidelberg.

Hornberg, C. and Weiler, E.W. (1984). High-affinity binding sites for abscisic acid on the plasmalemma of Vicia faba guard cells. Nature (London) 310, 321-324.

Jacobs, M. and Gilbert, S.F. (1983). Basal localization of the presumptive auxin transport carrier in pea stem cells. Science 220, 1297-1300.

Jacobs, M. and Short, T.W. (1986). Further characterisation of the presumptive auxin transport carrier using monoclonal antibodies. In "Plant Growth Substances 1985" (M. Bopp ed.), pp 218-226. Springer, Heidelberg.

Jacobs, W.P. (1952). The rôle of auxin in differentiation of xylem around a wound. American Journal of Botany 39, 301-309.

Jacobson, A. and Jacobson, L. (1981). Inhibitory effects of 2,3,5-triiodobenzoic acid on ion absorption, respiration, and carbon-metabolism in excised barley roots. Plant Physiology 67, 282-286.

Katekar, G.F. and Geissler, A.E. (1980). Auxin transport inhibitors IV. Evidence of a common mode of action for a proposed class of auxin transport inhibitors: the phytotropins. Plant Physiology 66, 1190-1195.

Kraus, E.J. and Mitchell, J.W. (1947). Growth-regulating substances as herbicides. Botanical Gazette 108, 301-349.

Leopold, A.C. and Guernsey, F.S. (1953). Auxin polarity in the Coleus plant. Botanical Gazette 115, 147-154.

Leopold, A.C. and Hall, O.F. (1966). A mathematical model of polar auxin transport. Plant Physiology 41, 1476-1480.

Leopold, A.C. and Lam, S.L. (1962). The auxin transport gradient. Physiologia Plantarum 15, 631-638.

Löbler, M. and Klämbt, D. (1985). Auxin-binding protein from coleoptile membranes of corn. II Localization of a putative auxin receptor. Journal of Biological Chemistry 260, 9854-9859.

Lomax, T.L., Mehlhorn, R.J., and Briggs, W.R. (1985). Active auxin uptake by zucchini membrane vesicles: quantitation using ESR volume and pH determinations. Proceedings of the National Academy of Sciences (USA) **82**, 6541-6545.

Marigo, G. (1979). Polyphenols et croissance végétale. Essai d'evaluation du rôle joué in vivo par les composés phénolques chez Lycopersicum esculentum. Thèse pour Docteur d'état, l'Université Paul Sabatier, Toulouse.

Marigo, G. and Boudet, A.M. (1977). Relations polyphénols-croissance. Mise en évidence d'un effet inhibiteur des composés phénoliques sur le transport polarisé de l'auxine. Physiologia Plantarum **41**, 197-202.

Mertens, R. and Weiler, E.W. (1983). Kinetic studies on redistribution of endogenous growth regulators in gravireacting plant organs. Planta **158**, 339-348.

Migliaccio, F. and Rayle, D.L. (1984). Sequence of key events in shoot geotropism. Plant Physiology **75**, 78-81

Milborrow, B.V. and Rubery, P.H. (1985). The specificity of the carrier-mediated uptake of ABA by root segments of Phaseolus coccineus L. Journal of Experimental Botany **36**, 807-822.

Mitchison, G.J. (1980a). A model for vein formation in higher plants. Proceedings of the Royal Society of London B. **207**, 79-109.

Mitchison, G.J. (1980b). The dynamics of auxin transport. Proceedings of the Royal Society of London B. **209**, 489-511.

Morey, P.R. and Cronshaw, J. (1968). Developmental changes in the secondary xylem of Acer rubrum induced by various auxins and 2,3,5-triiodobenzoic acid. Protoplasma **65**, 287-313.

Morgan, P.W., Beyer, E. Jr. and Gausman, H.W. (1968). Ethylene effects on auxin physiology. In "Biochemistry and Physiology of Plant Growth Substances" (F. Wightman and G. Setterfield eds.), pp 1255-1273. Runge, Ottawa.

Morgan, P.W. and Durham, J.I. (1972). Abscission: potentiating effect of auxin transport inhibitors. Plant Physiology **50**, 313-318.

Morris, D.A. (1977). Transport of exogenous auxin in two-branched pea seedlings. Planta **107**, 171-182.

Morris, D.A. (1979). The effect of temperature on the velocity of exogenous auxin transport in intact chilling-sensitive and chilling-resistant plants. Planta **146**, 603-605.

Morris, D.A. (1980). The influence of small direct electric currents in the transport of auxin in intact plants. Planta **150**, 431-434.

Morris, D.A., Kadir, G.O., and Barry, A.J. (1973). Auxin transport in intact pea seedlings (Pisum sativum L.). The inhibition of transport by 2,3,5-triiodobenzoic acid. Planta **110**, 173-182.

Morris, D.A. and Rubery, P.H. (1985). Effects of translation inhibitors on NPA-sensitive auxin net-uptake and efflux by Cucurbita pepo hypocotyl segments. Plant Physiology **77**, supplement, abstract 18.

Mulkey, T.J. and Evans, M.L. (1981). Geotropism in corn roots: evidence for its mediation by differential acid efflux. Science **212**, 70-71.

172

Naqvi, S.M. and Engvild, K.C. (1974). Action of abscisic acid on auxin transport and its relation to phototropism. Physiologia Plantarum 30, 283-287.

Niedergang-Kamien, E. and Skoog, F. (1956). Studies on polarity and auxin transport in plants. I. Modification of polarity and auxin transport by triiodobenzoic acid. Physiologia Plantarum 9, 60-73.

Nour, J.M. and Rubery, P.H. (1984). The uptake of gibberellin A_1 by suspension-cultured Spinacia oleracea cells has a carrier-mediated component. Planta 160, 436-443.

Osborne, D.J. and Mullins, M.G. (1968). Auxin, ethylene, and kinetin in a carrier-protein system for the polar transport of auxin in petiole segments of Phaseolus vulgaris. New Phytologist 68, 977-991.

Osborne, D.J. and Wright, M. (1977). Gravity-induced cell elongation. Proceedings of the Royal Society of London B. 199, 551-564.

Palmer, J.H. and Halsall, D.M. (1969). Effect of transverse gravity stimulation, gibberellin and indoleacetic acid upon polar transport of IAA^{C14} in the stem of Helianthus annuus. Physiologia Plantarum 22, 59-67.

Panigrahi, B.M. and Andus, L.J. (1966). Apical dominance in Vicia faba. Annals of Botany (New Series) 30, 457-473.

Pilet, P-E. (1965). Action of gibberellic acid on auxin transport. Nature (London) 208, 1344-1345.

Pilet, P-E. (1971). Abscisic acid action on basipetal auxin transport. Physiologia Plantarum 25, 28-31.

Rayle, D.L., Ouitrakul, R., and Hertel, R. (1969). Effects of auxins on the auxin transport system in coleoptiles. Planta 87, 49-53.

Rowntree, R.A. and Morris, D.A. (1979). Accumulation of ^{14}C from exogenous labelled auxin in lateral root primordia of intact pea seedlings (Pisum sativum L.). Planta 144, 463-466.

Rubery, P.H. (1979) The effects of 2,4-dinitrophenol and chemical modifying reagents on auxin transport by suspension-cultured crown gall cells. Planta 144, 173-178.

Rubery, P.H. (1980). The mechanism of transmembrane auxin transport and its relation to the chemiosmotic hypothesis of the polar transport of auxin. In "Plant Growth Substances 1979" (F. Skoog ed.), pp 50-60. Springer, Heidelberg.

Rubery, P.H. (1984). Auxin binding and membrane transport in relation to auxin action and transport. In "Membranes and Compartmentation in the Regulation of Plant Functions" (A.M. Boudet, G. Alibert, G. Marigo, P.J. Lea eds.). Annual Proceedings of the Phytochemical Society of Europe. pp 267-282. Clarendon, Oxford.

Rubery, P.H. (1986). The evolution of polar transport models. In "Plant Growth Substances 1985" (M. Bopp ed.), pp 197-202. Springer, Heidelberg.

Rubery, P.H. and Sheldrake, A.R. (1974). Carrier-mediated auxin transport. Planta 118, 101-121.

Rubinstein, B. and Leopold, A.C. (1963). Analysis of the auxin control of bean leaf abscission. Plant Physiology 38, 262-267.

Sachs, T. (1975).   The induction of transport channels by auxin.   Planta 127, 201-206.

Sachs, T. (1978).   Patterned differentiation in plants.   Differentiation 11, 65.

Schneider, G. (1970).   Morphactins: physiology and performance.   Annual Review of Plant Physiology 21, 499-536.

Scott, T.K. and Batra, M. (1973).   Effect of pH on auxin transport in the roots of Zea mays L.   Plant Physiology 51, supplement, abstract 68.

Sexton, R., Lewis, L.N., Trewavas, A.J., and Kelly, P. (1985).   Ethylene and abscission.   In "Ethylene and Plant Development" (J.A. Roberts and G.A. Tucker eds.), pp 173-196. Butterworth, London.

Sheldrake, A.R. (1973) The production of hormones in higher plants.   Biological Reviews 48, 509-559.

Sisler, E.C., Goren, R., and Huberman, M. (1985).   Effect of 2,5-norbornadiene on abscission and ethylene production in Citrus leaf explants.   Physiologia Plantarum 63, 1144-120.

Stenlid, G. (1976) Effects of flavanoids on polar transport of auxins.   Physiologia Plantarum 38, 262-266.

Sussman, M.R. and Gardner, G. (1980).   Solubilisation of the receptor for N-1-naphthylphthalamic acid.   Plant Physiology 66, 1074-1078.

Sussman, M.R. and Goldsmith, M.H.M. (1981).   The action of specific inhibitors of auxin transport on uptake of auxin and binding of N-1-naphthylphthalamic acid to a membrane site in maize coleoptiles.   Planta 152, 13-18.

Tamimi, S. and Firn, R.D. (1985).   The basipetal auxin transport system and the control of cell elongation in hypocotyls.   Journal of Experimental Botany 36, 955-962.

Thomson, K-S and Leopold, A.C. (1974).   In vitro binding of morphactins and 1-N-naphthylphthalamic acid in corn coleoptiles and their effects on auxin transport.   Planta 115, 259-270.

Wangermann, E. (1977).   Further localisation of auxin transport through internode segments.   New Phytologist 79, 501-504.

Wangermann, E. and Mitchison, G.J. (1981).   The dependence of auxin transport on cell length.   Plant, Cell and Environment 4, 141-144.

Wardlaw, C.W. (1953).   Action of triiodobenzoic acid and trichlorobenzoic acid on morphogenesis.   New Phytologist 52, 210-217.

Weintraub, R.L., Brown, J.W., Nickerson, J.C., and Taylor, K.N. (1952).   Studies on the relation between molecular structure and physiological activity of plant growth regulators. I. Abscission-inducing activity.   Botanical Gazette 113, 348-362.

White, J.C. and Hillman, J.R. (1972).   The use of morphactin and 2,3,5-triiodobenzoic acid in apical dominance studies.   Planta 107, 257-260.

ARE HORMONES INVOLVED IN ASSIMILATE TRANSPORT?

J.W. Patrick

Department of Biological Sciences, University of Newcastle, Newcastle, N.S.W.,
Australia

A continuous exchange of assimilates occurs across the boundary
of a higher plant cell throughout its development. The vascular
system provides the route through which assimilates are moved
throughout the plant at high rates over long distances. Based
on the intimate relationship between cell development and
assimilate transport, a long-considered hypothesis envisages
direct hormonal control of assimilate transport as part of the
co-ordinated regulation of plant development. Pharmacological
studies have demonstrated that component transport processes of
the source-path-sink system are sensitive to hormone action.
However, the significance of these observations in terms of
endogenous hormonal regulation of assimilate transport in the
whole plant awaits clarification.

INTRODUCTION

It is generally agreed that assimilate transport, both in the xylem and phloem, is
by mass flow. Thus, the rate (R) of assimilate transport can be described by the
product of transport velocity (V), cross-sectional area of the transport path (A)
and concentration of transported solute (C) i.e.

$$R = VAC \qquad (1)$$

with the flow velocity or volume flux (Jv) given by

$$Jv = Lp \quad P \text{ source-sink} \qquad (2)$$

where Lp is the hydraulic conductivity of the transport path and P the pressure
gradient between source and sink. The product of Lp and A provides an estimate of
the hydraulic conductance of the whole transport pathway.

Hormonal control of assimilate transport may be interpreted in terms of equations 1
and 2. This approach emphasizes the need to consider factors influencing flow
through the whole source-path-sink system when addressing the question of control.
This brief review attempts to define potential control points for assimilate
transport during sink development and assess possible models of hormonal control.

SOURCE/SINK LIMITATIONS OF ORGAN DEVELOPMENT

Depending upon developmental state and the prevailing physical environment,
assimilate gain by an organ can be either source-(assimilation rate less than the
potential rate of utilization) or sink-(potential assimilation rate greater than
the rate of utilization) limited (Wareing and Patrick, 1975). Any physical
limitation imposed by the vascular system would be indistinguishable from the
"source-limited" situation. In broad terms, most organs follow the same source/
sink developmental profile (Patrick, 1986). The cell division phase appears to be
source-limited for both photoassimilates and mineral ions. The cell expansion
phase is sink-limited for photoassimilate accumulation but mineral ion supply can
remain source-limited. While this condition is retained for storage sinks, the
mineral pool size is adequate to support photoassimilate accumulation but limits
the formation of polymers that incorporate mineral ions into their structures.

Interpreting the above analysis using the concept of limiting factors to deduce the probable control points for hormonal regulation of assimilate transport through the source-path-sink system leads to the following conclusions (for further discussion, see Patrick, 1986). In the case of meristematic sinks, the most effective control of assimilate transport would be mediated at the source of path components of the transport catena. In contrast, for cell expansion/storage sinks, photoassimilate transport would be most effectively controlled through regulation of photo-assimilate accumulation by the sink; control of mineral ion transport would be retained by the source-path complex. A preliminary and partial test of this hypothesis was undertaken using the developing pod of Phaseolus vulgaris plants as an experimental model.

Plants were pruned to trifoliate leaf 2 and the primary leaves supporting a single pod arising from the axis of trifoliate leaf 3. To examine whether pod-exported auxins acted directly on phloem transport (Patrick, 1979), basipetal auxin trans-port was blocked by applying 1-(2-carboxyphenyl)-3-phenylpropane-1,3-dione (CPD) (Katekar and Geissler, 1980) to the stem midway between the pod and source leaf. Transport of ^{14}C-photoassimilates to pods soon after anthesis was significantly slowed by CPD, but this effect was greatly diminished during the linear phase of seed fill (Table 1). In both cases, applying indole-3-acetic acid (IAA) immediately below the CPD-treatment site resulted in a restoration of ^{14}C-photoassimilate transport directly regulating either source activity (P source – equation 2) or path capacity (C or A – equation 1; Lp – equation 2) to control assimilate transport to the pod sink. The auxin control of assimilate transport is most pronounced for transfer to the cell division sink at pod set. With the developmental shift to sink-limitation during seed fill (Fader and Koller, 1985), this form of control, presumably still present (Table 1 and also see Patrick, 1979), loses significance. This could result from sink effects (i.e. minimisation of P sink – equation 2) exerting predominate control over assimilate transport.

Table 1 Effect of applying indole-3-acetic acid (IAA – 0.1% w/w in lanolin) below the site of 1-(2-carboxyphenyl)-3-phenylpropane-1, 3-dione (CPD – 1% w/w in lanolin) application to the stem mid-way between the pod and source leaf on ^{14}C photosynthate accumulation[a] by the pod at two stages of development.

Stem treatment	^{14}C-photosynthate accumulation (10^4dpm g^{-1})	
	Pod set	Seed fill
Control	228.4 + 39.3[b]	62.2 + 5.7
CPD	123.4 + 21.6	45.5 + 6.1
CPD + IAA	249.2 + 52.8	59.9 + 4.8

[a] The terminal leaflet of trifoliate leaf 2 was exposed to a 0.375 MBq pulse of ^{14}C-carbon dioxide six hours after applying the CPD and IAA treatments; the pods were harvested for radioassay after a further six hours.
[b] Standard error of the mean; eight replicates per treatment.

These observations indicate that elucidation of the rate-limiting component of the source-path-sink system should provide a sound basis on which to mount future investigations of hormonal control of assimilate transport. To this end, the following assessment of hormonal control of assimilate transport distinguishes the developmental state of the sink and the chemical nature of the transported spp (i.e. photoassimilates versus mineral ions).

HORMONAL CONTROL OF ASSIMILATE TRANSPORT TO MERISTEMS

Little is known of the factors regulating assimilate delivery to meristimatic sinks. Our analysis concludes that the source-path components are potential control points for hormonal regulation of assimilate transport to these sinks (see pp 176).

The relatively small quantities of assimilate imported by meristems (Layzell et al., 1981) indicates that the size of the assimilate transport pool at the source is unlikely to be limiting. Furthermore, because of their small size, assimilate consumption rates by apical meristems are unlikely to be perceived by source processes above the background of larger signals from cell expansion/storage sinks. The absence of any change in leaf photosynthesis following cytokinin-stimulation of photoassimilate transport to shoot apices (Bodson, 1984) provides tacit support for this proposition. Thus, the enhanced transport to these sinks in response to increased rates of assimilation (Bodson, 1984) may reflect a physical limitation imposed by the hydraulic conductance of the transport pathway (A and Lp of equations 1 and 2). The transpiration rate from most meristems is extremely low and hence assimilates are largely imported by phloem translocation, the symplastic continuum of which extends throughout shoot and root apices (Offler and Patrick, 1986). Equations 1 and 2 describe mass flow of assimilates (Murphy, 1986) from the phloem termini to each cell of a meristematic sink. Exudation studies demonstrate that fully-differentiated phloem networks have considerable spare transport capacity (Kallackaral and Milburn, 1984). In contrast, the hydraulic conductance of the undifferentiated portion of the pathway through the apical meristem could be significantly lower (Boyer, 1985) and hence represents the rate-limiting component for assimilate transport. The hydraulic conductance of the symplast pathway is undoubtedly determined by plasmodesmatal geometry. Little is known of the controls operating to set plasmodesmatal number. However, plasmodesmatal permeability to solutes appears to be regulated by cytoplasmic levels of calcium (Erwee and Goodwin, 1983) which in turn could serve as a second messenger for hormone action (Dieter, 1984). Recent reports suggest that abscisic acid (ABA) regulation of ion movements in guard cells depends on elevated levels of cytoplasmic calcium (de Silva et al., 1985). If this is a general phenomenon, then ABA elevation of cytoplasmic calcium would lead to decreases in plasmodesmatal permeability (Erwee and Godwin, 1983) and hence account for ABA inhibition of assimilate transport to shoot apices (Porter, 1981). Similarly, the rapid positive effects of cytokinins (Bodson, 1984) and gibberellins (Cottrell and Dale, 1986) on assimilate transport to shoot apices may result from hormone-induced decreases in cytoplasmic levels of calcium (Dieter, 1984). This model offers an experimentally testable hypothesis that has been examined in the case of floral evocation (Goodwin and Lyndon, 1983). The enhanced assimilate flux to florally-induced shoot apices was associated with a decrease rather than an increase in plasmodesmatal permeability (Goodwin and Lyndon, 1983). While the proposed model merits further investigation, the response of florally-induced apices (Goodwin and Lyndon, 1983) indicates other pathway controls must be operative to account for the increase in the apical pool size of sucrose (Bodson and Outlaw, 1985). One possibility is the regulation of an active transport mechanism propelling assimilate movement through the symplast.

The Munch pressure flow hypothesis of phloem translocation treats the sieve tube as a passive conduit. However, there is a growing body of evidence indicating that the phloem path has the capacity to propel flow directly (e.g. Minchin et al., 1983; Fensom et al., 1984). The requirement for the presence of auxin along the transport path of small sinks, such as decapitated stems (Patrick, 1979) and developing fruits (Table 1), could reflect auxin regulation of an active component of phloem translocation. Preliminary studies with decapitated bean stems treated with auxin have yielded data consistent with the latter hypothesis. Under conditions of steady-state ^{14}C-photoassimilate import into the decapitated stems, auxin was found to reverse the ^{14}C-photoassimilate gradient in the sieve tubes along the transport pathway (Fig. 1). Assuming that the ^{14}C-photoassimilate levels in the sieve tubes provide a relative estimate of sucrose concentrations, it is clear that energy needs to be expended to sustain auxin-promoted transport

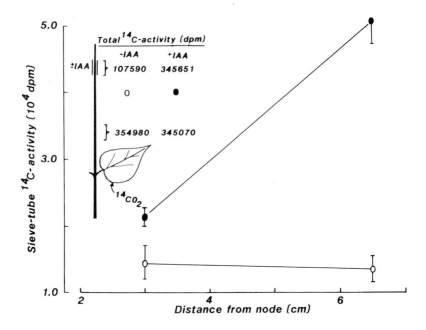

Fig. 1 Effect of IAA on the gradient of ^{14}C-photosynthate activity in the total stem tissue and sieve tubes* of decapitated stems of Phaseolus vulgaris L. (* Determined by microautoradiography. Bars represent standard errors of the mean; four replicates per treatment).

against the sucrose gradient. The nature of the proposed auxin-sensitive active mechanism of phloem translocation is uncertain. However, auxin has been shown to stimulate phloem loading in petioles (Baker, 1985), stems (Hayes and Patrick, 1985) and phloem bundles isolated from celery petioles (Daie et al., 1986). Sustained auxin-enhanced loading along the path would result in an increased translocation rate by maintaining assimilate concentration of the sap stream (equation 1). Such a mechanism avoids interference with phloem unloading through the symplast at the apical sinks. The cyclic waves of phloem loading and unloading proposed by Fensom et al., (1984) could be associated with the observed wave-like motion of basipetal auxin transport (Zajaczkowski et al., 1984). Alternatively, auxin may regulate potassium loading into the sieve tubes (Baker, 1985) which could determine the steepness of the turgor gradient to drive phloem translocation of sugars, even up a sugar concentration gradient (Lang, 1983 and see Fig. 1). Indeed, auxin could act by affecting the programmed turgor set points along the phloem pathway (Cram, 1983; Lang, 1983).

The proposed models for auxin action on the transport pathway are restricted to distances (cm) that can be adequately served by polar auxin transport. This requirement is satisfied by the spatial arrangement of photosynthetic leaves and shoot apices but certainly excludes root apices. Cytokinins, gibberellins and ABA have been detected in the phloem sap and hence could contribute to the regulation of pathway function. However, the absence of polarized transport by these hormones precludes them acting as directional signals for assimilate transport to specific regions. Nevertheless, their accumulation by meristems combined with local synthesis could serve to influence the hydraulic conductance of the symplast as proposed earlier.

HORMONAL CONTROL OF ASSIMILATE TRANSPORT TO CELL EXPANSION/STORAGE SINKS

Potential control of mineral ion and photoassimilate import by expansion growth and storage sinks could be exerted on different components of the source-path-sink system (see pp 176). The analysis commences with a consideration of xylem transport of mineral ions to the photosynthetic leaves. Since mineral ions are exported from the leaves with photoassimilates in the phloem, hormonal control of transport in the path-sink system is treated collectively for the two assimilate classes for this phase of their transport.

(a) Mineral Ion Transport to the Photosynthetic Leaves

The pattern of mineral ion transport alters during plant development. Vegetative growth of annual spp is supported by current root-assimilated mineral ions. With the onset of the reproductive phase, root assimilation declines and remobilization from the foliage predominates. The vegetative growth of perennials becomes progressively less dependent on root assimilation as the pool size of recycled ions increases. Therefore, with development in both annuals and perennials, the predominate source of mineral ions for growth switches from root assimilation to leaf remobilization.

Split-root experiments and manipulation of shoot growth demonstrate that mineral ion assimilation and subsequent translocation to the root xylem are subject to regulation by demand for ions from elsewhere in the plant (Clarkson, 1985). The focal point for this control would appear to be the electrogenic secretion of ions into the xylem (Clarkson, 1985). Shoot demand could be transmitted as the mineral ion concentration recirculated to the root in the phloem sap; the returned ions are envisaged to exert an allosteric regulation on the secretion step (de la Guardia et al., 1985). Root-produced cytokinins could determine the concentration of recirculated ions by controlling the degree of remobilization from the photosynthetic leaves (Simpson et al., 1982). Direct hormonal action on ion secretion to the xylem has been demonstrated for cytokinins and ABA. A rather confusing picture emerges with both stimulatory and inhibitory responses being reported. The physiological state of the root tissue could be a critical factor in selecting the direction of the response of ion secretion to a hormonal signal (Karmoker and van Steveninck, 1979) with an inhibitory action of ABA being the more typical response for whole plants (Karmoker and van Steveninck, 1979; Behl and Jeschke, 1981). In addition, ABA independently enhances vacuolar storage (Behl and Jeschke, 1981) possibly by increasing the set point of the homeostatically-regulated ion influx across the tonoplast (Cram, 1983). This latter response would permit the root to retain the capacity for mineral ion assimilation when shoot demand decreases. Abscisic acid could serve as a shoot signal to the root as it has been shown that it is rapidly translocated from shoot to root in the phloem (Brenner et al., 1985). Indeed, the phloem flux of ABA to the roots could be inversely related to shoot demand for photoassimilates and hence ions (Brenner et al., 1982).

Mass flow of mineral ions in the transpiration stream is described by equations 1 and 2. Preferential flow to the higher order leaves, which avoids futile recycling back to the roots, will be governed by transpiration-induced drops in leaf turgor, differences in petiolar hydraulic conductance (equations 1 and 2) and xylem-to-xylem transfer in the stem (Layzell et al., 1981). In dicotyledonous spp, the potential exists for developmental shifts in xylem Lp of the leaf petioles as new xylem elements are differentiated from the vascular cambium. The dimensions, and most importantly the radius (determinate of Lp) of the differentiating xylem elements is influenced by the axial gradients of hormones in the shoot (Neumann and Stein, 1984). The resultant diversion of root-produced cytokinins away from lower order leaves could amplify the effect of petiolar Lp changes by decreases in stomatal conductance. The resultant xylem flux determines mineral import by expanding leaves and stems (McNeil, 1976) as well as the transport pool size of ions in expanded leaves for phloem translocation to sinks of low transpiration flux. Mineral ion transfer from xylem to phloem takes place in both stems and leaves. Several mechanisms appear to exist for sinks to signal their demand for assimilates by influencing the levels of hormones in the source leaves. Root-produced cytokinins and gibberellins exported to the shoot in the transpiration stream reduce mineral ion return to the roots (e.g. Simpson et al., 1982). This results from the diversion of these hormones to young source leaves exporting to shoot sinks (see above) and their delaying action on leaf senescence and mineral ion remobilization (Simpson et al., 1982). While substantiation is needed, some evidence suggests that auxin conjugates (Hein et al., 1984) and gibberellins (Hoad et al., 1977) may move directly from shoot sinks to the photosynthetic leaves. Another model indicates that sinks may control the levels of leaf ABA indirectly by governing the rate of phloem export of ABA with the assimilates in response to sink demand (Brenner et al., 1982). Thus, the inhibition of phloem loading by ABA (Baker, 1985) could provide a mechanism for sink control (Brenner et al., 1982). The absence of any response of ion export to short-term changes in sink demand (Wolterbeek and de Bruin, 1986) indicates that the observed hormonal effects could be part of an adaptive control mechanism (Geiger and Fondy, 1985). These potential sink effects are superimposed on a developmental drift of mineral ion cycling from older foliage. The rate of this developmental drift could be indirectly regulated by hormones. Thus, release of potassium from the cytoplasm is governed by its apoplastic concentration (Pitman and Cram, 1977). Apoplast potassium levels decline as xylem delivery to the leaves progressively slows with age (see above) and, as a consequence, potassium export would be favoured. The concurrent reduction in cytokinin import facilitates the onset of senescence and remobilization of anions from macromolecules (Simpson et al., 1982). Sink demand, regulated by plant hormones, increases the export rate of mineral ions made available by the senescence process (Wareing and Seth, 1967). Having set the phloem concentration of mineral ions, further regulation of ion transport in the phloem depends on factors governing photoassimilate movement (Marshall and Wardlaw, 1973).

(b) Mineral Ion and Photoassimilate Transport from Source to Sink

Excess source-path capacity for photoassimilates may be sustained, at least in part, by sink-produced hormones. Alterations in the photosynthetic activity of leaves accompanying developmentally-related changes in assimilate demand (e.g. vegetative to reproductive - Geiger and Fondy, 1985) suggest sink regulation of photosynthesis, possibly by hormones (Brenner et al., 1982). Geiger and Fondy (1985) distinguish two levels of control of carbon fixation and allocation. Adaptive controls set the limits of key regulatory processes and these adjust slowly to altered external or internal conditions. Within these limits, carbon fluxes may respond instantaneously to feed-back signals. Plant hormones may operate at both levels. The potential for leaf photosynthesis, carbon allocation between storage and transport pools and phloem loading may be set and integrated by hormones (e.g. Brenner et al., 1982; Daie, 1986; Baker, 1985). The mechanism by which sinks may express their demand for assimilates through alterations in the source leaf levels of hormone is described in the previous section (see pp 179). The ABA model (Brenner et al., 1982) offers a plausible explanation for a mechanism of feed-back adjustment of photosynthesis regulated by stomatal resistance (Brenner et al., 1982) and phloem loading (Baker, 1985). The loci of hormone action on phloem loading by sucrose-proton symport remains uncertain, but may not involve control of the proton motive force through changes in the activity of the proton-pumping ATPase (Sturgis and Rubery, 1982). An additional possibility is that hormones regulate phloem loading by altering the set point of a turgor homeostat (Cram, 1983) governing the activity of a turgor-sensitive component of phloem loading (Smith and Milburn, 1980). These responses are only evinced if the system is operating within the limits of the adaptive controls (i.e. sink-limited - Geiger and Fondy, 1985). This could explain the absence of any auxin effect on carbon flows between various cellular compartments of attached leaves of wheat seedlings (Bauermeister et al., 1980). Hormonal control also could extend to the regulation of the adaptive control mechanism (Geiger and Fondy, 1985). For instance, the

180

activity of sucrose phosphate synthetase sets the capacity of the leaf for sucrose synthesis and hence export (Huber et al., 1985). Gibberellins (Brenner et al., 1985; Daie, 1986) and auxins (Daie, 1986) stimulate sucrose phosphate synthetase activity while ABA is inhibitory (Daie, 1986). However, for these responses to be expressed, they would need to be integrated with commensurate changes in the photosynthetic potential of the leaf and an adequate strength of the importing sinks (Geiger and Fondy, 1985).

The spare capacity of the source is shared by the phloem path (e.g. Kallackaral and Milburn, 1984). Vascular development is mediated by sink-produced hormones, and in particular, auxins and cytokinins (Jacobs, 1984). The constancy of the relationship between translocation rate and phloem cross-sectional area (Kallackaral and Milburn, 1984) suggests that the sink, through hormonal signals, anticipates its subsequent peak demand for photoassimilates during the cell division phase where growth potential is set. Maintenance of a relatively high hydraulic conductivity could depend on auxin regulation of callose deposition on the sieve plates (Thomas and Hall, 1975). The auxin-induced reloading model advanced earlier (see pp 178) would contribute to maintenance of an optimal translocation rate (equation 1).

The foregoing analysis indicates that, under sink-limitation, the rate of pressure-driven flow to a sink (see equation 2) is governed by the degree to which the turgor potential of the sieve tubes at the sink end of the phloem pathway can be depressed. The mechanism of turgor depression is determined by the cellular pathway of phloem unloading. The common route of phloem unloading is via the symplast (Offler and Patrick, 1986) probably by a continued mass flow of phloem sap through the sink symplast (Murphy, 1986).

The hydraulic conductance of the symplast undoubtedly remains the bottleneck for flow in expanding (Boyer, 1985) as well as mature storage sinks (e.g. Offler and Patrick, 1986). Therefore, hormonal regulation of plasmodesmatal permeability (see pp 177) could be significant in contributing to the attainment of the sink-limited condition. Nevertheless, for sink-limited transport of assimilate, regulation must solely be mediated through turgor depression of the sink cells. The acid invertase model proposed by Morris (1983) could function to provide carbon skeletons for growth and to generate osmoticum to maintain turgor for cell expansion (McNeil, 1976). However, acid invertase activity cannot directly influence turgor depression of the sink cells and hence phloem unloading via the symplastic route. In contrast, if symplast transfer from the phloem to sink cells is by diffusion, inversion of sucrose could be significant in determining the sucrose concentration gradient driving diffusion from phloem to sink cytosol (Morris 1983). Even so it is possible that vacuolar sucrose accumulation is the result rather than the cause of auxin-induced cell expansion (Cleland, 1986). The coupling between cell expansion and sugar accumulation in the vacuole could be mediated by a turgor-sensitive ATPase (Reinhold et al., 1984) providing the proton motive force to drive sucrose-proton antiport across the tonoplast (Briskin et al., 1985). The independence of sugar import and acid invertase activity is further illustrated by the finding that increases in the activity of acid invertase are similar in pollinated and non-pollinated ovaries, but only the former accumulate sugars (Walker and Hawker, 1976). Together, a case can be made for independent but integrated (possibly by the same hormone compliment) regulation of sugar import by and acid invertase activity of a sink region. For instance, hormone induced wall loosening (Cleland, 1986) provides a direct control of sink cell turgor and hence sugar import. Here it is envisaged that the turgor of the expanding cell acts as a signal (inverse) for assimilate demand which directly drives mass flow from the phloem through the sink symplast. The 3-fold difference in cell turgors of expanding and mature tissues (Boyer, 1985) indicates sufficient range exists for significant control of assimilate import regulated by sink cell turgor. Furthermore, the model is consistent with turgor-regulation of tonoplast transport of sugars described above and is amenable to experimental investigation.

A different set of conditions apply to phloem unloading through the sink apoplast. In this case, assimilate movement is across the opposing plasma membranes of the phloem or associated cells and those of the sink (Offler and Patrick, 1986). Storage of soluble sugars to high concentrations in vacuoles of some tissues (e.g. sugar beet tap root - Briskin et al., 1985) necessitates an additional energy-dependent transfer across the tonoplast. Independence of growth/storage rate from tissue sugar levels (e.g. Fader and Koller, 1985) indicates that the plasma membrane transport steps and apoplast diffusion have spare transport capacity. The rate-limiting steps are presumably enzymic consumption or transport across the tonoplast for vacuolar storage. For enzymic consumption, acid invertase (Morris, 1983) or sucrose synthase (Claussen et al., 1986) appear to be the key enzymes. Significant acid invertase activity may be found in the apoplast and vacuolar compartments (Morris, 1983). Rates of phloem unloading in corn kernels were found to be unaffected by the activity of apoplast acid invertase (Porter et al., 1985). This suggests the enzyme may play a more significant role in supplying substrate to the hexose porter on the plasma membranes of the sink cells. Hormone-induced changes in vacuolar acid invertase (Morris, 1983) as a contributing factor to sugar import by the sink depends on the sensitivity of the tonoplast and plasma membrane porters to transinhibition. At substrate saturation (i.e. sink-limitation) maximal transport velocity is the most significant kinetic property of the membrane porter determining the sugar flux. Decreases in vacuolar concentrations of sugars have only minor effects on the maximal velocity of the tonoplast sugar porter (Komor et al., 1981). Therefore, it is likely that hormone-induced changes in vacuolar acid invertase activity (Morris, 1983) is accompanied by commensurate but independent hormone-induced changes in the activities of membrane porters of sugars. For different reasons, similar conclusions apply to sucrose synthase located in the sink cytosol. This enzyme may function in storage sinks to regulate starch synthesis (Claussen et al., 1986) and the generation of UDP glucose for tonoplast transport by the group translocator (Thom and Maretzki, 1986). Unlike acid invertase (Morris, 1983), sucrose synthase activity does not appear to be sensitive to plant hormones. Rather, it is positively affected by cytoplasmic levels of sucrose (Claussen et al., 1986). Therefore, sucrose flux across the plasma membranes of the phloem and sink tissues are key regulatory points for expansion (acid invertase) as well as storage (sucrose synthase) sinks to control sugar import; cytoplasmic substrate availability for the growth or storage processes is determined by the activities of the sucrose cleaving enzymes. A strong case can be made that the membrane transfer to the sink apoplast from the phloem or associated cells is facilitated and possibly energised (Patrick, 1986). Accelerated phloem unloading induced by cytokinins and gibberellins can account for their stimulation of photoassimilate transport in decapitated stems without any alteration in the kinetic properties of sucrose accumulation by the sink cells (Hayes and Patrick, 1985). Similarly, unloading from legume seed coats responds rapidly and positively to ABA and cytokinins (Clifford et al., 1986). The dependence of the hormone effect on the presence of potassium (Clifford et al., 1986) suggests an action on facilitated membrane transport. Growth rates of seed from paired pods on the one plant, with cytokinin applied to one pod, indicate that hormonal regulation of photoassimilate unloading is only significant under source- limiting conditions (Table 2; ABA elicits a similar response - Clifford, Offler and Patrick, unpubl.).

This behaviour illustrates the requirements for an integrated response of all the key processes if enhanced accumulation is to result. This requirement could be met by ABA which stimulates sucrose accumulation by a number of sink tissues (Brun et al., 1986) as well as phloem unloading (Clifford et al., 1986). The strong correlation between seed ABA levels and growth rates of different genetic lines of soybean (Brun et al., 1986) provides qualified support for this hypothesis. If seed ABA levels predominantly result from import from the photosynthetic leaves (Brenner et al., 1982), then other controls must initiate photoassimilate import which is then autocatalytically amplified by the accumulated ABA.

Table 2. Dependence on source/sink ratio of the response of seed growth rates of Phaseolus vulgaris L. plants treated by a pedical infusion of 10^{-4}M benzyl adenine (BA); percent stimulation by BA given in brackets.

Limitation	Parameter	Control	10^{-4}M BA
Sink	Seed growth rate (mg day^{-1})	24.1	26.0 (8)
	Seed free-space sucrose concentration (mM)	169	175 (4)
Source	Seed growth rate (mg day^{-1})	13.9	17.1 (23)
	Seed free-space sucrose concentration (mM)	33	43 (30)

CONCLUSIONS

"Spray and pray" experiments provide unequivocal evidence that applied hormones can exert profound effects on assimilate transport which, in some instances, can lead to enhanced crop productivity (Weaver and Johnson, 1985). Treatment of target tissues shows that both loading (Pitman and Cram, 1977; Baker 1985; Daie et al., 1986) and unloading (Hayes and Patrick, 1985; Clifford et al., 1986) of assimilates across the membrane boundaries of the vascular tissues is directly affected by hormones. These actions can account for the overall response of assimilate transport through the source-path-sink system (e.g. Hayes and Patrick, 1986; Daie et al., 1986). Other than through control of vascular differentiation and hydraulic conductance, direct hormone action on longitudinal flow through the transport conduits remains problemmatical. The potential role of endogenous hormones as regulants of assimilate transport awaits clarification (see Lenton, 1984). Results using hormone agonists (Table 1) and isogenic lines (Brun et al., 1986) offer encouragement. The present review emphasizes the need to consider the whole source-path-sink system in a developmental context when designing experiments to explore this problem.

ACKNOWLEDGEMENTS

The unpublished studies were supported by grants from the Australian Research Grant Scheme and Monsanto Agricultural Products Company.

REFERENCES

Baker, D.A. (1985). Regulation of phloem loading. In "Regulation of Sources and Sinks in Plants" (B. Jeffcoat, A.F. Hawkins and A.D. Stead eds.), British Plant Growth Regulation Group, Monograph 12, 163-176.

Bauermeister, A., Dale, J.E., Williams, E.J. and Scobie, J. (1980). Movement of ^{14}C- and ^{11}C-labelled assimilate in wheat leaves: the effect of IAA. Journal Experimental of Botany 31, 1199-1209.

Behl, R. and Jeschke, W.D. (1981). Influence of abscisic acid on unidirectional fluxes and intracellular compartments of K^+ and Na^+ in excised barley root segments. Physiologia Plantarum 53, 95-100.

Bodson, M. (1984). Assimilates and evocation. In "Light and the Flowering Process" (D. Vince-Prue, B. Thomas, K.E. Cockshull eds.), pp 157-169. Academic Press, New York.

Bodson, M. and Outlaw, W.H. (1985). Elevation in the sucrose content of the shoot apical meristem of Sinapsis alba at floral evocation. Plant Physiology 79, 420-424.

Boyer, J.S. (1985). Water transport. Annual Review of Plant Physiology 36, 473-516.

Brenner, M.L., Hein, M.B., Schussler, J., Daie, J. and Brun, W.A. (1982). Coordinate control : The involvement of ABA, its transport and metabolism. In "Plant Growth Substances" (P.F. Wareing ed.), pp 343-352. Academic Press, New York.

Brenner, M.L., Brun, W.A., Schussler, J. and Cheikh, N. (1985). Effects of endogenous and exogenous plant growth substances on development and yield of soybeans. In "Plant Growth Substances" (M. Bopp ed.), pp 380-386. Academic Press, New York.

Briskin, D.P., Thornley, W.R. and Wyse, R.E. (1985). Membrane transport in isolated vesicles from sugar beet tap root. Plant Physiology 78, 871-875.

Brun, W.A., Brenner, M.L. and Schussler, J. (1986). Translocation of abscisic acid and assimilates in soybean. In "Phloem Transport" (J. Cronshaw, W.J. Lucas and R.T. Giaquinta eds.), pp 589-596. Alan R. Lis. Inc., New York.

Clarkson, D.T. (1985). Factors affecting mineral nutrient acquisition by plants. Annual Review of Plant Physiology 36, 77-115.

Claussen, W., Loveys, B.R. and Hawker, J.S. (1986) Influence of sucrose and hormones on the activity of sucrose synthase and acid invertase in detached leaves and leaf sections of eggplants (Solanum melongena L.) Journal of Plant Physiology 124, 345-357.

Cleland, R.E. (1986). The role of hormones in wall loosening and plant growth. Australian Journal of Plant Physiology 13, 93-103.

Clifford, P.E., Offler, C.F. and Patrick, J.W. (1986). Growth regulators have rapid effects on photosynthate unloading from seed coats of Phaseolus vulgaris L. Plant Physiology 80, 653-637.

Cottrell, J.E. and Dale, J.E. (1986). The effects of photoperiod and treatment with gibberellic acid on the concentration of soluble carbohydrates in the shoot apex of spring barley. New Phytologist 102, 365-373.

Cram, W.J. (1983). Chloride accumulation as a homeostatic system: Set points and peturbations. The physiological significance of influx isotherms, temperature effects and the influence of plant growth substances. Journal Experimental Botany 34, 1484-1502.

Daie, J. Hormone-mediated enzyme activity in source leaves. Plant Growth Regulation, (in press).

Daie, J., Watts, B., Aloni, B. and Wyse, R.E. In vitro and in vivo modification of sugar transport and translocation in celery by phytohormones. Plant Science, (in press).

184

de la Guardia, M.D., Fournier, J.M. and Benlloch, M. (1985). Effect of potassium status on K^+ (Rb^+) uptake and transport in sunflower roots. Physiologia Plantarum **63**, 176-180.

de Silva, D.L.R., Cox, R.C., Hetherington, A.M. and Mansfield, T.A. (1985). Suggested involvement of calcium and calmodulin in the response of stomata to abscisic acid. New Phytologist **101**, 555-563.

Dieter, P. (1984). Calmodulin and calmodulin-mediated processes in plants. Plant, Cell and Environment **7**, 371-380.

Erwee, M.G. and Goodwin, P.B. (1983). Characterization of the Egeria demsa Planch. leaf symplast. Inhibition of the intercellular movement of fluorescent probes by group II ions. Planta **158**, 320-328.

Fader, G.M. and Koller, H.R. (1985). Seed growth rate and carbohydrate pool sizes of the soybean fruit. Plant Physiology **79**, 663-666.

Fensom, D.S., Thompson, R.G. and Alexander, K.G. (1984). Stem anoxia temporarily interrupts translocation of ^{11}C-photosynthate in sunflower. Journal of Experimental Botany **35**, 1582-1594.

Geiger, D.R. and Fondy, B.R. (1985). Responses of export and partitioning to internal and environmental factors. In "Regulation of Sources and Sinks in Plants" (B. Jeffcoat, A.F. Hawkins and A.D. Stead eds.), British Plant Growth Regulator Group Monograph **12**, pp 177-194.

Goodwin, P.B. and Lyndon, R.P. (1983). Synchronisation of cell division during transition to flowering in Silene apices not due to increased symplast permeability. Protoplasma **116**, 219-222.

Hayes, P.M. and Patrick, J.W. (1985). Photosynthate transport in stems of Phaseolus vulgaris L. treated with gibberellic acid, indol-3-acetic acid or kinetin. Effects at the site of hormone application. Planta **166**, 371-379.

Hein, M.B., Brenner, M.L. and Brun, W.A. (1984). Effects of pod removal on the transport and accumulation of abscisic acid and indol-3-acetic acid in soybean leaves. Plant Physiology **76**, 955-958.

Hoad, G.V. Loveys, B.R. and Skene, K.G.M. (1977). The effect of fruit removal on cytokinins and gibberellin-like substances. Planta **136**, 25-30.

Huber, S.C., Kerr, P.S. and Kalt-Torres, W. (198). Regulation of sucrose formation and movement. In "Regulation of Carbon Partitioning in Photosynthetic Tissue" (R.L. Heath and J. Preiss eds.), pp 199-214. Waverly Press, Baltimore.

Jacobs, W.P. (1984). Functions of hormones at the tissue level of organization. In "Hormonal Regulation of Development II. The Functions of Hormones from the Level of the Cell to the Whole Plant", Encyclopaedia of Plant Physiology, New Series, Vol. **10** (T.K. Scott ed.), pp 149-171. Springer-Verlag, Berlin.

Kallackaral, J. and Milburn, J.A. (1984). Specific mass transfer and sink-controlled phloem translocation in castor bean. Australian Journal of Plant Physiology **11**, 483-490.

Karmoker, J.L. and van Steveninck, R.F.M. (1979). The effect of abscisic acid on the uptake and distribution of ions in intact seedlings of Phaseolus vulgaris cv. Redland Pioneer. Physiologia Plantarum **45**, 453-459.

Katekar, G.F. and Geissler, A.E. (1980). Auxin transport inhibitors. IV. Evidence of a common mode of action for a proposed class of auxin transport inhibitors : The phytotropins. Plant Physiology 66, 1190-1195.

Komor, E., Thom, M. and Maretzki, A. (1981). The mechanism of sugar uptake by sugar cane suspension cells. Plant Physiology 153, 181-192.

Lang, A. (1983). Turgor-regulated translocation. Plant, Cell and Environment 6, 683-689.

Layzell, D.B., Pate, J.S., Atkins, C.A. and Canvin, D.T. (1981). Partitioning of carbon and nitrogen and the nutrition of root and shoot apex in a nodulated legume. Plant Physiology 67, 30-36.

Lenton, J.R. (1984). Are plant growth substances involved in the partitioning of assimilates to developing reproductive sinks? Plant Growth Regulation 2, 267-276.

McNeil, D.L. (1976). The basis of osmotic pressure maintenance during expansion growth in Helianthus annuus hypocotyls. Australian Journal of Plant Physiology 3, 311-324.

Marshall, C. and Wardlaw, I.F. (1973). A comparative study of the distribution and speed of movement of ^{14}C assimilates and foliar-applied ^{32}P-labelled phosphate in wheat. Australian Journal of Plant Physiology 26, 1-13.

Minchin, P.E.H., Lang, A. and Thorpe, M.R. (1983). Dynamics of cold induced inhibition of phloem transport. Journal Experimental Botany 34, 156-162.

Morris, D.A. (1983). Hormonal regulation of assimilate partition : Possible mediation by invertase. British Plant Growth Regulator Group Monograph 6, 23-35.

Murphy, R. (1986). Symplastic sieve tube unloading in seed coats of Phaseolus vulgaris is a necessary requirement for pressure-driven translocation. In "Phloem Transport" (J. Cronshaw, W.J. Lucas and R.T. Giaquinta eds.), pp 259-262. Alan R. Liss, Inc., New York.

Neumann, P.M. and Stein, Z. (1984). Relative rates of delivery of xylem solute to shoot tissue : Possible relationship to sequential leaf senescence. Physiologia Plantarum 62, 390-397.

Offler, C.E. and Patrick, J.W. (1986). Cellular pathway and hormonal control of short-distance transfer in sink regions. In "Phloem Transport" (J. Cronshaw, W.J. Lucas and R.T. Giaquinta eds.), pp 295-306. Alan R. Liss, Inc., New York.

Patrick, J.W. (1979). Auxin-promoted transport of metabolites in stems of Phaseolus vulgaris L. Further studies on effects remote from the site of hormone application. Journal Experimental Botany 30, 1-13.

Patrick, J.W. Assimilate partitioning. Hortscience, (in press).

Pitman, M.G. and Cram, W.J. (1977). Regulation of ion content in whole plants. Society for Experimental Biology, Symposium vol. xxxi pp 391-424.

Porter, N.G. (1981). The directional control of sucrose and asparagine transport in lupin by abscisic acid. Physiol Plant 53, 279-284.

Porter, G.A., Knieval, D.P. and Shannon, J.C. (1985). Sugar efflex from maize (Zea mays L.) pedicel tissue. Plant Physiology 77, 524-531.

Reinhold, L., Siden, A. and Volokita, M. (1984). Is modulation of the rate of proton pumping a key event in osmoregulation? Plant Physiology **75**, 846-849.

Simpson, R.J., Lambers, H. and Dalling, M.J. (1982). Kinetin application to roots and its effect on uptake, translocation and distribution of nitrogen in wheat (Triticum aestivum) grown with a split root system. Physiologia Plantarum **56**, 430-435.

Smith, J.A.C. and Milburn, J.A. (1980). Osmoregulation and control of phloem-sap composition in Ricinus communis L. Planta **148**, 28-34.

Sturgis, J.N. and Rubery, P.H. (1982). The effects of indol-3-yl-acetic acid and fusicoccin on the kinetic parameters of sucrose uptake by discs from expanded primary leaves of Phaseolus vulgaris L. Plant Science Letters **24**, 319-326.

Thom, M. and Maretzki, A. (1986). Comparison of some characteristics of uridine diphosphate glucose-dependent sucrose synthesis in isolated vacuoles and tonoplast vesicles. In "Phloem Transport" (J. Cronshaw, W.J. Lucas and R.T. Giaquinta eds), pp 93-102. Alan R. Liss, Inc., New York.

Thomas, B. and Hall, M.A. (1975). The effect of growth regulators on wound-stimulated callose formation in Salix viminalis L. Plant Science Letters **4**, 9-15.

Walker, R.R. and Hawker, J.S. (1976). Effect of pollination on carbohydrate metabolism in young fruits of Citrullus lanatus and Capsicum annuum. Phytochemistry **15**, 1881-1884.

Wareing, P.F. and Patrick, J.W. (1975). Source-sink relations and the partition of assimilates in the plant. In "Photosynthesis and Productivity in Different Environments" (J.P. Cooper ed.), pp 481-499. Cambridge University Press.

Wareing, P.F. and Seth, A.K. (1967). Ageing and senescence in the whole plant. Society for Experimental Biology Symposium, vol. **xxi**, pp 543-548.

Weaver, R.J. and Johnson, J.O. (1985). Relation of hormones to nutrient mobilization and the internal environment of the plant: The supply of mineral nutrients and photosynthate. Encyclopaedia Plant of Physiology New Series, vol. 11, pp 3-36. Springer-Verlag, Berlin.

Wolterbeek, H. and de Bruin, M. (1986). The import and redistribution of several cations and anions in tomato leaves. Journal of Experimental Botany **37**, 331-340.

Zajaczkowski, S., Wodzicki, T.J. and Romberger, J.A. (1984). Auxin waves and plant morphogenesis. In "Hormonal Regulations of Development II. The functions of Hormones from the Level of the Cell to the Whole Plant", Encyclopaedia of Plant Physiology, New Series, Vol. 10 (T.K. Scott ed.), pp 244-262. Springer-Verlag, Berlin.

A STRUCTURED EVALUATION OF THE INVOLVEMENT OF ETHYLENE AND ABSCISIC ACID IN PLANT RESPONSES TO AERATION STRESS

Michael B. Jackson,

University of Bristol, Department of Agricultural Sciences, Long Ashton Research Station, Long Ashton, Bristol, BS18 9AF, England

It is argued that applying a set of clearly defined criteria can effectively reveal the strengths and weaknesses of experimental evidence implicating endogenous hormones in naturally occurring developmental processes. Most reviews do not make such structured assessments. This often leads to a 'safety first' approach in which the central issue of assessing hormone involvement in development is largely avoided in favour of discussing merely the biochemical or physiological consequences of applying hormones to plants.
This chapter attempts a critical, structured evaluation of evidence implicating ethylene or abscisic acid in the development of epinastic curvatures or stomatal closure that follow quickly from soil flooding. It also assesses the extent to which these findings relate to plant performance at higher and lower levels of organisational complexity. For both epinasty and stomatal closure, many of the test criteria for establishing regulatory roles for ethylene or abscisic acid are at least partially satisfied thereby rendering a contrary view difficult to sustain. Shortcomings are also revealed that point a way forward for future research.

INTRODUCTION

Despite a wealth of detailed information describing the actions of applied hormones, review writers seem increasingly unwilling to implicate endogenous plant hormones in the regulation of naturally occurring developmental events (see chapters in Wilkins, 1984). This uncertainty may have several causes. One of these could be the narrow focus of much hormone research, since the prevalent tendency is to study simplified (and perhaps artifactual) systems and their idiosyncrasies as ends in themselves. Such an approach gives only limited help when we ask questions of how plants come to look and perform the way they do in natural or agricultural situations. A second cause of uncertainty could be the failure of many who write about hormones to apply to data under consideration criteria that must be met if a hormonal explanation is to be accepted. Absence of a clear structure for appraising a large and diverse literature inevitably discourages more circumspect writers from expressing an opinion concerning the involvement of endogenous hormones in development. However, those more committed to the hormonal cause may for the same reason resort to a series of anecdotal claims for the prowess of endogenous plant hormones (see most chapters in Scott, 1984).

In keeping with the theme of this book, a set of criteria is used here to evaluate claims that changes in ethylene or abscisic acid concentration bring about certain plant responses to restricted aeration. The results reveal both strengths and shortcomings in the evidence that readily form the basis for critical discussion and planning further research. The criteria used (Table 1) owe much to rules for establishing biological activity published almost thirty years ago by Jacobs (1959). These criteria also try to accommodate the view of Passioura (1979) that research at the lower levels of plant organisation (e.g. molecular, sub-cellular) should link closely with questions raised at higher levels of organisation (eg. tissues, organs, whole plants) and that in turn these should relate to ecological aspects of plant behaviour. Without such integration, research at any one level when prosecuted alone, risks being viewed as parochial or obscure.

Table 1 Criteria for implicating a hormone in the regulation of a naturally-occurring developmental phenomenon

---

Principal criteria

(i)   Correlation. Joint occurrence between the timing of developmental change and alterations to the endogenous hormone content. The ideal is precedence by the hormonal change, commensurate with its speed of action.

(ii) Duplication. Reproduction of the phenomenon by re-creating quantitatively, changes in the internal concentrations of hormone measured when the process occurred naturally.

(iii) Deletion and Re-instatement. (a) Prevention or inhibition of phenomenon by removing or decreasing the internal hormone titre. (b) Reversing the effect of (a) by demonstrably re-instating quantitatively the original internal hormone levels. (c) Inhibiting the phenomenon by interfering reversibly with the action of the hormone, preferably using a non-toxic, competitive inhibitor.

(iv) Chemical Specificity. The evidence in (i-iii) should not apply to other substances found in plants, other than to precursors.

(v)   Relevance to Higher Levels of Organisation. The developmental process studied should occur beyond the confines of the laboratory and relate to performance in environments to which organs, whole plants or populations are naturally subject.

(vi) Relevance to Lower levels of Organisation. The association between the action of exogenously supplied hormone and the naturally occurring phenomenon is retained at cellular, sub-cellular and biochemical levels. Ideally criteria (i-iv) should apply to each aspect examined.

(vii) Generality. The extent to which the proposed hormonal controls apply to other taxonomic groups with similar developmental traits should be established.

CASE No. 1   ETHYLENE AND EPINASTIC LEAF CURVATURE IN FLOODED TOMATO PLANTS

Epinastic leaf curvature in tomatoes and other species (Doubt, 1917) is one of the most familiar effects of exogenously applied ethylene. This downward re-orientation of leaves is the consequence of accelerated expansion by adaxial cells of the petiole and possibly some slowing of growth on the opposing abaxial side (Crocker et al., 1932; Palmer, 1972). The leaves of tomato plants growing in soil that is suddenly waterlogged also develop epinastic curvatures (Turkova, 1944). The extent to which this curvature reflects a causal involvement of naturally produced ethylene, and any significance this may hold for whole-plant performance in over-wet conditions, is assessed using the criteria of Table 1.

(i) Correlation

Much evidence links epinastic curvature of flooded plants to increases in endogenous ethylene. The ethylene concentration in internal gas extracted by partial vacuum from whole leaves of tomato plants more than doubles when the soil is waterlogged for sufficient time (54h) to promote extensive epinasty in the petioles of those extracted leaves (Jackson and Campbell, 1975). Gas extracted from epinastic petioles themselves is also enriched with ethylene to a similar extent (Jackson and Campbell, 1976b). Closer correlations in location and in time have been established by monitoring rates of ethylene production, (free of interference from wound-induced

190

ethylene production), by 20mm-long segments taken from the zone of epinastic curvature at the petiole base (Jackson and Campbell, 1976a). After 24 h flooding, epinastic curvature and ethylene production increase in tandem and continue to do so for a further 24h, by which time epinastic curvature has neared completion (Jackson et al., 1978). Similar results but with ethylene production assayed on a whole-shoot basis (i.e. with no discrimination between epinastic and non-epinastic tissue), have also been obtained under rather different environmental conditions by Bradford and Dilley (1978). The principal factor in flooded soil that initiates epinasty is oxygen deficiency (Jackson and Campbell, 1976b; Bradford and Dilley 1978). When the root systems of intact tomato plants are exposed to decreasing partial pressures of oxygen in solution cultures (air contains approx. 20.8 KPa O_2), the highest concentration of oxygen that promotes epinasty (3KPa) also raises the ethylene content of the petioles (Jackson and Campbell, 1976b). When half of a vertically divided root system is exposed to oxygen deficiency, the leaf connected to it by xylem elements becomes epinastic and does so in association with faster rates of ethylene production (Jackson, 1980).

All the quoted analyses of ethylene were made using gas-solid chromatography that employed retention time of authentic ethylene standards to identify ethylene in experimental samples. This would be an inadequate basis for identifying the non-gaseous plant hormones extracted with organic solvents because of the absence of tests to increase the chemical specificity of the assay (e.g. mass spectrometry, UV isomerisation). However, the chances of another compound from plants co-chromatographing with ethylene on alumina, Porapak or similar chromatography column packing is extremly small because the number of volatile compounds in plants is very much less than non-volatiles. Also, these column packings only elute non-polar substances at the modest temperatures used for ethylene analysis (approx. $120^{\circ}C$ or less), thus excluding from the flame ionisation detector almost all organics except low molecular weight hydrocarbons. There are very few low molecular weight hydrocarbons similar in size to ethylene and therefore co-chromatography with another substance is improbable. However, ethane is one such gas and authors do not always state that their chromatography systems discriminate between ethane and ethylene. Confidence could be heightened by the use of a photo-ionisation detector, which is highly sensitive to ethylene but much less responsive to ethane.

The preceding correlative evidence linking the timing and extent of epinasty in flooded tomatoes to increased ethylene seems strong and is backed-up by the following biochemical evidence. The additional ethylene formed in the epinastic leaves of flooded tomato plants is thought to be derived from precursors or promotors of ethylene production, such as 1-aminocyclopropane-1-carboxylic acid (ACC), passing from the anoxic roots to the shoots via the xylem (Jackson and Campbell, 1976b; Bradford and Yang, 1980). A linear relationship has been found between the extent of epinasty and the flux of ACC in xylem sap extracted by vacuum during the first 84h of flooding. The increases in xylem-ACC precede increases in petiolar ethylene production and epinastic cuvature by approximately 12h. Re-oxygenating the soil by drainage reverses these trends (Bradford and Yang, 1980). Immersing, for 6h, the cut ends of detached shoots in similar concentrations of ACC to those found in xylem sap, gives rise to epinastic curvatures and to fluxes of ACC through the stele comparable with those seen in flooded plants. Future work is needed to demonstrate that flooding actually enriches the petioles with ACC. This may prove difficult since Amrhein, et al. (1982) could not find ACC in the leaves of flooded tomatoes, although increases in ACC concentrations of the roots correlated closely with the development of epinastic curvature. Since ACC is converted very quickly to ethylene in well-aerated shoot tissue, chemical inhibitors of this conversion may be needed in order to demonstrate actual enrichment of shoot tissues with the precursor.

(ii) Duplication

Ethylene gas applied to tomato plants readily duplicates the effect of flooding on epinasty. Tomato plants with well-aerated roots become epinastic within 24h of applying 0.007Pa of ethylene or more to the shoots (Jackson and Campbell 1975;

1976b). Sensitive techniques have shown curvature within 1h of treatment and that 0.001Pa ethylene is sufficient to illicit a response (Crocker et al., 1932; Leather et al., 1972). When larger concentrations of ethylene (1.0-10.0Pa) are supplied to the roots, petiolar epinasty results from the internal passage of a small proportion of this ethylene into the leaves. The greater the concentration of ethylene applied to the roots the greater the angle of epinastic curvature after 6-50h. The increase in ethylene extractable from the epinastic petioles by partial vacuum (i.e. doubling or tripling), when 1.0Pa ethylene is given via the roots, approaches that measured in the petioles of flooded plants displaying similar amounts of epinastic curvature (Jackson and Campbell, 1975). Quantitative links have also been established between the extent of epinasty and the rate of petiolar ethylene production by applying different amounts of the ethylene precursor ACC (Bradford and Yang, 1980). Concentrations of ACC that promote epinasty also stimulate ethylene production to rates similar to those seen in petioles of flooded plants undergoing epinasty.

Since tomato plants growing in well-aerated soil respond so readily to applications of ethylene or its precursor, it seems unlikely that epinastic curvatures caused by soil flooding result from significantly enhanced sensitivity or responsiveness to ethylene. This conclusion is strenthened by experiments with plants bearing a second separate adventitious root system but with only the lower original root system made oxygen deficient. The presence of the upper, aerated roots might be expected to inhibit epinastic curvature by decreasing ethylene activity, possibly by exporting substances such as cytokinins that can antagonize ethylene action (Jackson and Campbell, 1979). However, the presence of aerated roots above the waterlogged ones does not markedly decrease epinasty, and ethylene production also remains largely unchanged (Jackson and Campbell, 1979).

(iii) Deletion or Re-instatement

If increases in ethylene are indeed reponsible for promoting epinasty in flooded plants, then removing or depleting the supply of endogenous ethylene to the leaves, or inhibiting the action of ethylene chemically, should depress curvature. Futhermore, epinasty should be re-instated when the shortfall in ethylene content or activity brought about by deletion is made good by exogenous applications of the gas or its precursor. In this way specificity of action is established more certainly.

Removing anaerobic roots, the putative source of ethylene precursor and thus of extra ethylene present in the shoots of flooded plants prevents epinasty, although the leaves do retain their ability to respond to applied ethylene (Jackson and Campbell, 1976b). A more sophisticated approach has been to use chemical inhibitors of ACC bio-synthesis (Bradford et al., 1982). Amino-oxyacetic acid (AOA) and aminoethoxyvinylglycine (AVG) are examples of such inhibitors. Since both inhibit pyridoxal phosphate-dependent enzymes, it must be recognised that they may have unwanted side-effects such as interference with water uptake by roots (Bradford et al., 1982) and with pyridoxal phosphate reactions not connected with ethylene formation. In accord with their reputed activity as inhibitors of ACC biosynthesis, application of AOA and AVG to anaerobic root systems of tomato plants almost completely stops the flux of ACC from roots, with a concommitant elimination of both petiole epinasty and flooding-induced increased ethylene production by petioles (Bradford et al., 1982). It is unfortunate that almost no data are available to demonstrate the specificity of action of these inhibitors. This could be checked by applying ethylene or ACC to see if the action of AOA and AVG could be reversed. Amrhein and Schneebeck (1980) have claimed that AOA at least, does not interfere with epinastic growth per se. Absence of any test of specificity of action applies also to otherwise persuasive experiments with cobalt chloride, an inhibitor of ethylene production from ACC (Bradford et al., 1982). This chemical inhibits epinasty increasingly as larger doses given to plants with anaerobic roots progressively slow-down petiolar ethylene production.

Silver nitrate, carbon dioxide, benzothiadiazole, 3,5 -diiodo-4-hydroxybenzoic acid (DIHB) each inhibit several effects of applied ethylene, including epinasty.

Likewise, they inhibit epinasty when given to flooded tomatoes (Bradford and Dilley, 1978; Jackson and Campbell, 1976b; Wilkins et al., 1978), thereby adding further credance to the idea that flooding promotes epinasty through ethylene action. Again, no attempt seems to have been made to establish the specificity of these inhibitors of ethylene action. This is particularly important since silver nitrate, benzothiadiazole and DIHB can be toxic and thus conceivably inhibit epinasty simply by acting as non-specific growth inhibitors. The use of 2,5-norbornadiene, a competitive, non-toxic inhibition of ethylene activity (Sisler et al.,1985) it might seem to avoid such problems but has yet to be tested on flooded tomatoes.

(iv) Chemical Specificity

Ethylene is not the only natural plant product capable of promoting epinasty when supplied to tomato plants; indoleacetic acid (IAA) is also very active and there is evidence (in sunflower rather than tomato) that endogenous auxin concentrations increase in the shoot during soil waterlogging (Phillips, 1964; Wample and Reid, 1979). Could this hormone be at least co-equal with ethylene in regulating epinasty in flooded plants? Arguments against this proposal include (a) available analyses of endogenous IAA are not chemically definitive; (b) increases in auxin levels in flooded plants are slow to develop (e.g. 14d, - Phillips, 1964) or develop after increases in ethylene (in Vicia faba - Hall et al., 1977)); (c) the weight of evidence is extremely slim if examined using Criteria (i-iv); (d) auxin may promote epinasty only by virtue of its ability to stimulate ethylene production (Palmer, 1985). This is not to say that the presence of auxin in the petiole is unimportant for epinasty. The limited results on this question (Palmer, 1985; Leather et al., 1972; Kang, 1979) suggest that auxin must be present for maximum responsiveness to ethylene. However, control of epinasty during waterlogging seems unlikely to reside in changing auxin concentration.

(v) Relevance to Higher Levels of Organization

Epinasty is a visually prominent and characteristic response of several species to soil flooding. However, the consequences, if any, for overall growth or survival remain to be established. On intuitive grounds it seems likely that epinasty would decrease the total amount of solar radiation intercepted (Waggoner, 1966) and thus slow transpiration. This could help offset the tendency of the shoots to wilt engendered by an increase in resistance to water entry into roots caused by oxygen shortage (Jackson et al., 1978; Bradford and Hsiao, 1982). One can only conclude that while claims for ethylene as a regulator of petiole epinasty in flooded plants appear quite well founded, the work remains vulnerable to criticisms of triviality until physiological consequences of epinasty are established experimentally. This in turn might give some guidance to its ecological significance. Tests could usefully exploit chemical means of decreasing epinasty in flooded plants mentioned earlier. It is suprising that in a recent review of the ecological role of hormones, experimental approaches of this kind were neither surveyed nor advocated (Salisbury and Marinos, 1985).

(vi) Relevence to Lower Levels of Organization

It is axiomatic that the notion of ethylene regulation of epinasty would be substantiated by finding a range of celluar and sub-cellular characteristics of flooding-induced epinasty that could satisfy criteria (i-iv) of Table 1. Unfortunately, very little is known of the pattern of cell growth along and across the petiole of ethylene-treated plants (Palmer, 1972; Crocker et al., 1932) and flooded plants have not been studied. Cell growth kinetics, fine-structure of cells, cell-wall acidification, enzyme changes, calcium re-distribution, protein, nucleic acid and carbohydrate metabolism, ethylene binding and breakdown, have all been totally neglected. Furthermore, since the cells involved are readily locatable in advance of the reponse, this may be useful in identifying properties that confer localized ethylene responsiveness.

(vii) Generality

It would be comforting to find similar hormonal controls of morphogenetic phemomena in a wide variety of species and across contrasting taxonomic groups. However, it is entirely possibe that independent lines of evolution have bestowed different mechanisms for the control of similar developmental features. The link between epinasty and ethylene production in the leaves of flooded plants has been studied closely only in tomato. Thus, it would be unwise to assume the findings apply equally well to other species. However, limited evidence suggests a similar ethylene-based control mechanism exists also in sunflower. Flooding and exogenous ethylene both promote epinasty in this species and flooding can increase the concentration of ethylene in gases extracted from the sunflower shoot (Kawase, 1974). Futhermore, Crocker et al. (1932) identified 89 species or cultivars that develop epinastic curvatures when exposed to ethylene. A proportion of these can be expected to display epinasty when flooded, suggesting there is a good chance of extending the findings obtained with tomato to other taxonomic groups.

CONCLUSIONS FROM CASE 1

Experimental work of the 'correlation' and 'duplication' kind firmly support the notion of a causative link between the incidence of epinasty in waterlogged tomato plants and increased ethylene concentration or production in the petioles. The link is strengthened by the diversity of experimental methods used and the quantitative nature of the evidence. 'Deletion' and 're-instatement' experiments taking surgical or chemical approaches add futher convincing support although there is some doubt about the specificity of action of the inhibitors employed. The ability of applied auxins to promote epinasty casts some doubt upon the chemical 'specificity' of ethylene as the only natural regulator of epinasty in flooded plants. However, the overall case for a rival regulatory role for auxin in such plants is slim at present. There is no experimental evidence of the consequences of epinasty for the whole plant or for the survival prospects of waterlogged tomato plants. Furthermore, almost nothing is known about epinasty at the cellular and biochemical levels. Applying criteria (i-iv) of Table 1 to events at these lower levels of organisation would not only consolidate the case for the notion of ethylene as the natural regulator of epinasty in flooded plants but may also improve our understanding of the mechanism of action of the hormone.

CASE No. 2   ABSCISIC ACID AND RAPID STOMATAL CLOSURE IN FLOODED PEA PLANTS

Stomatal closure in the face of environmental stress is well documented and frequently precipitated by a loss of leaf hydration. Increased abscisic acid (ABA) synthesis is thought to mediate in this response although the case is complicated by observations that stomata usually close in advance of increases in total leaf ABA. Attempts have been made to explain this discrepancy in terms of turgor loss causing a highly localised re-distribution of ABA into guard cells that would not be detected by hormone analysis of intact leaf laminae (Dörffling et al., 1980) or in terms of localised ABA transport from water-stressed roots to the leaf epidermis (see Davies et al. this volume). However, direct evidence is lacking. The situation is different in waterlogged pea plants because stomata have been found to close in the absence of hydration loss by leaf tissue. Nevertheless, despite the absence of foliar water deficits, there is evidence implicating increased foliar ABA concentrations in this closure (Jackson and Drew, 1984; Jackson, 1985; Jackson and Hall, 1987). The strength of the case and its significance for plant survival will now be evaluated using the criteria of Table 1.

(1) Correlation

When compost supporting plants at the 5-to 7-leaf stage is waterlogged, large decreases in leaf conductance (interpreted as stomatal closure) take place on each of the following 3d in association with up to ten-fold increases in ABA in the leaves (Jackson, 1985). Similar results, although with some differences of detail, have recently been obtained by Davies and collaborators (see this volume). Extensive stomatal closure is seen during the first few hours of the second photoperiod after waterlogging starts, in association with larger leaf water potentials, more highly hydrated leaves and slower transpiration. Abscisic acid concentrations are also greater in these plants, the increase commencing during the preceding dark period, if not earlier. Numerical relationships between day-time conductances and the associated concentration of foliar ABA in the same leaves indicate that stomata begin to close whenever ABA rises above control values. Minimum apertures are attained when ABA concentrations reach about one third of maximum (Jackson, 1985; Jackson and Hall, 1987).

It seems unlikely that flooding markedly increases the sensitivity of stomata to ABA or to other unknown promotors of closure. If this was the case, large differences in the leaf conductances of flooded and non-flooded plants would have been found at similar ABA concentrations.

(2) Duplication

When ABA is applied to freshly detached pea leaves via the transpiration stream, stomata close within 15 min. An exogenous concentration of $0.1\,mmol\ m^{-3}$ closes stomata and raises extractable ABA in the leaf lamina to concentrations closely similar to those found in waterlogged plants by the same methods of extraction and analysis. Some control over the extent of closure can also be achieved by varying the external concentration of ABA, suggesting that the size of stomatal apertures in flooded plants could be regulated by changing concentrations of endogenous ABA.

Abscisic acid increases can be brought about not only as a result of waterlogging but by incubating excised leaves for up to 3d with their petioles in vials of water. These leaves behave in a similar way to those attached to waterlogged plants, i.e. their ABA content increases as the stomata close and laminae hydrate. The increase in ABA is presumably a result of accumulation of hormone produced by the leaf but not exported because of the absence of sinks in the root system (Jackson and Hall, 1987).

(iii) Deletion and Re-instatement

Inhibitors of ABA biosynthesis or action are not available. However, a mutant of pea that is partially deficient in ABA offers the opportunity for deletion and re-instatement type experiments. Measurements of ABA in the leaves of mutant and non-mutant plants grown under high humidity show the mutant to contain about one third the concentration of ordinary plants (Jackson and Hall, 1987). Increases in ABA concentration of mutant plants also fail to match those of non-mutant plants when both are waterlogged for the same length of time. In accord with the hypothesis that ABA concentrations determine the extent of closure, conductance values are greater in waterlogged mutants than those in waterlogged non-mutants. Unfortunately re-instatement experiments in which the stomatal response to making good the shortfall of endogenous ABA in waterlogged mutants have not been carried out. Furthermore, it is not entirely clear that mutants are as sensitive to ABA as non-mutants, although work with epidermal strips suggests this may be true (Donkin et al., 1983).

(iv) Chemical Specificity

Abscisic acid is not uniquely able to influence stomatal aperture at concentrations that can occur in plants. Carbon dioxide and potassium ions are also active in this way. There is evidence that waterlogging can inhibit potassium uptake by roots of peas (Jackson, 1979; Zhang and Davies, 1986) and it is thus possible that any resulting potassium deficiency in leaves contributes to closure of the stomata of flooded plants. Measurements of carbon dioxide in the leaves of flooded plants (tomatoes) show no large increases, making this gas an unlikely regulator of stomata (Jackson and Campbell, 1976b; Bradford, 1983). All-trans-farnesol is another naturally occurring substance that can close stomata (Wellburn et al., 1974) although no measurements of this substance have been made in flooded plants.

(v) Relevance to Higher Levels of Organisation

Pea plants in a wide variety of growing conditions ranging from growth cabinets, glasshouses, to outdoor lysimeters and field conditions are damaged severely by only a few days of waterlogging (Jackson, 1979; 1985). A conspicuous symptom of the injury is leaf necrosis and desiccation, despite an ability to close stomata quickly in response to flooding. But it is also true that leaves remain highly turgid for at least 3-4d before they degenerate if flooding persists. The ABA-mediated stomatal closure thus appears to offer protection from rapid wilting and desiccation during this early period. Without stomatal closure at this time wilting could be predicted as a consequence of the high resistance to water entry that is a property of oxygen deficient roots. This deduction is supported by the behaviour of the ABA deficient mutant, which wilts severely within the first 24-48h of waterlogging, unless grown in highly humid conditions. In one test, leaf water potentials (bars) of non-waterlogged, plants were $-6.1^+_- 0.7$ and $-3.4^+_-0.1$ for the wilty mutants and non-wilty type respectively. Waterlogging for 2d changed these readings to $-10.9^+_-0.7$ and $-4.7^+_-0.4$ ($^+_-$S.E.,n=5). Clearly, in the absence of marked increases in ABA and stomatal closure, flooding inflicts severe decreases in water potential on the foliage of pea plants at an early stage.

(vi) Relevance to Lower Levels of Organisation

The reader is referred to Raschke (1979) for a detailed analysis of the physical and biochemical basis of stomatal closure. It is inappropriate here to summarise the large literature on this subject. Since no studies have been made at this level on the stomatal movements of flooded plants it can only be assumed that, as in other situations such as closure induced by darkness or lack of carbon dioxide, it involves the transport or generation of osmotically effective substances such as potassium, chloride and malate in guard cells. Pertinent experiments might usefully explore the extent to which the effects of applied ABA parallel those taking place in the stomata of waterlogged plants.

(vi) Generality

It seems likely that the picture described above for peas may apply to other herbaceous species, particularly the tomato, where stomata also close in association with increased leaf water potentials (Jackson et al., 1978; Bradford and Hsiao, 1982), and in several woody species including Populus, Salix, Eucalyptus and Ulmus (Pereira and Kozlowski, 1977). Unpublished results of Jackson and Hall show that, ABA also increase in the foliage of waterlogged tomatoes as stomata close. In the ABA-deficient tomato mutant 'flacca', stomatal closure is much less extensive (Jackson and Hall, 1987) and as with peas, the penalty for this is severe wilting within 24-48h of waterlogging.

CONCLUSIONS FROM CASE 2

Stomatal control in flooded plants has received less experimental attention than petiole epinasty and is unable to benefit from any chemical control of ABA biosynthesis in the way epinasty research has gained from chemical controls over ethylene production. Abscisic acid is also more difficult to extract and measure reliably at physiological concentrations. Nevertheless, 'correlation' and 'duplication' experiments point to a regulatory role for the increasing amounts of ABA that accumulate in the leaves of flooded peas. Strengths of the evidence include the close correlations with time between increased ABA and stomatal closure, the link between extracted ABA concentrations and the extent of closure; the similarity between the concentrations of ABA extracted from flooded plants with closing stomata and of that extracted from leaves supplied with sufficient exogenous ABA to close stomata. 'Deletion' type studies using an ABA deficient mutant reinforce these data since its limited ability to close stomata when waterlogged is related to only modest increases in ABA during flooding. The 'specificity' of ABA as the principal influence on the stomata of flooded will be greatest during the first 1-3d. At later times stomatal aperture may become increasingly affected by factors other than ABA (e.g. potassium deficiency, slower photosynthesis) as flooding proceeds. These studies have some bearing on the tolerance of plants to flooded conditions since it is clear that in the absence of prompt stomatal closure and associated increases in ABA, foliage becomes prematurely dehydrated. Avoidance of severe wilting soon after flooding begins may hold survival value.

REFERENCES

Amrhein, N., Breuing, F., Eberle, J., Skorupka, H. and Tophof, S. (1982). The metabolism of 1-aminocyclopropane-1-carboxylic acid. In "Plant Growth Substances 1982" (P.F. Wareing ed.), pp 249-258. Academic Press, London.

Amrhein, N. and Schneebeck, D. (1980). Prevention of auxin-induced epinasty by -aminooxyacetic acid. Physiologia Plantarum 49, 62-64.

Bradford, K.J. (1983). Effects of soil flooding on leaf gas exchange of tomato plants. Plant Physiology 73, 475-479.

Bradford, K.J. and Dilley, D.R. (1978). Effects of root anaerobiosis on ethylene production, epinasty and growth of tomato roots. Plant Physiology, 61, 506-509.

Bradford, K.J. and Hsiao, T.C. (1982). Stomatal behaviour and water relations of waterlogged tomato plants. Plant Physiology 70, 1508-1513.

Bradford, K.J., Hsiao. T.C. and Yang, S.F. (1982). Inhibition of ethylene synthesis in tomato plant subjected to anaerobic root stress. Plant Physiology 70, 1503-1507.

Bradford, K.J. and Yang, S.F. (1980). Xylem transport of 1-aminocyclopropane-1-carboxylic acid, an ethylene precursor, in waterlogged plants. Plant Physiology 65, 322-326.

Crocker, W.P., Zimmerman, P.W. and Hitchcock, A.E. (1932). Ethylene-induced epinasty of leaves and the relation of gravity to it. Contributions from Boyce Thompson Institute 4, 177-218.

Donkin, M.E., Hull, T., Martin, E.S. and Wang, T.L. (1983). The physiology of a wilty mutant of Pisum sativum under simulated water stress conditions. Pisum Newsletter 15, 18-19.

Dörffling, K., Tietz, D., Streich, J. and Ludewig, M. (1980). Studies on the rôle of abscisic acid in stomatal movements. In "Plant Growth Substances 1979" (F. Skoog, ed.), pp 274-285. Springer-Verlag, Berlin.

Doubt, S.L. (1917). The response of plants to illuminating gas. Botanical Gazette 63, 209-223.

Hall, M.A., Kapuya, J.A., Sivakumaran, S. and John, A. (1977). The rôle of ethylene in the response of plants to stress. Pesticide Science 8, 217-233.

Jackson, M.B. (1979). Rapid injury to peas by soil waterlogging. Journal of the Science of Food and Agriculture 30, 143-152.

Jackson, M.B. (1980). Aeration in the nutrient film technique of glasshouse crop production and the importance of oxygen, ethylene and carbon dioxide. Acta Horticulturae 98, 61-78.

Jackson, M.B. (1985). Responses of leafed and leafless peas to soil waterlogging. In "The Pea Crop. A Basis for Improvement" (P.D. Hebblethwaite, M.C. Heath and T.L.K. Dawkins, eds.), pp 163-172. Butterworths, London.

Jackson, M.B. and Campbell, D.J. (1975). Movement of ethylene from roots to shoots, a factor in the responses of tomato plants to waterlogged soil conditions. The New Phytologist **74**, 397-406.

Jackson, M.B. and Campbell, D.J. (1976a). Production of ethylene by excised segments of plant tissue prior to the effect of wounding. Planta **129**, 273-274.

Jackson, M.B. and Campbell, D.J. (1976b). Waterlogging and petiole epinasty in tomato: the rôle of ethylene and low oxygen. The New Phytologist **76**, 21-29.

Jackson, M.B. and Campbell, D.J. (1979). Effects of benzyladenine and gibberellic acid on the response of tomato plants to anaerobic root environments and to ethylene. The New Phytologist **82**, 331-340.

Jackson, M.B. and Drew, M.B. (1984). Effects of flooding on growth and metabolism of herbaceous plants. In "Flooding and Plant Growth" (T.T. Kozlowski, ed.), p 105. Academic Press, Orlando.

Jackson, M.B., Gales, K. and Campbell, D.J. (1978). Effect of waterlogged soil conditions on the production of ethylene and on water relationships in tomato plants. Journal of Experimental Botany **29**, 183-193.

Jackson, M.B. and Hall, K.C. (1987). Early stomatal closure in waterlogged pea plants is mediated by abscisic acid in the absence of foliar water deficits. Plant, Cell and Environment, **10** (in press).

Jacobs, W.P. (1959). What substance normally controls a given biological process? 1. Formulation of some rules. Developmental Biology **1**, 527-533.

Kang, B.G. (1979). Epinasty. In "Physiology of Movements". Encyclopedia of Plant Physiology New Series, Vol. 7 (W. Haupt and M.E. Feinleib eds.) pp 647-667. Springer-Verlag, Berlin.

Kawase, M. (1974). Rôle of ethylene in induction of flooding damage in sunflower. Physiologia Plantarum **31**, 29-38.

Leather, G.R., Forrence, L.E. and Abeles, F.B. (1972). Increased ethylene production during clinostat experiments may cause leaf epinasty. Plant Physiology **49**, 183-186.

Palmer, J.H. (1972). Rôles of ethylene and indol-3yl-acetic acid in petiole epinasty in Helianthus annuus and the modifying influence of gibberellic acid. Journal of Experimental Botany **23**, 733-743.

Palmer, J.H. (1985). Epinasty, hyponasty and related topics. In "Hormonal Regulation of Development. III. Rôle of Environmental Factors". Encyclopedia of Plant Physiology New Series, Vol.11 (R.P. Pharis and D.M. Reid eds.), pp 139-168. Springer-Verlag, Berlin.

Passioura, J.B. (1979). Accountability, philosophy and plant physiology. Search **10**, 347-350.

Pereira, J.S. and Kozlowski, T.T.(1977). Variations among woody angiosperms in response to flooding. Physiologia Plantarum **412**, 184-192.

Phillips, I.D.J. (1964). Root-shoot hormone relations. II. Changes in endogenous auxin concentration produced by flooding the root system in Helianthus annuus. Annals of Botany **28**, 37-45.

Raschke, K. (1979). Movements of stomata. In "Physiology of Movements". Encyclopedia of Plant Physiology New Series, Vol. 7. (W. Haupt and M.E. Feinleib eds.), pp 383-441. Springer-Verlag, Berlin.

Salisbury, F.B. and Marinos. N.G. (1985). The ecological rôle of plant growth substances. In " Hormonal regulation of development III. Rôle of Environmental Factors". Encyclopedia of Plant Physiology New Series, Vol. 11 (R.P. Pharis and D.M. Reid eds.), pp 707-766. Springer-Verlag, Berlin.

Scott, T.K., ed., (1984). "Hormonal Regulation of Development II. The Functions of Hormones from the Level of the Cell to the Whole Plant". Encyclopedia of Plant Physiology New Series, Vol. 10. Springer Verlag, Berlin.

Sisler, E.C., Goren, R. and Huberman, M. (1985). Effects of 2,5-norbornadiene on abscission and ethylene production in citrus leaf explants. Physiologia Plantarum 63, 114-120.

Turkova, N.S. (1944). Growth reactions in plants under excessive watering. Comptes Rendus (Doklady) de l'Academie des Sciences de l'URSS 42, 87-90.

Waggoner, P.E. (1966). Decreasing transpiration and the effect upon growth. In "Plant Environment and Efficient Water Use (W.H. Pierre, D. Kirkham, J. Pesek and R. Shaw eds.), pp 49-72. American Society of Agronomy and Soil Science Society of America, Madison.

Wample, R.L. and Reid, D.M. (1979). The rôle of endogenous auxins and ethylene in the formation of adventitious roots and hypocotyl hypertrophy in flooded sunflower plants (Helianthus annuus L.). Physiologia Plantarum 44, 219-226.

Wellburn, A.R. Ogunkami, A.B., Fenton, R., and Mansfield, T.A. (1974). All-trans-farnesol: a naturally occurring anti-transpirant. Planta 120, 255-263.

Wilkins, H., Alejar, A.A. and Wilkins, S.M. (1978). Some effects of halogenated hydroxybenzoic acids on seedling growth. In "Opportunities for Chemical Plant Growth Regulation". BCPC Monograph No. 21. pp 83-94. British Crop Protection Council, Croydon.

Wilkins, M.B., ed., (1984). "Advanced Plant Physiology". Pitman, London.

Zhang, J. and Davies, W.J. (1986). Chemical and hydraulic influences on the stomata of flooded plants. Journal of Experimental Botany, 37, (in press).

HORMONES AS CHEMICAL SIGNALS INVOLVED IN ROOT TO SHOOT COMMUNICATION OF EFFECTS OF CHANGES IN THE SOIL ENVIRONMENT

W.J. Davies[1], J.C. Metcalfe[1], U. Schurr[2], G. Taylor[1] and J. Zhang[1]

[1]Department of Biological Sciences, University of Lancaster, Bailrigg, Lancaster LA1 4YQ, England

[2]Lehrstuhl für Pflanzenökologie, Universität Bayreüth, 8580 Bayreüth, Postfach 10 12 51, Federal Republic of Germany

Variations in leaf water relationships can have marked effects on shoot growth and many aspects of leaf physiology. There is also accumulating evidence that following soil drying or flooding many physiological changes occur in the leaf under circumstances where leaf water potentials and turgors are not affected. It is suggested that roots are extremely sensitive to changes in the soil environment and that they may have the capacity to 'measure' the availability of soil water and transfer this information as a chemical signal to the shoot. Indeed, this type of measurement must take place if plants are to 'optimise' their water use with respect to water availability. This paper assesses the possible candidates for chemical signals moving from roots to shoots and suggests that ABA may have a central role to play in root to shoot communication.

INTRODUCTION

An increase in size and complexity can be an extremely hazardous undertaking for a plant. The essential substate for growth, carbon, is acquired only at the expense of losing water. Since the maintenance of turgor is also an essential part of the growth process the course that plants must steer in order to attain a successful solution to this dilemma is often a tortuous one. The problem is further complicated by irregular and unpredictable rainfall. In a scholarly analysis, Cowan (1982) has attempted to identify some of the characteristics of plants which enable them to grow and develop more quickly without diminishing the probability of survival, and to increase the probability of survival without diminishing their growth rate. Cowan has expounded the principle of optimisation as the risk of water use balanced against the benefit of carbon fixation in a changing environment, particularly with regard to declining soil water supply between rainfall episodes. Cowan's analysis and a similar analysis by Jones (1980), suggest that in order effectively to optimise gas exchange between rainfall episodes, which might be equated with successful growth and development in a competitive situation, plants must exhibit the capacity to 'measure' the amount of water available to them in the soil and modify their physiology accordingly. This chapter suggests a mechanism whereby plants might achieve this end.

STOMATAL CONDUCTANCE AND SOIL WATER STATUS

When a plant is growing in drying soil, the decline in water availability will eventually bring about some decline in stomatal conductance. This response apparently often arises from a fall in leaf turgor due to limited water transport from roots. Careful observation suggests, however, that stomata of some plants may close as soil dries, even though leaf turgor remains high (see e.g. Bates & Hall, 1981; Davies & Sharp, 1981; Schulze, 1986). Three recent experiments have shown clearly that under some circumstances, stomatal conductance may be related to the water status of the soil and therefore to the availability of water, rather than being linked directly to the bulk water relations of the leaves. Because of the

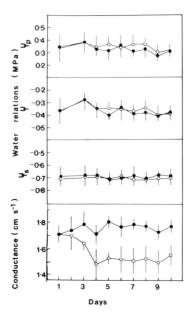

Fig. 1 <u>Water relations and conductance of Commelina leaves from plants with roots</u> <u>split between two pots.</u> Treatments were a) water applied to both halves of root system (closed symbols) or b) water withheld from one half of root system after day 1 (open symbols). Points are means + S.E. Modified from Zhang <u>et al</u>. (1987).

intimate hydraulic contact between the stomata and the other leaf cells, this is clearly a surprising observation.

Blackman & Davies (1985) have divided roots of maize plants between two pots and allowed transpirational water loss to dry the soil around half of each root system. Soil around the other half of the root was kept well watered. This treatment had no significant effect on the water relations of leaves of these plants, compared to plants rooted in two pots which were both well watered. Despite this, plants with part of their root system in dry soil showed only partial stomatal opening suggesting that soil conditions had an effect on stomata which was independent of any hydraulic effect. We have recently repeated this experiment with <u>Commelina</u> seedlings and achieved the same result (Fig. 1).

A relationship between leaf conductance and the percentage of extractable soil water around the roots of <u>Helianthus</u> has been described by Turner <u>et al</u>. (1985). Leaf conductance decreased when about two thirds of the extractable water in the soil had been utilized, irrespective of the leaf water status. In a similar experiment, Gollan <u>et al</u>. (1986) have allowed wheat plants to dry the soil around their roots and, not unexpectedly, this treatment has resulted in stomatal closure (Fig. 2a). Ingeniously, however, they have pressurised the roots of some plants (see Passioura, 1980) to raise the turgor of the shoot without influencing the turgor of the roots nor the matric potential of the soil. Again, stomata closed as the soil dried, even though shoots were kept at full turgor (Fig. 2b).

It is clear from the experiments cited above that soil drying has an additional, presumably, chemical effect on stomatal behaviour that is independent of the

202

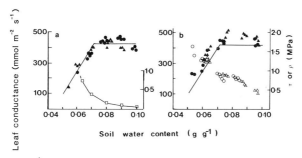

Fig. 2 <u>Leaf conductance of wheat plants as a function of soil water content</u>
a) Plants whose leaf water potentials were uncontrolled during the monotonic drying
of the soil. Soil water suction (□) is also shown. b) Plants which were kept
constantly at full turgor during the drying of the soil by application of a
balancing pressure to the roots (△○). Results for two plants (triangles and
circles) are shown. The solid line in b. is a summary of the relationship shown in
a. Modified from Gollan <u>et al</u>. (1986).

transport of water to the leaves. This change must reflect a change in root
physiology and may also influence aspects of leaf physiology other than the
stomta. Certainly, leaf expansion is reduced when water is witheld from plants and
this can occur even though leaves apparently show high turgors (eg. Michelena &
Boyer, 1982). There is, however, much controversy over measurements of water
relations of growing cells and there may be other explanations for an apparent lack
of correlation between leaf growth and turgor (see eg. Cosgrove, 1986). Flooding
(see Jackson, this volume), and salt stress (eg. Termaat <u>et al</u>., 1985) will also
limit shoot growth and restrict stomatal aperture, even when leaf turgors are
unaffected. Presumably these responses also reflect changes in root functioning
and modifications in the transport of chemical information from roots. Leaf water
relations are clearly not always a reliable indication to the stomata of the
changing edaphic environment. Chemical information moving from roots may therefore
be an important influence on leaf physiology, enabling the plant to regulate its
response to environmental stress.

ROOT GROWTH AND WATER RELATIONS IN DRYING SOIL

Drying of the soil around roots does not always, as might be expected, reduce root
growth. Some species show short-term stimulation in root growth (eg. Sharma &
Ghildyal, 1977; Malik <u>et al</u>., 1979). Continued root growth in drying soil has been
linked to the capacity to sustain turgor in the root tip (Sharp & Davis, 1979).
Eventually, however, turgors are reduced. Such changes would be expected to
influence directly the rate of synthesis of those growth substances which are
apparently produced in root tips. Turgor reductions and presumed stress-induced
changes in wall properties will reduce root growth rates and thereby reduce water
and mineral uptake, sink activity and biosynthesis of amino acids and growth
substances. All of these changes will be expected to influence shoot physiology.
As the soil in the immediate vicinity of the root dries, we might expect that a
vapour gap will develop between the root and the soil (eg. Faiz & Weatherley,
1982). This is a controversial question but reduced contact between the plant and
the soil may further reduce water and mineral uptake. Reduced water flux to shoots
will in itself reduce the transfer of chemical information.

Tips of maize roots in the dry half of a split root system (see above) can show
reduced turgor even though tips of roots in wet soil have substantially higher root
water potentials and turgors (Davies <u>et al</u>., 1986). We have argued previously that

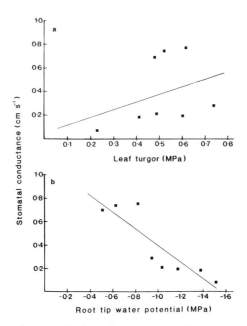

Fig. 3 Relationships between leaf conductance of Lolium plants and a) leaf turgor (y = 0.657x - 0.054. r = 0.35) and b) root tip water potential (y = 0.71x + 1.112. r = 0.83). Measurements were taken in the middle of the light period as plants dried the soil over a 3 week period. Modified from Metcalfe and Davies (1987).

this type of response may occur because root tips are comparatively isolated hydraulically due to only restricted xylem development near the root tip (Sharp & Davies, 1979). Careful observations of comparative root and shoot water relations can show that when water is witheld from soil, root tip water potentials and turgors start to decline before decreases in shoot turgor can be detected (Sharp, 1981; Metcalfe & Davies, 1987). These changes can correlate well with restriction in stomatal conductance. In Lolium plants, stomata close as soil dries but leaf turgor does not decline and there is no correlation between leaf turgor and leaf conductance (Fig. 3a). Stomatal behaviour is not obviously correlated with declining root turgor, but this is a difficult variable to estimate and more work is required in this area, perhaps with a pressure probe. There is a good correlation between leaf conductance and root water potential (Fig. 3b) raising the possibility that the flux of some chemical moving into the root in the transpiration stream may have a controlling influence on stomata in this instance.

We consider now the type of chemical information moving to leaves and specifically assess the evidence that soil drying influences the synthesis of growth substances in roots as well as the uptake and flux of nutrients to leaves.

NATURE OF THE CHEMICAL INFORMATION CONVEYED FROM ROOTS TO SHOOTS

Intensive research over many years has revealed that the stomatal complex is sensitive to a variety of stimuli (see eg. Mansfield & Davies, 1984). Some redundancy in control stimuli presumably results in reliability in the control of gas exchange. The complex chemical information moving to the shoot will be the sum total of the various functions of the root and we might therefore expect that a change in the soil environment which alters root growth or physiology will influence, at the very least, the synthesis of growth substances and amino acids and the uptake of nutrients. It would be unrealistic to consider the influence of one class of compounds in isolation from the others. In concentrating our attentions here on growth substances it is important to note that individual systems will show differing sensitivity to individual growth substances depending on the influence of other growth substances or nutrients.

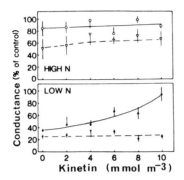

Fig. 4 Leaf conductance of cotton plants which were either well supplied with nitrogen or nitrogen deficient. Leaves were treated with ABA at 1 mmol m^{-3} (——) or 3 mmol m^{-3} (- - - -) and a range of concentrations of kinetin. Modified from Radin et al. (1983).

(a) Variation in the Sensitivity of Stomata to Growth Substances

One of the clearest examples of nutrient supply influencing the sensitivity of stomata to an application of a growth substance is provided by the work of Radin et al. (1982) with cotton. ABA has only a small effect on stomata of cotton plants which are well supplied with nitrogen but the effect is enhanced in nitrogen-deficient leaves (Fig. 4). In low-N leaves, stomatal responses to low concentrations of ABA could be almost blocked by concurrent applications of kinetin. Blackman & Davies (1983) have shown that cytokinins can also override the influence of ABA on maize stomata.

Even in the leaves of well-watered plants there is quite a large amount of ABA (eg. Hartung et al., 1982) and therefore a reduction in the transport of nitrogen and/or cytokinin to leaves as a result of some form of perturbation of the root environment might be expected to close stomata by changing their sensitivity to the ABA present in the leaf.

(b) Effects of Soil Drying or Flooding on Nutrient Uptake

When the soil dries, uptake of nutrients can be markedly reduced (see eg. Nye & Tinker, 1977). This can be because of the decreased availability of nutrients to roots or because of a change in the uptake properties of the roots themselves. Shaner & Boyer (1976) have shown that soil drying reduced the uptake of nitrate by maize roots. The primary cause of the decreased nitrate flux was a decrease in the ability of the roots to supply nitrate to the transpiration stream. When the decreased nitrate transport by the roots was coupled with the decreased transpiration at low water potential, the combined effects on nitrate flux were large. Interestingly, the activity of nitrate reductase in maize leaves was

205

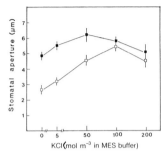

Fig. 5 <u>Effects of increasing potassium concentration on stomatal apertures of pea</u>
<u>plants in abaxial epidermis which was removed from leaves of control plants (closed</u>
<u>symbols) or plants with roots flooded with fresh water 14d previously (open</u>
<u>symbols).</u> Points are means of 60 observations + S.E. Modified from Zhang & Davies
(1986).

responsive to variation in nitrate flux even when the over-all nitrogen status of
the leaves remained the same. The authors refer to this response as a desiccation-
altered signal.

Kozlowski & Pallardy (1984) have reviewed the effects of flooding on the mineral
nutrition of plants and have noted that these are many and varied. Zhang & Davies
(1986) have shown recently that flooding of pea plants greatly restricts potassium
uptake and that potassium application to leaves, incubated in conditions which are
ideal for stomatal opening, can reverse flood-induce restriction of stomatal
aperture (Fig. 5). The likely effect of a flood-induced potassium deficiency in
leaves is to increase the sensitivity of stomata to any ABA present in or arriving
at the leaf (Wilson <u>et al</u>., 1978; Snaith & Mansfield, 1982b) and it is important
therefore to obtain information on the effects of the treatment on the balance of
growth substances in the plant. With a few recent exceptions (eg. Hubick <u>et al</u>.,
1986) most studies concentrate on the effects of environmental perturbation on a
single regulator. More comprehensive studies are required.

(c) Cytokinins in Xylem Sap as Indicators of Changes in the Root Environment

In the 20 years since the observation by Itai & Vaadia (1965) that kinetin-like
activity in root exudate of sunflower plants was reduced by soil drying there have
been many suggestions that such a response could provide a link between root
physiology and stomatal behaviour. Early reports that stomata of many species were
insensitive to applied cytokinins (Luke & Freeman, 1968) have been superceded by
reports of stomatal responses to cytokinin by monocot and dicot C_3 and C_4
plants and by CAM plants (eg. Jewer & Incoll, 1980; 1981; Blackman & Davies, 1983;
Radin <u>et al</u>., 1982). Blackman & Davies (1984) have suggested that inappropriate
plant material and experimental conditions might explain early reports of stomatal
insensitivity to cytokinins.

Since the pioneering work of Itai and co-workers there have been many other reports
that cytokinin synthesis by roots can be influenced by soil drying (see Jewer &
Incoll, 1987) and flooding (eg. Burrows and Carr, 1969). Nevertheless, good
quantitative estimates of effects of soil drying on contents of cytokinins in
leaves are still required. The traditional view that synthesis of cytokinins is
restricted to root tips is now being challenged (eg. Salama & Wareing, 1979; Chen &
Petschow, 1978) and if cytokinins are also synthesised in meristems of shoots it is
difficult to see how modifications in transport from the roots can have a very

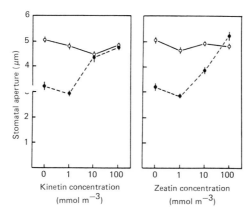

Fig. 6 Effects of increasing concentrations of cytokinin on stomatal aperture of maize plants which were grown with roots split between two pots. Epidermis was removed from plants which either received water on both halves of the root system (———) or received water on only one half of the root system for 5 d prior to this treatment (- - - -). Points are means of 60 observations $\pm$ S.E. Modified from Blackman & Davies (1985).

sensitive influence on stomata. Jewer and Incoll (1987) have suggested, however, that the very large number of root meristems relative to shoot meristems may mean that roots can exert a dominant influence on cytokinin balance.

We have described above a split-root experiment where maize plants showed restricted stomatal opening when part of their root system was allowed to dry the soil (Blackman & Davies, 1985). Interestingly, application of cytokinin to the leaves of these plants, incubated under conditions which were ideal for stomatal opening, reopened stomata to apertures exhibited by control plants (Fig. 6). One conclusion from this experiment is that stomatal opening in plants with partially dried roots is restricted by reduced cytokinin contents of leaves. Even if cytokinin synthesis is restricted to roots, there are several difficulties with this conclusion. Most importantly, the treatment will result in at most a 2-fold decrease in the transport of anything manufactured by the root. The dose response (Fig. 6) does not imply the degree of sensitivity required for our hypothesis. Possibly the sensitivity of the stomata in the intact plant to decreases in cytokinin transport is enhanced by modification in the balance of other growth substances and nutrients.

(d) Ethylene as an Indicator of a Change in the Root Environment

Plant water deficit can substantially enhance ethylene production by leaves (eg. Wright, 1977) and increases have been implicated in several of the plant's physiological responses to water deficit (see Bradford & Hsiao, 1982a). In water-logged plants, the ethylene precursor ACC is exported from the roots in increased quantities and converted to ethylene in the shoot (Bradford & Yang, 1980). Flooded plants often show coincident epinasty of petioles and stomatal closure (eg. Bradford & Hsiao, 1982b) and ethylene will promote epinasty. It is generally accepted, however, that ethylene has no effect on stomata (Pallaghy and Raschke, 1972) and Bradford & Hsiao (1982b) were unable to find a stomatal response to ACC supplied in the transpiration stream, apparently ruling out this physiologically active component known to be transported in the xylem as the causal agent in flood-induced stomatal closure. Interestingly, however, Tissera & Ayres (1986) have recently reported that the stomata of rust-infected Vicia leaves show only limited opening and that rust infection potentiates production of wound ethylene. Inhibition of opening was also induced when rust-infected leaves were supplied with ACC through the petiole. Inhibition of opening was reversed by inhibitors of the action of ethylene. These results show that under certain conditions, stomata can be sensitised to ethylene and it is not hard to imagine that this might be brought about by the myriad of chemical changes which are induced by flooding of roots (eg. Jackson & Kowalewska, 1983) or by soil drying.

(e) Production of Abscisic Acid in Roots and the Regulation of Shoot Physiology

Despite several early reports to the contrary, it is now apparent that many species have the capacity to synthesise ABA in their roots (eg. Walton et al., 1976; Lachno, 1983; Cornish & Zeevaart, 1985). At first sight, however, it is not clear how ABA originating in roots could specifically influence stomata, when leaves themselves synthesise ABA and often have a very high ABA content. Recent information on compartmentation of ABA within leaves suggests, however, that leaves of well-watered plants have most of their ABA sequestered within the chloroplasts which act as anion traps (see eg. Cowan et al., 1982). The first response to water deficit may be a release of ABA from the chloroplasts (Cornish & Zeevaart, 1984; Schulze, 1986), perhaps as a result of a reduction in stomatal pH (Hartung et al., 1981). There are now two reports that ABA may be synthesised in guard cells (Weiler et al., 1982; Cornish & Zeevaart, 1986) but unless epidermal turgor falls, the concentration of ABA in the apoplast immediately adjacent to the guard cell plasmalemma will be low (Behl & Hartung, 1986). This is now thought to be the site of action for ABA on the guard cell (Hartung, 1983).

In a series of important papers in the 1970s, Meidner argued that the inner walls of the epidermal cells and the walls of the guard cells themselves were more important sites of water loss than previously had been thought (see eg. Meidner, 1975). As well as the evidence of his own experiments, Meidner cited experiments where tracers added to the transpiration stream are often found deposited in the walls of the epidermis. These conclusions suggest that a proportion of any ABA in the transpiration stream can move directly to the sites of action on the guard cell plasmalemma. If leaf turgor does not decline, then this ABA can act independently of any ABA already in the leaf and sequestered in the chloroplast. Modified synthesis and transport of ABA from roots may therefore provide a direct link between changing root water status and the stomata. Weyers & Hillman (1979) have noted that a relatively high proportion of ^{14}C-ABA fed to Commelina leaves through the transpiration stream was detected in the epidermis. They showed that radioactivity appeared in the epidermis before significant stomatal closure had taken place.

We now consider evidence that the increased production of ABA by roots subjected to soil drying and flooding correlates in time with restriction in stomatal aperture.

ABA PRODUCTION BY ROOTS AND STOMATAL CLOSURE OF FLOODED PLANTS

Our recent experiments have confirmed the observations of others (see Jackson – this volume) that flooding of pea plants results in stomatal closure within a few hours of root innundation (Fig. 7) despite the fact that no leaf water deficit develops (Zhang & Davies, 1986). In our experiments there was no statistically significant increase in ABA content of shoots until the second day of flooding, 36 h after root innundation. Interestingly, ABA contents of roots of flooded plants increased significantly at the beginning of the second day of flooding, 22 h after root innundation and 14 h before the increase in ABA in the shoots (Zhang & Davies, 1987). These results suggest that roots of pea plants have the capacity to produce ABA in response to flooding and confirm the suggestion of Cornish & Zeevaart (1985) that levels of endogenous ABA in roots can rise appreciably before changes in leaf water status occur. ABA contents of roots appear to increase within a few hours of the innundation of roots and these increases correlate well

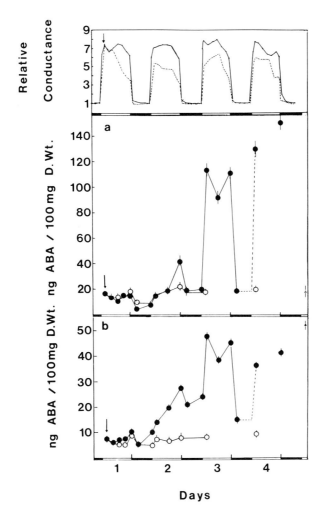

Fig. 7 Effects of flooding on relative stomatal conductance and ABA content of leaves (a) and roots (b) of pea plants. Plants were first flooded at point shown by arrow. Stomatal conductance of control plants (———) and flooded plants (- - - -) was measured with a viscous flow porometer. ABA contents of flooded plants are shown by closed symbols and open symbols show ABA contents of control plants. Points are mean ± S.E. Modified from Zhang & Davies (1987).

with restriction of stomatal aperture. Nevertheless, the first statistically significant increase in ABA content does not occur until the beginning of day 2. It is difficult to assess how large an increase in ABA production by roots will be necessary before epidermis is enriched sufficiently to close stomata. Presumably, only a proportion of the ABA produced by roots will be exported but since the epidermis has a comparatively small volume and the process is cumulative, it may be that stomata can very sensitively respond to a change in the environment around

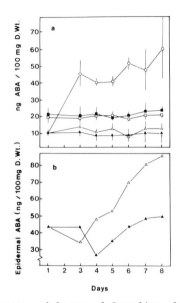

Fig. 8 ABA content of roots and leaves of Commelina plants which were grown with their roots split between two pots. Control plants received water onto both pots throughout the experimental treatment, while the other treatment was to withold water from one half of the root system from day 1. a) ABA contents of leaves (□ ■) and roots (○△▲) are shown. Roots from drying soil (○—○), roots from wet soil (△—△), roots from control plant (▲—▲), leaves from control plants (■—■), leaves from plants with part of their root system in drying soil (□—□), b) ABA content of epidermis removed from control plants (▲—▲) or epidermis of plants with part of their root system in drying soil (△—△). In a) points are means ± S.E. In b) there is no significant increase in ABA in the epidermis of control plants, while the t value for the linear regression showing an increase in epidermal ABA content of plants with roots in drying soil is highly significant. Modified from Zhang et al. (1987).

their roots. It is necessary to ask how stomata can respond to the increased production of ABA by roots, even though ABA contents of leaves are apparently not enhanced.

ABA PRODUCTION BY ROOTS AND STOMATAL CLOSURE OF PLANTS IN DRYING SOIL

We have shown above that when maize plants are grown with roots split betwen two rooting containers, and one part of the root system is allowed to dry the soil, then stomata can close despite the existence of a high turgor in the leaves. We have repeated this experiment with Commelina plants and produced the same result (see Fig. 1), with some restriction of stomatal conductance evident on the third day and a substantial restriction apparent on the fourth day after water was first witheld from part of the root system. It is apparent that very soon after water was first witheld from half of the root system of some plants, ABA contents of these roots increased substantially (Fig. 8). There was no increase in ABA contents of roots in wet soil. When the whole leaf was sampled for ABA, there was no detectable increase in ABA content which would obviously explain the limitation in stomatal conductance. It is possible to sample abaxial epidermis of Commelina

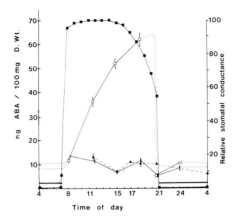

Fig. 9 Relative stomatal conductance (■) and ABA content of leaves from well
watered Commelina plants. ABA contents of abaxial epidermis (○), ABA content of
mesophyll with adaxial epidermis (▲), ABA content of whole leaf (x). Points are
mean + S.E. Modified from Zhang et al. (1987).

for ABA and it is clear from Fig. 8 that there was a substantial increase in the
ABA content of the epidermis on the fourth day after water was first withheld from
the root. This observation correlates in time with the restriction in stomatal
aperture. It is important to emphasize that at no time was there any evidence of
the development of leaf water deficit and therefore the results taken as a whole
indicate that stomata are responding to increased epidermal ABA contents, with ABA
originating from the roots (Zhang et al., 1987). Synthesis of ABA in roots of
Commelina is apparently very sensitive to small changes in root water relations.

STOMATAL BEHAVIOUR AND ABA IN THE EPIDERMIS OF COMMELINA

We have looked in detail at the distribution of ABA in the leaves of well-watered
Commelina plants as a function of time of day (Fig. 9). It is apparent that ABA
builds up in the abaxial epidermis as the light period progresses and that this
increase correlates reasonably well with a gradual restriction of stomatal aperture
towards the end of the day. Importantly, there is no detectable enhancement of ABA
content of the mesophyll (with adaxial epidermis) and the increase in epidermal ABA
is not detectable when the whole leaf is analysed for ABA. This experiment
confirms that stomatal closure shown in Figs. 7 and 8 and in previous experiments
(eg. Blackman & Davies, 1985) which was not accompanied by any obvious increase in
ABA content of the shoot, might have been caused by enhancement of the ABA content
of the epidermis, with this ABA arising from the roots. Clearly, further
experiments are needed to substantiate, this hypothesis. The difference between
ABA contents of 'wet' and 'dry' roots of split root plants is further confirmation
that root ABA originated in roots of Commelina and was not transported to the roots
from the shoots, as is suggested for other plants (eg. Hoad, 1975).

CONCLUSIONS

We have argued above that stomatal behaviour and possibly other aspects of leaf
physiology can be controlled by chemical information moving from roots
independently of any hydraulic influence. It is important to note that the
physiology of leaves of flooded plants may also be influenced by a build up of
shoot-sourced material which is not distributed to roots as a result of a reduction

in sink strength (eg. Jackson, 1985). This is another important manifestation of root to shoot communication. We have tended to ignore such effects for plants growing in drying soil, since root growth is often increased by such treatments and therefore sink strength will also be increased. Eventually, however such effects will become important.

Much of the chemical information moving from the root to the shoot will be modified as a result of altered root functioning as the soil dries. The preceeding discussion suggests that the stomata can sense this change in function and that their responses are modified accordingly. While it is likely that several growth substances and nutrients interact in their effects on stomata it is perhaps worth emphasising the importance of ABA in this chemical complex. The transport of cytokinin, (gibberellins?) and soil nutrients may initially be reduced by only a few percent as a result of soil perturbation. In contrast, root ABA content and therefore presumably transport to and accumulation in shoots may be enhanced by an order of magnitude or more by the same treatment. Stomatal responses to growth substances vary linearly with the log of the growth substance concentration. Therefore one would conclude that ABA might play a central role in root to shoot communication of the effects of root perturbation, with variation in other chemical information acting to increase the sensitivity of shoot systems to ABA accumulation. In this role, ABA fulfils some of the criteria for a realistic definition of a plant hormone or signal. It apparently moves from its site of synthesis (roots) to another site (stomata) which will not synthesise ABA unless the water relations of the leaf are perturbed. It is true that ABA synthesis is by no means the only function of the root but enhanced production by roots may not simply reflect modified root growth and function. A few roots in dry soil may convey chemical information via enhanced ABA synthesis while total root growth may even be enhanced, due to compensation by other roots in wet soil. The number of roots in dry soil at any given time will be useful information for optimisation of water use with respect to available water.

ACKNOWLEDGEMENTS

We thank the AFRC, the Government of the People's Republic of China and Studienstiftung des Deutschen Volks for financial support and our colleagues for helpful discussions.

REFERENCES

Bates, L.M. and Hall, A.E. (1981). Stomatal closure with soil water depletion not associated with changes in bulk leaf water status. Oecologia 50, 62-65.

Behl, R. and Hartung, W. (1986). Movement and compartmentation of abscisic acid in guard cells of Valerianella locusta; effects of osmotic stress, external H^+-concentration and fusicoccin. Planta (in press).

Blackman, P.G. and Davies, W.J. (1983). The effects of cytokinins and ABA on stomatal behaviour of maize and Commelina. Journal of Experimental Botany 34, 1619-1626.

Blackman, P.G. and Davies, W.J. (1984). Age-related changes in stomatal response to cytokinins and ABA. Annals of Botany 54, 121-125.

Blackman, P.G. and Davies, W.J. (1985). Root to shoot communication in maize plants of the effects of soil drying. Journal of Experimental Botany 36, 39-48.

Bradford, K.J. and Hsiao, T.C. (1982a). Physiological responses to moderate water stress. In "Physiological Plant Ecology II" (O.L. Lange et al., eds.), pp 263-324. Springer-Verlag, Berlin.

Bradford, K.J. and Hsiao, T.C. (1982b). Stomatal behaviour and water relations of waterlogged tomato plants. Plant Physiology 70, 1508-1513.

Bradford, K.J. and Yang, S.F. (1980). Xylem transport of l-aminocyclopropane-l-carboxylic acid, an ethylene precursor, in waterlogged tomato plants. Plant Physiology 65, 322-326.

Burrows, W.J. and Carr, D.T. (1969). Effect of flooding the root system of sunflower plants on the cytokinin content of the xylem sap. Physiologia plantarum 22, 1105-1112.

Chen, C.M. and Petschow, B. (1978). Cytokinin biosynthesis in cultured rootless tobacco plants. Plant Physiology 62, 861-865.

Cornish, K. and Zeevaart, J.A.D. (1984). Abscisic acid metabolism in relation to water stress and leaf age in Xanthium strumarium. Plant Physiology 76, 1029-1035.

Cornish, K. and Zeevaart, J.A.D. (1985). Abscisic acid accumulation by roots of Xanthium strumarium L. and Lycopersicon esculentum Mill. in relation to water stress. Plant Physiology 79, 653-658.

Cornish, K. and Zeevaart, J.A.D. (1986). Abscisic acid accumulation by in situ and isolated guard cells of Pisum sativum L. and Vicia faba L. in relation to water stress. Plant Physiology 81, 1017-1021.

Cosgrove, D.J. (1986). Biophysical control of cell growth. Annual Review of Plant Physiology 37, 377-405.

Cowan, I.R. (1982). Regulation of water use in relation to carbon gain in higher plants. In "Physiological Plant Ecology II" (O.L. Lange et al., eds.), pp 589-614. Springer-Verlag, Berlin.

Cowan, I.R., Raven, J.A., Hartung, W. and Farquhar, G.D. (1982). A possible role for abscisic acid in coupling stomatal conductance and photosynthetic carbon metabolism in leaves. Australian Journal of Plant Physiology 9, 489-498.

Davies, W.J. and Sharp, R.E. (1981). The root: a sensitive detector of a reduction in water availability? In "Mechanisms of Assimilate Distribution and Plant Growth Regulators" (J. Kralovic ed.), pp 53-67. Slovak Society of Agriculture, Prague.

Davies, W.J., Metcalfe, J. Lodge, T.A. and Ross da Costa, A. (1986). Plant growth substances and the regulation of growth under drought. Australian Journal of Plant Physiology 13, 105-125.

Faiz, S.M.A. and Weatherley, P.E. (1982). Root contraction in transpiring plants. New Phytologist 92, 333-343.

Gollan, T., Passioura, J.B. and Munns, R. (1986). Soil water status affects the stomatal conductance of fully turgid wheat and sunflower leaves. Australian Journal of Plant Physiology 13, 459-464.

Hartung, W. (1983). The site of action of abscisic acid at the guard cell plasmalemma of Valerianella locusta. Plant Cell and Environment 6, 427-428.

Hartung, W., Heilmann, B. and Gimmler, H. (1981). Do chloroplasts play a role in abscisic acid synthesis? Plant Science Letters 22, 235-242.

Hartung, W., Gimmler, H. and Heilmann, B. (1982). The compartmentation of abscisic acid, of ABA-biosynthesis, ABA-metabolism and ABA-conjugation. In "Plant Growth Substances 1982" (P.F. Wareing ed), pp 325-334. Academic Press, London.

Hoad, G.V. (1975). Effect of osmotic stress on abscisic acid levels in xylem sap of sunflower. Planta **124**, 25-29.

Hubick, K.T., Taylor, J.S. and Reid, D.M. (1986). The effect of drought on levels of ABA, cytokinin, gibberellins and ethylene in aeroponically grown sunflower plants. Journal of Plant Growth Regulation **4**, 139-151.

Itai, C. and Vaadia, Y. (1965). Kinetin-like activity in root exudate of water stressed sunflower plants. Physiologia plantarum **18**, 941-944.

Jackson, M.B. (1985). Responses of leafed and leafless peas to soil waterlogging. In "The Pea Crop. A Basis for Improvement". (P.B. Hebblethwaite et al., eds.), pp 163-172. Butterworths, London.

Jackson, M.B. and Kowalewska, A.K.B. (1983). Positive and negative messages from roots induce foliar desiccation and stomatal closure in flooded pea plants. Journal of Experimental Botany **34**, 493-506.

Jewer, P.C. and Incoll, L.D. (1980). Promotion of stomatal opening in the grass Anthephora pubescens Nees. by a range of natural and synthetic cytokinins. Planta **150**, 218-221.

Jewer, P.C. and Incoll, L.D. (1981). Promotion of stomatal opening in detached epidermis of Kalanchoe by natural and synthetic cytokinins. Planta **153**, 317-318.

Jewer, P.C. and Incoll, L.D. (1987). Cytokinins and water relationships. In "Cytokinins: Plant Hormones in Search of a Role". (R. Horgan and B. Jeffcoat eds.) British Plant Growth Rgulator Group Monograph **14** (in press).

Jones, H.G. (1980). Interaction and integration of adaptive responses to water stress: the implications of an unpredictable environment. In "Adaptation of Plants to Water and High Temperature Stress" (N.C. Turner and P.J. Kramer eds.) pp 353-365. Wiley, New York.

Kozlowski, T.T. and Pallardy, S.G. (1984). Effects of flooding on water, carbohydrate and mineral relations. In "Flooding and Plant Growth" (T.T. Kozlowski, ed.), pp 47-164. Academic Press, New York.

Lachno, D.R. (1983). ABA and IAA in maize roots subject to water, salt and mechanical stress. In "Growth Regulators in Root Development" (M.B. Jackson and A.D. Stead eds.) pp 37-54. British Plant Growth Regulator Group Monograph **10**.

Luke, H.H. and Freeman, T.E. (1968). Stimulation of transpiration by cytokinins. Nature **217**, 873-874.

Malik, R.S., Dhankar, J.S. and Turner, N.C. (1979). Influence of soil water deficits on root growth of cotton seedlings. Plant and Soil **53**, 109-115.

Mansfield, T.A. and Davies, W.J. (1984). Abscisic acid and water stress. Biochemical Society Transactions **11**, 557-560.

Meidner, H. (1975). Water supply, evaporation and vapour diffusion in leaves. Journal of Experimental Botany **26**, 666-673.

Metcalfe, J. and Davies, W.J. (1987). Root water relationships and stomatal behaviour of pasture grasses. Submitted to Journal of Experimental Botany.

Michelena, V.A. and Boyer, J.S. (1982). Complete turgor maintenance and low water potentials in the elongating regions of maize leaves. Plant Physiology **69**, 1145-1149.

214

Nye, P.H. and Tinker, B. (1977). "Solute Movement in the Soil-Root Systems". Blackwells, Oxford.

Pallaghy, C.K. and Raschke, K. (1972). No stomatal response to ethylene. Plant Physiology 49, 275-276.

Passioura, J.B. (1980). The transport of water from soil to shoot in wheat seedlings. Journal of Experimental Botany 31, 333-345.

Radin, J.W., Parker, L.L. and Quinn, G. (1982). Water relations of cotton plants under nitrogen deficiency. V. Environmental control of abscisic acid accumulation and stomatal sensitivity to abscisic acid. Plant Physiology 70, 1066-1070.

Salama, A.M. El-O. A. and Wareing, P.G. (1979). Effects of mineral nutrition on endogenous cytokinin in plants of sunflower. Journal of Experimental Botany 30, 971-981.

Schulze, E-D. (1986). Carbon dioxide and water vapour exchange in response to drought in the atmosphere and in the soil. Annual Review of Plant Physiology 37, 247-274.

Shaner, D.L. and Boyer, J.S. (1976). Nitrate reductase activity in maize leaves. II. Regulation by nitrate flux at low leaf water potential. Plant Physiology 58, 555-509.

Sharma, R.B. and Ghildyal, B.P. (1977). Soil water-root relations in wheat : water extraction rates of wheat roots that developed under dry and moist conditions. Agronomy Journal 69, 231-233.

Sharp, R.E. (1981). Mechanisms of turgor maintenance in Zea mays. Ph.D. thesis. University of Lancaster.

Sharp, R.E. and Davies, W.J. (1979). Solute regulation and growth by roots and shoots of water stressed maize plants. Planta 147, 43-49.

Snaith, P.J. and Mansfield, T.A. (1982). Stomatal sensitivity to abscisic acid : can it be defined? Plant Cell and Environment 5, 309-311.

Termaat, A., Passioura, J.B. and Munns, R. (1985). Shoot turgor does not limit growth of NaCl-affected wheat and barley. Plant Physiology 77, 869-872.

Tissera, P. and Ayres, P.G. (1986). Endogenous ethylene affects the behaviour of stomata in epidermis isolated from rust infected faba bean (Vicia faba). New Phytologist 104, 53-61.

Turner, N.C., Schulze, E-D. and Gollan, T. (1985). The responses of stomata and leaf gas exchange to vapour pressure deficits and soil water content. II. In the mesophytic herbaceous species Helianthus annuus. Oecologia 65, 348-355.

Walton, D.C., Harrison, M.A. and Cote, P. (1976). The effects of water stress on abscisic acid levels and metabolism in roots of Phaseolus vulgaris L. and other plants. Planta 131, 141-144.

Weiler, E.W., Schnabl, H. and Hornberg, C. (1982). Stress-related levels of abscisic acid in guard cell protoplasts of Vicia faba L. Planta 154, 24-28.

Weyers, J.D.B. and Hillman, J.R. (1979). Sensitivity of Commelina stomata to abscisic acid. Planta 146, 623-628.

Wilson, J.A., Ogunkanmi, A.B. and Mansfield, T.A. (1978). Effects of external potassium supply on stomatal closure induced by abscisic acid. Plant Cell and Environment 1, 199-201.

Wright, S.T.C. (1977). The relationship between leaf water potential and the levels of abscisic acid and ethylene in excised wheat leaves. Planta 134, 183-189.

Zhang, J. and Davies, W.J. (1986). Chemical and hydraulic influences on the stomata of flooded plants. Journal of Experimental Botany 37, 1479-1491.

Zhang, J. and Davies, W.J. (1987). ABA in roots and leaves of flooded pea plants. Journal of Experimental Botany (in press).

Zhang, J., Schurr, U. and Davies, W.J. (1987). Control of stomatal behaviour by abscisic acid synthesised in roots. Submitted to Journal of Experimental Botany.

HORMONE INVOLVEMENT IN DAYLENGTH AND VERNALIZATION CONTROL OF

REPRODUCTIVE DEVELOPMENT

W.W. Schwabe

Dept. of Horticulture, Wye College (University of London),
Nr. Ashford, Kent TN25 5AH, England

The effects on flowering of the five established plant hormones are discussed briefly followed by a consideration of the specific flowering hormone, and also natural inhibitors of flowering. Auxins appear to be involved in inhibition of flowering when in excess and also in de-vernalization and abortion of inflorescences, e.g. in Chrysanthemum. Gibberellins (GAs) may be causally linked to juvenility and inhibition of floral bud formation in fruit trees, yet in long day (LD) plants and those requiring vernalization GAs can often be promotive, also in some conifer families they will induce male and female cone formation. The role of abscisic acid (ABA) seems linked to GA effects which can be counteracted, while ethylene effects are related directly or indirectly to auxin effects. The role of cytokinins seems as yet uncertain. The existence of a natural flowering hormone, though often queries, seems still fairly certain. It appears to be the product of a 'factory' in the leaf, operating at a distance on some tissue in the target meristems, but little fundamentally new information has emerged in the recent past. By contrast the existence of a natural flowering inhibitor has had strong confirmation, though it may not be as specific as a promoter. It can be extracted, and re-introduced into leaves of another plant, and appears to operate on several short day (SD) species.

INTRODUCTION

A discussion of hormone effects involved in the morphogenetic processes leading to flowering, particularly when environmentally induced by vernalization or appropriate photoperiod treatment, requires a definition of the term "hormone". However, since at this meeting such definitions will have been attempted several times, it will be simpler merely to list the type of chemical messengers which will be considered. They comprise the following: auxins (which includes derivatives - and where necessary synthetic analogues); cytokinins such as zeatin, zeatin riboside, isopentenyl-aminopurine (including also kinetin and other synthetic compounds); gibberellins (including all effective natural compounds and recent synthetic analogues); abscisic acid (including xanthoxin) as well as ethylene (including ethylene generating compounds). In addition to these, the more specific flowering substance (florigen/anthesin) and antiflorigenic substances need to be considered.

The topic of Photoperiod and Hormones has recently been reviewed very thoroughly by Vince-Prue (1985), who cites no fewer than 350 references, most of which reflect on flowering behaviour. Earlier reviews include Cleland (1982) and Chailakhyan (1982), as well as Zeevaart (1976 and 1978). Several others are quoted by Vince-Prue.

Inasmuch as it is legitimate and possible to generalize, an attempt will be made to discuss the effects of each of the five known natural hormone groups. This will be followed by consideration of the specific flowering hormone 'florigen' and endogenous inhibitor(s).

Plate 1 <u>Xanthium strumarium flowering in continuous light after repeated exposure to x-rays</u> (approx. 1500-2000 rads in 10 doses).

AUXIN

Since the early days, quite soon after the actual discovery of auxin, its involvement with flowering has been suspected and a number of possible modes of its activity have been postulated (e.g. Cholodny, 1939) and since at that time no other plant hormones were known, everything was explained in terms of this hormone alone.

As is only too well known, a great deal of effort was spent on determining endogenous levels of IAA, almost entirely by use of bioassay techniques. While this did not really allow qualitative identification (hence the use of such terminology as "auxin-like activity"), not all this work should now be disregarded, but clearly some of the more crucial findings would need to be confirmed with the modern specific physical or immunochemical techniques. Where growth has been activated by any of a variety of treatments and active leaf production and growth is promoted, it would not be unexpected to find higher auxin levels. There is a good deal of agreement that in long photoperiods higher auxin levels can be detected in many plant species than under SD, but a causal link between such quantitative differences and effects on flowering depend on confirmation by other experimental techniques.

In general terms it seems from the older literature onwards that, auxin – (indol-3-yl acetic acid, IAA) - is inhibitory to flowering when present in excess. This was easily demonstrated by applying IAA or synthetic analogues exogenously which then led to the suppression or reduction of flowering. This was particularly so in the case of short-day requiring species, but similar inhibitory effects have been quoted for long-day plants, though, in this category some flowering promotion has also been recorded (see Lang, 1959). What is less certain is, whether the effect is a direct one, or an indirect one via stimulation of ethylene production.

Some of the unfavourable effects of IAA on flowering, in a quantitative sense, may be attributed to enhancing apical dominance which simply depressed lateral flower formation, and the early observation by Gorter (1949) that TIBA could enhance the amount of flowering in the tomato may have been due to "anti-auxin" action of TIBA in preventing its transport through the tissue.

While Bonner and Thurlow (1949) were the first to demonstrate the inhibitory effect of applied IAA, no work has been done on the possibility of reducing the native internal levels, in order to induce flowering in non-inductive conditions.

Many years ago some tests were carried out by this author with a view to achieving this. At that time a paper by Skoog (1935) has suggested that the treatment of plants with x-rays resulted in morphogenetic effects resembling low auxin levels, suggesting that there was internal destruction of auxin by short-lived organic peroxide ions.

In those early experiments Xanthium plants were used, the plants being held under continuous light (daylight plus incandescent light). They were exposed to a series of dosages of X-ray, and quite drastic deformations of leaf shape, generally simpliciation and size reduction, were induced as well as much shortening of the stems. The abnormalities induced in this way, were too large to allow conclusions as to "normal" effects of SD induction. However, when plants were exposed instead of repeated low dosages, they remained normal in appearance, and, in fact, flowering was induced a spite of continuous illumination. For a variety of reasons which seemed valid at the time, the data was never published, but recently these experiments were repeated and the same effects obtained (Plate 1), i.e. flowering in continuous light without morphogenetic damage.

This would then suggest that flowering in SD of Xanthium is indeed associated with lower auxin levels, especially in the terminal bud and the young leaves contained therein, the presumptive source of much of the apical auxin.

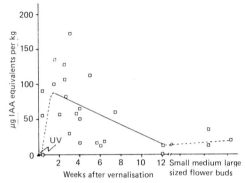

Fig. 1 (After Tompsett and Schwabe, 1974)
IAA equivalents for auxin-like activity in extracts from vernalized plants in short
days at 28°C□ and from unvernalized plants at 28°C in short day (mean of 6
extracts)▲ (UV). Equation of best-fitting line y = 96.96-6.86x (solid line on
diagram).

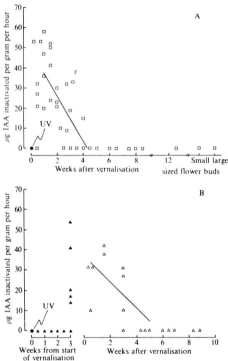

Fig. 2 (After Tompsett and Schwabe, 1974).
A. Auxin-oxidizing enzyme activity in extracts from vernalized plants in short days
at 28°C □ and from unvernalized plants in short day at 28°C (mean of 11 extracts)
●(UV). Equation of best-fitting line y = 49.84-11.43x (solid line on diagram).
B. Auxin-oxidizing enzyme activity in extracts from plants sampled during 3 weeks
chilling ▲ , from vernalized plants in short day at 20°C△ and from unvernalized
plants in short day at 20-5°C (mean of 20 extracts) ●(UV). Equation of
best-fitting line y = 36.44-6.19x (solid line on diagram).

In the Chrysanthemum, too, auxin appears to play a substantial role in flowering and related morphogenetic events. Bioassaying for auxin-like activity revealed no detectable amounts in the shoot tips of unvernalized plants, nor was there any during the chilling period itself (Tompsett and Schwabe, 1974). However, immediately upon return to warm, growing temperatures, there was a big rise in activity, and perhaps surprisingly, this was accompanied by a marked auxin-oxidase activity, which again was not detectable in unvernalized material. The levels of both gradually declined over the succeeding weeks until the plants became floral. Very high dosages of exogenously applied indol-3-yl-butyric acid (IBA) caused de-vernalization (Schwabe, 1970). This effect simulated the effect of natural conditions. Thus, severe and prolonged shading causes de-vernalization and is believed to be the mechanism by which the basal shoots and stolons on the plant attain the unvernalized condition, which explains the need for annual vernalization and which is essentially the reason why the Chysanthemum is a perennial plant. The same effect of shading, or LD-treatment, or exogenous application of IAA or IBA controls the further development of the inflorescence buds - all three methods being able to cause abortion of the inflorescence - provided the critical developmental stage of the marginal florets forming gynoecia has not been passed. Before this stage, all three methods can cause abortion - after this stage none is effective and development proceeds unhindered. The young florets themselves then become a source of auxin supply and when florets are removed at the stage when the entire inflorescence is approximately 0.75 to 1.00 cm in diameter, elongation of the inflorescence peduncle is prevented, but normal growth can be restored by auxin application as a lanolin paste (500 ppm) into the receptacle cup. (Schwabe, 1968).

Another important morphogenetic response which is affected by auxin is sex differentiation. In the Cucurbitaceae and other families there is much evidence that auxin application can cause feminization; thus, in the cucumber, production of female flowers is accelerated, and in other species similar effects may be induced, e.g. female flowers may form on the tassel of auxin-treated maize plants, (see also below). These examples are given to indicate the various responses that can be induced by the same hormone, depending on the developmental stages and type of the receptor tissue.

THE ROLE OF THE GIBBERELLINS

Again, there is no doubt of the involvement of this group of plant hormones in the regulation of flowering, even though the effects are quite varied.

Juvenility

In many, especially woody, species flowering and floral initiation cannot take place until the young plant has reached the stage when favourable environmental conditions can bring about floral induction. This change to a condition when the plant becomes capable of responding to favourable conditions (stimuli) has often been referred to as a 'phase-change'. In many plants it is a once-and-for-all transition occurring some time after the seedling stage but with a degree of reversibility at the change-over time. It may take place within days, months or even many years from seed germination; in other species it would appear to be an annual event, dependent on the growth of shoots and the distance from their own roots (Schwabe and Al-Doori, 1973; Frydman and Wareing, 1973). In the case of the juvenile condition, the role of gibberellins appears to be one of inhibition of flowering, with the GAs emanating from the roots, moving in an upward direction, and for example in the black currant (Ribes nigrum its efficacy depending on the distance between the roots and shoot tip. In species with this response, applied GAs, say, as foliar sprays have proved equally inhibitory, and Luckwill (1970) has shown that naturally-produced GA by other plant parts than the roots, such as young fruits may similarly inhibit flower-bud initiation for the following season. The detailed results of the extensive Long Ashton research cannot be given here, but it is clear that basically similar responses have been found in a number of species of woody dicotyledons.

Plate 2   Peach seedlings grown from unchilled seeds without (dwarf) and with GA$_3$ treatment and chilled control.

By contrast very effective promotion of male and female cones has been induced in conifers from several families (especially the Cupressaceae and Taxodiaceae) exposed to gibberellin application, especially under raised temperature conditions. No specific GA molecule has been identified as 'active', but the less polar molecules were generally more effective in promoting floral development (Pharis et al., 1970, 1980; Ross and Pharis, 1976).

Among herbaceous plants a similar contrast appears to obtain: a whole range of long day plants and/or plants requiring chilling or vernalization treatment, can be induced to become floral when treated exogenously with gibberellins (Lang, 1957). The correlation between LD behaviour and substitution for LD by GAs is not, however, complete; in general terms plants forming rosettes in non-inductive SD or in the unvernalized condition are apparently more responsive to GA, than others which do not show this morphological response. Moreover, there are also differences in the responses to different GA molecules which was shown most interestingly by Michniowick and Lang (1962), who showed that different species were preferentially induced by some GAs while others were not susceptible to other gibberellins. By contrast, numerous SD plants (such as strawberry, Nicotiana tabacum and Kalanchoe are positively inhibited from flowering even in favourable SD by exogenously-applied GAs.

On the basis of these empirical results one could be tempted to classify species into two categories, those promoted by GAs and those inhibited by GAs, but of course this would be a total oversimplication. Once again we know very little of the possible mode of action of GA, but there are some indications that treatments like chilling do not result in a response equivalent to a single dose application of GA, but rather the equivalent to establishing a pathway for the production of a functional GA supply over a considerable period. In the Chrysanthemum, as the result of chilling, raised GA levels are detectable for many weeks (Fig. 3) from the end of chilling. In other cases it seems that an exogenous application of GA can have the same effect, thus treating a 'dwarf peach seedling' with a heavy dose of GA restores normal growth (equivalent to a chilled seedling) without reversion to the dwarf condition (Plate 2), a situation which may perhaps be regarded as 'autocatalytic'.

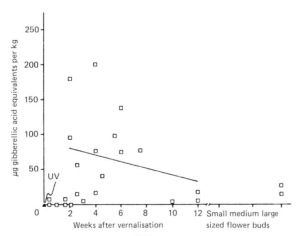

Fig. 3 (After Tompsett and Schwabe, 1974)
Gibberellic acid equivalents for gibberellin-like activity in extracts from vernalized plants at 28°C in short days □ and from unvernalized plants in short days at 28°C (mean of eight extracts) ▲ (UV). Equation of best-fitting line y = 95.14-5.73x (sold line on diagram).

Environmentally induced changes in GA content generally suggest increased amounts in LD conditions and this applies to species ranging from conifers to herbaceous plants. For a useful compilation of assay results see Vince-Prue (1985).

THE CYTOKININS

The role of this group of plants hormones in the regulation of flowering is still very uncertain and controversial. The most rapid change recorded as a reduction in cytokinins in Xanthium leaf and root exudates after a single SD (Henson and Wareing, 1974 and 1977a & b) suggesting a negative role in flowering in this SD plant. This contrasted with the results of Beever and Woolhouse (1973) with another SD plant Perilla frutescens, which showed an increase after 20 SD's, roughly the time required for floral induction. It may of course be that cytokinin content is much more dependent on root growth and activity and transport from the root to the tops. This would certainly apply to unpublished work by Ahmad and Schwabe, and Ahmad (1976), with the Chrysanthemum, where root activity and growth appeared to be the main controlling factors. With present knowledge it would seem to be unwise to attribute a major role to cytokinins in floral induction.

ETHYLENE

The role of ethylene appears to be fairly closely linked to that of auxins, and in a number of instances the inhibitory effects of auxin on flowering have now been attributed to a release/production of ethylene by the treated plants, making the auxin effect an indirect one. Thus interference with induction by auxin application in Xanthium, Perilla, Pharbitis and Chrysanthemum has been explained in this manner (cf. Abeles, 1967; Zhadanova, 1950; Suge, 1972). In Cucumis melo L., endogenous ethylene appears to regulate sex expression, by favouring gynaecious flowering (Byers et al., 1972).

Perhaps the most interesting of the ethylene effects and certainly the one with the most economic significance is the positive induction of flowering in several members of the Bromeliacease (cf. Nickel, 1983).

ABSCISIC ACID

The role of abscisic acid and some of its metabolic precursors, such as xanthoxin, again seems only rather remotely related to flowering. Some earlier suggestions of a directly promotory reaction of flowering (Wareing and El Antably, 1970) can, it would seem, be attributed to the antagonism of ABA to gibberellin effects. Clearly ABA does not generally promote flowering in SD plants and in Kalanchoe it and xanthoxin are markedly inhibitory even in inductive SD conditions (Schwabe, 1972). Moreover, it has been shown that in LD requiring species ABA is again antagonistic to induction, possibly also via its interaction with gibberellin, e.g. Lolium temulentum is prevented from flowering by ABA even after LD induction (Evans, 1960).

OTHER SUBSTANCES

A number of other substances have been shown to influence flowering in particular species and under particular conditions. Among these salicylic acid and some chelators have been noted as actively promoting in the Lemnaceae (see Cleland et al., 1982 for a review), but it would seem unprofitable to generalize from these genera to the higher plants overall.

Attempts to find parallels with mammalian systems involving steroids, especially as far as sex determination is concerned (see there) have regularly failed, ever since the earliest attempts by Löve and Löve (1945).

SEX DETERMINATION AND SPECIFICITY OF NATURAL PLANT GROWTH REGULATORS

Perhaps the most specific effects ascribed to the natural plant hormones in flowering are that of regulating and modifying the determination of sex of individual flowers. Generally, it is claimed that the gibberellins promote maleness, and the auxins and cytokinins female development, although the actual mechanism would yet need to be elucidated. However, a series of unpublished experiments by Schwabe and Sekak and Sekak (1983) have cast some doubt on this specificity, especially when cytokinins are also involved. Results of Srinivasan and Mullins (1979), in which fruit development from tendril anlagen in Vitis by cytokinin treatment was brought about, suggested a less specific pattern. The new results cannot be detailed here, but they tend to indicate that the mode of application of the growth substances, the developmental stage of the tissue, etc. may be more important than has hitherto been appreciated. Thus, cytokinin application can result in the production of male flowers on female inflorescences of Xanthium and equally female flowers in male Xanthium inflorescences, as well as the formation of functional gynoecia and subsequent fruit formation in Mercurialis annua. This rather suggests that the action is not so much sex specific, but rather exerted through affecting meristem size, competitive sink strength and/or apical dominance. These same, and possibly simpler and more direct effects may therefore also be involved in their efficacy in the induction processes.

THE NATURAL FLOWERING HORMONE 'FLORIGEN' (ANTHESIN)

In spite of continued active research, very little fundamentally new information has been added to that available for a good many years now, though perhaps some aspects have become clearer in relation to the flowering inhibitor researches (cf. below). Hence it would seem superfluous to cite old data or to repeat well-known information. Instead it is likely to be more effective to cite the few salient and well-established facts. Normally, the apical meristem tissue is the receptive site for the cold stimulus of vernalization, and the leaf the sensory organ for photoperiod; in some instances even very small and unexpanded leaves are fully capable of responding to daylength, e.g. Kleinia articulata (Kulkarni and Schwabe, 1984). The leaf reaction is a quantitative one (as is the cold response of meristematic cells in the apex), a fact which tends to be commonly overlooked since so much of work on photoperiodism has been concentrated on those, relatively few, species in which the response is very rapid and evoked after only a short dark period (e.g. Xanthium strumarium or Pharbitis nil) or a single LD cycle (Sinapis alba or Lolium temulentum). In most species the induction process is a cumulative one, moreover, this cumulative effect operates in the induced leaf itself. Thus in Kalanchoe no flowering whatever results if ten leaves or leaf pairs are given, say 2 or 3 short days, yet a single leaf given 12 short days gives almost maximum induction, which can mean hundreds of flowers per plant. The conclusion is clearly that the mechanism (factory) for making flowering stimulus needs to be established, not just a dosage response which could be added up from different leaves. This fact has nowhere been demonstrated better than in the grafting experiments of Zeevaart (1958) where one leaf could be grafted successively to a number of Perilla plants inducing each to flower in turn, until the one and only induced leaf itself succumbed to old age. A Perilla plant induced by such a leaf could not, however, serve as a donor itself. Whether this is the normal pattern for LD plants as well or for all SD species remains to be established, but no clear evidence to the contrary is known to the author.

The factory then grows with each extra inductive photoperiodic cycle, and in Kalanchoe it has been suggested that this is on an exponential scale, resulting roughly in a doubling for every extra inductive cycle (Schwabe and Wimble, 1976). The output from the factory, florigen, then moves to the target meristem where the morphogenetic transformation to an inflorescence or flower is enacted, always provided no inhibition prevents the export from the induced leaf; at that point 'evocation' may be said to occur.

The transmission may, as generally suspected, go with the sucrose-transport stream in the phloem, as shown both by rates of movement and other evidence. While the factory may represent a new enzyme system, the translocatable substance is still totally undefined. Numerous attempts in the past to extract and re-introduce it into non-induced plants have signally failed, in spite of the occasional sporadic claim to have done so. What are the implications of these failures? These, too, are still the same as those put forward many years ago; it could be that a large molecule is involved, or it could be a highly unstable one, or again some moiety linked to another molecule (two-component system) – we do not know. The most recent attempts by Purse (1984) to make phloem extracts in the presence of chelating agents have not led to a solution. The earlier suggestion by Chailakhyan and Lozhnikova (1961) of a combination with gibberellin has not proved very fruitful either. A somewhat similar suggestion by Bernier's group (see Bodson, 1984) concerns the co-involvement of fresh assimilate in evocation. What does seem to be reasonably well established, at least by way of a lack of evidence to the contrary, is, that the transportable stimulus itself is the same for all higher plants for which it has been established – a quite remarkable fact, if true.

How does the stimulus operate? At least in quite a number of species it seems as if there is an activation of the sub-apical meristem (perhaps a normally 'quiescent' area). Clearly not all tissues are reached by hormonal substances ascending towards apices, or the target tissues are not competent to respond, e.g. gibberellins will only in a few cases cause elongation of the youngest 2 or 3 internodes at the apex, whereas auxin transport inhibitors such as TIBA or naphthylphthalalamic acid will do so regularly – only the ivy responds to GAs in this region (Schwabe, 1984). However, this possible activation is probably only one aspect (see also Bernier, 1981).

INHIBITION AND INHIBITORS OF FLOWERING

Rather like the elusive florigen, natural flowering inhibitors have a long history. In LD Plants one of the earliest suggestions of inhibitors is due to Lang and Melchers (1943), a theme taken up again by the same author many years later (Lang et al., 1977). Inhibition by an unknown factor, produced in unfavourable daylengths in Kalanchoe blossfeldiana was discussed by Harder (1948) and later by Schwabe (1959). One of the problems with physiological inhibition is the fact that the agents are generally less specific than those given promotory reactions. Thus in Kalanchoe flowering inhibition due to exogenous application has been shown first for auxin (Harder and van Senden, 1949), then for gibberellic acid (Hardet and Bünsow, 1958) and later still for abscisic acid and xanthoxin, as well as for the natural inhibitor, which for reasons of convenience may be referred to as antiflorigen (Schwabe, 1972). In several LD plants, e.g. Spinacea oleracea, abscisic acid has been shown to have anti-floral activity (Evans, 1966).

However, disregarding the activity of the synthetic hormones or their analogues, what do we know about the natural anti-florigen?

In Kalanchoe which has been most thoroughly studied from this point of view, we know that there really is a specific substance with such action. We know that it is formed in LD, that it soon reaches a maximal level at which it no longer increases, regardless of the duration of the unfavourable photoperiodic treatment. In Kalanchoe this maximum is reached in 2-3 long days. In other species e.g. Hibiscus it may accumulate for longer (Ren et al., 1982). We know that it is made in the leaves and interferes with the establishment of the factory making florigen. The inhibitor can be extracted, as a simple press-sap, is effective with or without centrifugation, can be re-injected into leaves being induced by SD and reduces or stops induction. This fact alone is far stronger evidence for its existence than the elusive florigen has so far been able to command. Moreover, it has recently been possible to show that it is not specific to Kalanchoe and that at least one other SD species can be inhibited as well. It is not present in induced leaves, i.e. it is truly a product, quantitatively dependent upon photoperiod. Its chemical composition has not yet been established, but it should be possible to do so, since a valid bioassay is available. Its mode of action appears to be in the leaf-interfering with the florigen production. Another inhibitor of secret composition was recently revealed by Jaffe (Jaffe and Bridle, 1987) at the Nottingham Easter School. It seems likely that other inhibitors may yet be identified, e.g. in Kleinia articulata there is a powerful transport inhibitor which prevents transport to the stem apex and which emanates from very young, unexpanded leaves (Kulkarni and Schwabe, 1984).

In fact, this situation has been reported on numerous occasions ever since Chailakhyan's classical experiments of inducing only part of single leaves (Chailakhyan, 1945), where the stimulus fails to pass through non-induced leaf areas, or where the presence of a non-induced leaf between the induced one and the target apex prevents the latter from being transformed. Unfortunately, the mode of operation of this type of inhibition is not yet known, though some possible methods were discussed by the author on an earlier occasion (Schwabe and Papafotiou, 1987).

REFERENCES

Abeles, F.B. (1967). Inhibition of flowering in Xanthium pennsylvanicum by ethylene. Plant Physiology 42, 608-609.

Ahmad, S. (1976). "Effects of Environment and Applied Growth Substances on Endogenous Cytokinins in Chrysanthemum morifolium cv. Sunbeam". Ph.D. thesis, London University. pp 317.

Beever, J.E. and Woolhouse, H.W. (1973). Increased cytokinin from root systems of Perilla frutescens and flower and fruit development. Nature 246, 31-32.

Bernier, G., Sachs, R.M. and Kinet, J.M. (1981). "The Physiology of Flowering". Vol. 2. CRC Press, Boca Raton, Florida.

Bodson, M. (1984). Assimilates and Evocation. In "Light and the Flowering Process" (D. Vince-Prue, B. Thomas and K.E. Cockshull eds.), pp 157-169. Academic Press, London.

Bonner, J. and Thurlow, J. (1949). Inhibition of photoperiodic induction in Xanthium by applied auxin. Botanical Gazette 110, 613-624.

Byers, R.E., Baker, L.R., Sell, H.M., Herner, R.C. and Dilley, D.R. (1972). Ethylene : A natural regulator of sex expression in Cucumis melo L. Proceedings of the National Academy of Science, 69, 717-720.

Chailakhyan, M.K.H. (1945) Photoperiodism of individual parts of the leaf, its halves. Comptes Rendus Doklady Academii nauk SSSR, Academy of Sciences URSS, 47, 220-224.

Chailakhyan, M.K.H. (1982). Hormonal substances in flowering. In "Plant Growth Substances" (P.F. Wareing ed.), pp 645-655. Academic Press, London.

Chailakhyan, M.K.H. and Lozhnikova, V.N. (1961). Gibberellin-like substances in higher plants and their effect on growth and flowering Fiziologia Rastenije, 7, 432-438.

Cholodny, N.G. (1939). The internal factors of flowering. Herbage Reviews, 7, 223-247.

Cleland, C.F. (1982). The chemical control of flowering - a status report. In "Plant Growth Substances" (P.F. Wareing ed.), pp 635-644. Academic Press, London.

Cleland, C.F., Tanaka, O. and Fledman, L.J. (1982). Influence of plant growth substances and salicylic acid on flowering and growth in the Lemnaceae (duckweeds). Aquatic Botany 13(1) (Special Issue), 3-20.

Evans, L.T. (1960). Inflorescence initiation in Lolium temulentum L. II. Evidence for inhibitory and promotive processes involving transmissible products. Australian Journal of Biological Science 13, 429-440.

Evans, L.T. (1966). Inhibitory effect on flower induction in a long-day plant. Science 151, 107-108.

Frydman, V.M. and Wareing, P.F. (1973). Phase change in Hedera helix L. II. The possible role of roots as a source of shoot gibberellin-like substances. Journal of Experimental Botany 24, 1139-1148.

Gorter, C.J. (1949). The influence of 2,3,5-triiodobenzoic acid on the growing points of tomatoes. Proceedings Koninglijke Nederlandse Akademie Van Wetenscharpen, 52, 1185-1193.

Harder, R. (1948). Vegetative and productive development of Kalanchoe blossfeldiana, as influenced by photoperiodism. Symposia of the Society for Experimental Biology 2, 117-138. Cambridge University Press, Cambridge.

Harder, R. and Bünsow, R. (1958). Über die Wirkung von Gibberellin auf Entwicklung un Blütenbildung der Kurztagpflanze Kalanchoe blossfeldiana. Planta 51, 201-222.

Harder, R. and Van Senden, H. (1949). Antagonistische Wirkung von Wuchsstuff und "Blühormon". Naturwissenschaften 11, 348.

Henson, I.E. and Wareing, P.F. (1974). Cytokinins in Xanthium strumarium L.: a rapid response to short-day treatment. Physiologia Plantarum 32, 185-187.

Henson, I.E. and Wareing, P.F. (1977a). Cytokinins in Xanthium strumarium L.: the metabolism of cytokinins in detached leaves and buds in relation to photoperiod. New Phytologist 78, 27-33.

Henson, I.E. and Wareing, P.F. (1977b). Cytokinins in Xanthium strumarium L.: some aspects of the photoperiodic control of endogenous levels. New Phytologist 78, 35-45.

Jaffe, M.J. and Bridle, K.H. (1987). A new strategy for the identification of native plant photoperiodically regulated flowering substances. In "The Manipulation of Flowering" (J.G. Atherton ed.), pp 279-287. 45th East School in Agricultural Science, University of Nottingham.

Kulkarni, V.J. and Schwabe, W.W. (1984). Differences in graft transmission of the floral stimulus in two species of Kleinia. Journal of Experimental Botany 35, 422-430.

Lang, A. (1957). The effects of gibberellin upon flower formation. Proceedings of the National Academy of Sciences, U.S.A. 43, 709-717.

Lang, A. (1959) The influence of gibberellin and auxin on photoperiodic induction. In "Photoperiodism and Related Phenomena in Plants and Animals" Publ. No. 55, (R.B. Withrow ed.), pp 329-350. American Association for the Advancement of Science, Washington, D.C.

Lang, A. and Melchers, G. (1943). Die photoperiodische Reaktion von Hyoscyamus niger. Planta 33, 653-702.

228

Lang, A. Chailakhyan, M.C. and Frolova, J.A. (1977). Promotion and inhibition of flower formation in a day-neutral plant in grafts with a short-day plant and a long-day plant. Proceedings of the National Academy of Sciences U.S.A. 74, 2412-2416.

Löve, A. and Löve, D. (1945). Experiments on the effect of animal sex hormones on dioecious plants. Arkiv für Botanik, 32A, 1-60.

Luckwill, L.C. (1970). The Control of Growth and Fruitfulness of Apple Trees. In "Physiology of Tree Crops" (L.C. Luckwill ed.), pp 237-254. Academic Press, London.

Michniewicz, M. and Lang, A. (1962). Effect of nine different gibberellins on stem elongation and flower formation in the cold-requiring and photoperiodic plants grown under non-inductive conditions. Planta 58, 549-563.

Nickel, L.G. (1983). Plant Growth Regulating Chemicals Vol. II. CRC Press, Boca Raton, Florida.

Purse, J. (1984). Phloem exudate of Perilla crispa and its effects on flowering of P. crispa shoot explants. Journal of Experimental Botany 35, 227-238.

Pharis, R.P., Ross, S.D. and McMullan, E. (1980). Promotion of flowering in the Pinaceae by gibberellins. III. Seedlings of Douglas fir. Physiologia Plantarum 50, 119-126.

Pharis, R.P., Ruddat, M.D.E., Glenn, J.L. and Morf, W. (1970) A quantitative requirement for long days in the induction of staminate strobili by gibberellin in the conifer Cupressus arizonica. Canadian Journal of Botany 48, 653-658.

Ren, X.C., Zhang, J-Y., Luo, W-H. and Jin, S-P. (1982). Flower inhibitory effects of long days preceding the inductive short days on SDP Hibiscus cannabinus cv. South Selected. Acta Phytophysiol Sinica 8, 214-221.

Ross, S.D. and Pharis, R.P. (1976). Promotion of flowering in the Pinaceae by gibberellins. I. Sexually mature non-flowering grafts of Douglas fir. Physiologia Plantarum 36, 182-186.

Schwabe, W.W. (1959). Studies of long-day inhibition in short-day plants. Journal of Experimental Botany 10, 317-329.

Schwabe, W.W. (1968). Effects of photoperiod and temperature on flowering of the Chrysanthemum. Scientific Horticulture 20, 89-94.

Schwabe, W.W. (1970) The possible role of plant hormones in the devernalization of the Chrysanthemum. In "Cellular and Molecular Aspects of Floral Induction" (G. Bernier ed.), pp 358-365. Longman, London.

Schwabe, W.W. (1972). Flower inhibition in Kalanchoe blossfeldiana. Bioassay of an endogenous inhibitor and inhibition by (+) abscisic acid and xanthoxin. Planta 103, 18-23.

Schwabe, W.W. (1984). Phyllotaxis. In "Positional Controls in Plant Development" (P.W. Barlow and D.J. Carr eds.), pp 403-440. Cambridge University Press, Cambridge.

Schwabe, W.W. and Al-Doori, A. (1973) Analysis of a juvenile-like condition affecting flowering in the Black Currant (Ribes nigrum). Journal of Experimental Botany 24, 969-981.

Schwabe, W.W. and Papafotiou, M. (1987). The Flowering Problem. In "The Manipulation of Flowering" (J.G. Atherton ed.), pp 351-359. 45th Easter School in Agricultural Science. University of Nottingham.

Schwabe, W.W. and Wimble, R.H. (1976). Control of flower initiation in long- and short-day plants - a common model approach. In "Perspectives in Experimental Biology. Vol. II, Botany" (N. Sunderland ed.), pp 41-57. Pergamon, Oxford.

Sekak, A. (1983). "Studies on Hormonal Regulation of Sex Differentiation of Monoecious (Xanthium strumarium L.) and Dioecious (Mercurialis annua L.) Plants". Ph.D. thesis, London University, pp 283.

Skoog, F. (1935). The effect of X-irradiation on auxin and plant growth. Journal of Cellular and Comparative Physiology, 7, 227-268.

Srinivasan, C. and Mullins, M.G. (1978). Control of flowering in the grapevine (Vitis vinifera L.) Formation of inflorescences in vitro by isolated tendrils. Plant Physiology 61, 127-130.

Suge, H. (1972). Inhibition of photoperiodic floral induction in Pharbitis nil by ethylene. Plant and Cell Physiology 13, 1031-1038.

Tompsett, P.B. and Schwabe, W.W. (1974). Growth hormone changes in Chrysanthemum morifolium. Effects of environmental factors controlling flowering. Annals of Botany 38, 269-285.

Vince-Prue, D. (1985). Photoperiod and Hormones. In "Hormonal Regulation of Development III. Role of Environmental Factors", Encyclopedia of Plant Physiology. New Series. Vol. 11. (R.P. Pharis and D.M. Reid eds.), pp 308-364. Springer Verlag, Berlin.

Wareing, P.F. and El-Antably, H.M.M. (970). The possible role of endogenous growth inhibitors in the control of flowering. In "Cellular and Molecular Aspects of Floral Induction" (G. Bernier ed.), pp 285-303. Longman Group, London.

Zeevaart, J.A.D. (1958). Flower formation as studied by grafting. Mededelingen van de Landbouwhogeschool Wageningen 58, 1-88.

Zeevaart, J.A.D. (1976). Physiology of flower formation. Annual Review of Plant Physiology 27, 321-348.

Zeevaart, J.A.D. (1978). Transmission of the floral stimulus between four different photoperiodic response types in the Crassulaceae. Plant Physiology 61 Supplement 14, No. 72.

Zhadanova, L.P. (1950). Significance of the gaseous regime for the passage of the light stage in plants. Doklady Akademii Nauk SSSR 70, 715-718.

TROPISMS AS INDICATORS OF HORMONE-MEDIATED GROWTH PHENOMENA

I.R. MacDonald[1] and J.W. Hart[2]

[1]The Macaulay Institute for Soil Research, Craigiebuckler, Aberdeen AB9 2QJ, Scotland
[2]Dept of Plant Science, University of Aberdeen, Aberdeen AB9 2UD, Scotland

The characteristic features of growth-regulating hormones, viz., action remote from the site of production and response linked to changes in concentration, are considered in relation to the kinetics of tropic curvature. The differential growth which follows the application of a geotropic stimulus to seedling hypocotyls, is shown to consist of two distinct phases which are separable in time and location. The primary response occurs within minutes of geostimulus and consists of growth inhibition on the upper surface and growth stimulation on the lower surface. The secondary response takes place one to two hours later and involves a basipetal resumption of growth in a non-growing region of the hypocotyl. It is in the secondary response that the characteristics of hormonally-mediated growth are most prominently displayed. The resumption of growth has a non-nutritional dependence on the presence and orientation of the apex and there is convincing evidence of a basipetal migration of differential growth, indicative of longitudinal message transmission, along the hypocotyl. Evidence is also presented that is consistent with the involvement of auxin in the primary tropic response, viz., horizontal hypocotyls immersed in a solution of IAA continue to grow at an equal rate on both upper and lower surfaces, whereas those similarly exposed to a solution of GA show the normal georesponse. A new model is proposed to account for tropic curvature in both roots and shoots in terms of hormonal movement and differential auxin sensitivities of closely adjacent tissues.

INTRODUCTION

Plant hormones and tropisms are inseparable, at least when viewed historically. It was research in the area of tropic responses that originally led to the concept of growth regulation by hormones (see Heslop-Harrison, 1980). Paradoxically, some of the results of more recent studies in this area have been used as evidence against the notion that hormones are involved in the regulation of plant growth (Firn and Digby, 1980; Trewavas, 1981). Hence it may be said that the historical link between tropisms and plant hormones continues to the present day, albeit with a seemingly dramatic switch in emphasis.

A tropism is defined as a directional response of a plant organ to some directional environmental stimulus. There are some non-growth tropic responses. For instance, heliotropism, or sun-tracking, as shown by many leaves and flowers, usually results from reversible turgor changes in specialised pulvinar cells. On the other hand, most tropic responses are based upon differential growth between the two sides of the curving organ. The type of tropism is named after the environmental stimulus that induces it. Phototropism and geotropism are the most universally evident tropisms but thigmotropism, a directional response to touch or physical contact, is a marked characteristic of the tendrils or stems of many climbing plants. Directional responses to nutrients or other chemicals (chemotropism) and to water (hydrotropism) are known to occur in special instances, e.g., during the growth, respectively, of pollen tubes and of certain roots. However, although these are indeed directional responses to localised environmental stimuli, it is not clear whether such responses to chemical stimuli have the same sort of basis, either of perception or of growth regulation, as tropic responses to the physical factors of light, gravity or touch. The term autotropism is used to describe the straightening of a tropistically-curving organ after it has attained the required orientation, but it is arguable whether this phenomenon is a tropism in the strict sense of the term. The straightening action does not seem to be a response to an external, environmental stimulus. Neither is it simply a response to gravity since it occurs in geostimulated roots that are subsequently placed on a klinostat (Larsen, 1953). Moreover, the growth reactions involved in autotropic straightening in a geocurving organ, occur long before the organ reaches the vertical position.

The classic, and still the most widely accepted hypothesis proposed to account for the more obvious forms of tropic behaviour, i.e., positive and negative geotropism and phototropism, is that which developed from the independent researches of N.G. Cholodny and F.W. Went in the 1920s. Since its general presentation by Went and Thimann (1937), it has become somewhat popularised in successive generations of textbooks, and it may be useful to restate its original postulates. These are:

1. Dependence on auxin. The growth of a plant organ is dependent on auxin which is synthesised in the tip.
2. Tip perception. A directional environmental stimulus brings about an asymmetric redistribution of auxin in the tip of the organ.
3. Message transmission. The asymmetry in auxin distribution is transported longitudinally along the organ to produce a response in another region.
4. Concentration dependence. The tropic response represents a growth response to altered auxin levels resulting in growth stimulation and growth inhibition on the opposite sides of the curving organ.
5. Differential sensitivity of roots and shoots. The opposite responses of roots and shoots to gravity is a consequence of their differing sensitivity to auxin, the prevailing level in geostimulated roots becoming supra-optimal for maximum growth.

In recent years certain difficulties and doubts regarding the general validity of the Cholodny-Went theory have been high-lighted and the theory openly challenged. For the most part these difficulties revolve round the validity or otherwise of the auxin gradient and the nature of the actual growth responses during tropic curvature. The difficulties may be grouped as follows:

1. The apex of the organ need not be present for tropic curvature to begin. This calls into question the postulates concerning both tip perception and basipetal transmission of auxin (Firn et al., 1981).
2. In many cases of tropic curvature an auxin gradient either cannot be demonstrated at all or is considered to be of insufficient magnitude to account for the observed differences in growth rate on either side of the organ (Digby and Firn, 1976).
3. It has been claimed that the major growth event responsible for tropic curvature in shoots is actually growth inhibition on the concave side, making the concept of auxin-stimulated growth superfluous (Digby and Firn, 1979).
4. It has further been claimed that the tropic response occurs simultaneously along the length of a responding organ, making redundant the concept of message transmission (Firn and Digby, 1980).

Such claims and observations have led to suggestions that neither auxin nor any other hormone is involved in transmitting information or in regulating growth during the tropic response. In this article we endeavour to demonstrate that many of the characteristics of tropic behaviour do imply the operation of, indeed the necessity for, a mechanism consonant with the Cholodny-Went model especially in respect of long-distance communication and co-ordination of growth responses during curvature. However, some aspects of the original concept require modification, and we here propose a more refined model, based upon differential tissue sensitivities, to account for auxin regulation of tropic curvature.

CHARACTERISTICS OF HORMONE-MEDIATED GROWTH

There has always been a certain difficulty in agreeing upon the definition, or even the general meaning, of the word 'hormone' in its application to plants (Audus, 1965). Most descriptions of plant hormones portray them as naturally-produced substances that regulate or control plant activity by acting in minute amounts, with a separation between the sites of production and response. There are difficulties associated with each of these aspects, particularly in using them to distinguish a hormone from other naturally produced substances such as vitamins, where minute amounts of chemical have large effects on growth and development. However, there are two features which are crucial to any concept of a hormone. These are:

1. Action at a distance. By this it is meant that events occurring in one area or tissue, produce a response in another area. Whether the distance should be measurable in cm or microns is never specified but the concept does imply some transmission or movement of a substance.
2. Control by concentration. By this it is meant that any alteration in the concentration or activity of the hormone will effect a predictable level of growth response. It also carries the implication that a latent growth response may be initiated by the presence of the hormone in appropriate concentration.

In recent years the concept of hormonal transmission has been more explicitly defined to include the idea of target tissues, that is tissues in which the cells capable of responding to a hormone are exclusively located; but this development has not fundamentally altered the classical view of hormonal regulation. Basically, then, in considering tropisms as indicators of hormone-mediated growth, we are concerned with demonstrating the existence of non-nutritional control by one region over the behaviour of, or responses in, another region, this control being exerted through the transmission of a specific organic compound. We now examine the characteristic features of tropic responses to see to what extent they reflect the characteristics of hormone-mediated growth.

CHARACTERISTICS OF TROPIC RESPONSES

1 Growth Rate Changes during Tropic Curvature

It has been established by our own work (MacDonald et al., 1983) and that of others, (Cosgrove, 1981) that the normal, seemingly continuous, straight growth of a hypocotyl comprises bursts of growth that are discontinuous in both space and time. The total overall growth of a hypocotyl is actually made up of discrete zonal growth rates along and across the organ, and these rates are continually changing. Although no regular or predictable pattern to these changes has yet been described, the manner in which growth rate tends to rise and fall at any one point on the hypocotyl suggests that successive waves of growth spiral along the organ. Such a situation presumably is related to, or forms the basis of, nutational behaviour, and it has serious implications for the investigation of growth responses to tropic or any other environmental stimulation. For example, the stage of the dynamically-changing straight growth pattern should be known at the time of onset of an experimental treatment if valid conclusions are to be made about the significance of any changes in growth rates immediately subsequent to the treatment. Such information would also indicate whether the experimental treatment was producing its effect simply by amplifying existing oscillations in growth patterns, or by imposing a completely new pattern of growth on the system — alternatives which imply quite different underlying mechanisms. This aspect may assume greater importance in future work aimed at determining more precisely the timing of growth events consequent upon a tropic stimulation.

Meantime, however, the tropically-induced gross changes in growth rate can be described with some confidence (MacDonald et al., 1983). When a hypocotyl is placed horizontally, the initial changes in growth rates occur within ten or, at most, twenty minutes (Berg et al., 1986), and consist of a marked inhibition of growth on the upper surface and an acceleration of growth on the lower surface of the organ. Subsequent events over the next few hours involve growth stimulation and inhibition on each side of the hypocotyl as the organ curves upwards and then straightens autotropically (see Fig. 1). A similar sequence of growth responses occurs during phototropic curvature, with an initial inhibition of growth on the lit side and a stimulation of growth on the shaded side of a unilaterally irradiated hypocotyl (Hart et al., 1982). Moreover, since, in phototropism, the growth rate on the shaded side is greater than that which occurs if the seedlings are returned to total darkness, it is apparent that real stimulation occurs on the convex side, rather than simply a release from light inhibition of growth. The details of the growth responses in phototropism are complicated by the

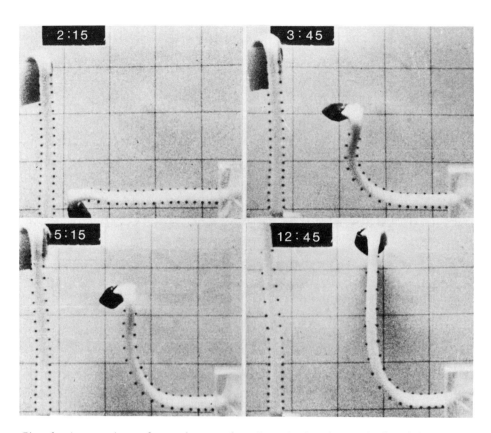

Fig. 1 A comparison of growth as a function of time in vertical and horizontal sunflower seedlings. Note the delayed development of curvature in zones 10-12 (numbering from the apical end) of the horizontal seedling and in the absence of any corresponding growth in the basal third of the vertical seedling.

superimposition of other, non-phototropic, effects of light. For example, it has been established that the common inhibition of hypocotyl straight growth by blue light is a separate response from phototropism (Cosgrove, 1985; Rich et al., 1985). From this it follows that the details of growth responses during phototropic curvature could vary according to the protocol used for tropic stimulation. Different degrees of growth inhibition are seen in phototropically curving cress hypocotyls depending on whether the seedlings have been pretreated in light or darkness before being exposed to unilateral irradiation (Hart et al., 1982).

The results of other investigators are in general agreement with this picture of growth inhibition and stimulation during curvature. The York group have emphasised inhibition as the major feature responsible for hypocotyl curvature (Digby and Firn, 1979) although they also report growth stimulation (Macleod et al., 1986). Similarly growth stimulation on the convex side of tropically-curving coleoptiles (Jaffe et al., 1985; Baskin et al., 1985) and roots (Barlow and Rathfelder, 1985) has also been described. Therefore, both growth inhibition and stimulation seem to be general features of the tropic response. The question which now confronts us is whether these changes in growth rate are hormonally-mediated.

2 Migration of the Tropic Responce

A crucial test of hormone-mediated growth is whether or not there is any indication of 'action at a distance'. The original studies of Dolk (1936) seemed to establish

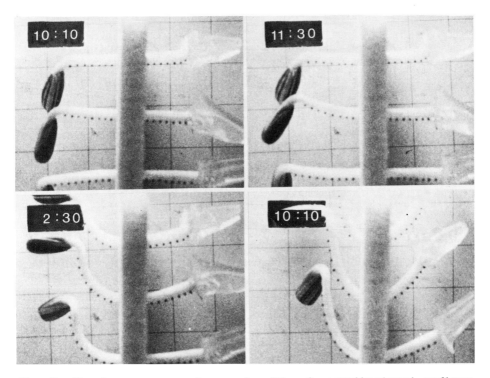

Fig. 2 <u>Time-lapse sequences from a cine film of centrally-pivoted sunflower seedlings undergoing geotropic curvature.</u> Note the absence of curvature in the basal ends for at least one hour following the commencement of curvature at the apical ends.

that in the course of a tropic response, the region of curvature moved along the responding organ in a basipetal direction. However, this view has been disputed by other workers who have claimed that curvature is initiated simultaneously along the length of the organ and that any seeming migration of curvature is an artifact brought about by autotropic straightening being basipetally imposed along the curvature (Digby and Firn, 1979; Trewavas, 1981). We hold to the view that there is a real migration of the tropic response along the hypocotyl and that this can be seen in a number of different ways.

A time-lapse sequence of a geotropic response shows that the region of curvature does in fact move during the response (Fig 1). In addition to any movement due to autotropic straightening, it can be clearly seen that the previously-straight basal regions eventually become curved. However, it could be argued that the initial straightness of the basal regions in the early stages of the response is due to the slower development of curvature, rather than to a later initiation of curvature. That the tropic responses do indeed occur earlier in the apical regions can be visually demonstrated in another type of experiment.

A horizontal hypocotyl can be anchored about half-way along its axis such that each end is free to move upwards in response to gravity. Firn et al. (1981) first performed this experiment and observed that both ends did curve upwards. They put this forward as evidence that curvature commenced simultaneously in all growing regions of the hypocotyl. However, for this conclusion to be justified it has to be demonstrated not just that both ends bend upwards, but that they do so at the same time, though not necessarily at the same rate. Whether both ends begin curvature simultaneously depends, in fact, on the point of anchorage of the hypocotyl. If the hypocotyl pivots at a point where differential growth is occurring on either side of the anchorage point, each end will show simultaneous uplift, the extent of the curvature being determined by the respective growth rates. In experiments with horizontal hypocotyls pivoted at different locations along the axis, we have shown that a position can be found at which the behaviour of the two ends is markedly distinct, the movement of the apical end preceding that of the basal end by 1 - 2 hours (Fig. 2). This clearly indicates a temporal separation of events along the hypocotyl.

Basipetal migration of tropic curvature can also be demonstrated by consideration of the actual growth responses. We have already indicated that a significant feature of the tropic response is growth stimulation on the convex side of the curving organ. A closer examination of growth during geotropic curvature of a hypocotyl shows that the region of greatest growth stimulation moves along the lower side of the organ from the apex towards the base (MacDonald et al., 1983). This basipetal migration of growth is particularly clear if the algebraic difference between the growth rates of the upper and lower sides is considered (Table 1). In the more apical regions this difference attains a maximum value within the first hour, but only in later hours does it reach high values in the more basal zones. A basipetal geocurvature of roots (Barlow and Rathfelder, 1985) and the photocurvature of coleptiles (Baskin et al., 1985) suggesting that migration of growth rate changes is a characteristic feature of a tropic response.

Finally, we have shown that during the later stages of tropic curvature, the basipetal migration of growth results in the actual initiation of growth in previously non-growing basal zones of the lower side (Hart and MacDonald, 1984). This resumption of growth can be seen from a comparison of the marked basal zones of geostimulated and unstimulated hypocotyls (Fig. 1).

3 The Role of the Apex in Tropic Curvature

A basic tenet of the Cholodny-Went theory is that the apex is intimately involved both in the perception of the tropic stimulus and in the regulation of the tropic response. However, it has been repeatedly demonstrated that tropic curvatures can occur not only in the absence of the apex (Iwami and Masuda, 1974) but even in

Table 1   The curvature index of successive zones from the apex downwards of etiolated cucumber hypocotyls undergoing geotropism.

Curvature index*

	Time (h) from commencement of geostimulus				
Zone	0	1	2	3	4
1	165	66	66	-132	242
2	-66	264	132	-488	44
3	11	330	176	-330	-132
4	-66	176	286	-124	-418
5	88	374	352	-132	-110
6	-11	110	308	71	-66
7	0	264	264	212	-132
8	-22	198	264	430	0
9	-11	154	198	112	88
10	-11	66	154	211	-22
11	-11	44	22	22	198
12	-15	-88	22	66	-22
Total	11	1958	2244	-42	-330

*   This value is the algebraic difference between the growth rates on either side of each zone. Low numbers indicate nearly equal growth on both sides. Negative values indicate autotropic correction. High positive values indicate geocurvature. The region of maximum upward curvature in each hour is encircled. Values are taken from MacDonald et al. (1983) quod vide for further details.

isolated segments of an organ (see references in Firn et al., 1981). Such findings have been used as evidence that the apex does not have a role in the tropic responses of whole organs (Firn et al., 1981). However, in considering the role of the apex in tropic growth, it must be made clear what precisely is meant by 'the tropic response' - specifically, whether it refers to an incipient, partial curvature in a local region, or to the fully completed reorientation of the whole organ. Evidence has already been published indicating that the presence of a certain amount of apical tissue is necessary for full expression of the geotropic response in sunflower hypocotyls (MacDonald and Hart, 1985). Furthermore this effect of the apex is not simply by way of supplying nutritional or energy requirements since detaching the cotyledons while leaving the apical bud intact, has no effect on the extent of tropic curvature or on growth, at least over a 24 hour period.

This involvement of the apex in the tropic response is not limited merely to a requirement for its presence. The full expression of the response, both in terms of the completeness of bending and the appearance of growth in the basal regions of the hypocotyl, requires that the apex itself must be horizontal. For example, if a hypocotyl is gently flexed so that the apex is kept vertical when the basal half is horizontal (Fig. 3), there is no resumption of growth in the basal regions. That is, unless the apex itself is geostimulated, one characteristic feature of the georesponse does not occur. Conversely, if a seedling is fixed in such a way that the apical end is maintained in a horizontal orientation, while the root end is unrestricted, the root end swings right over describing a semi-circle (Fig. 4). In other words, if the apex is prevented from reorientating itself, growth continues to be stimulated irrespective of the orientation of the intermediate zones. A

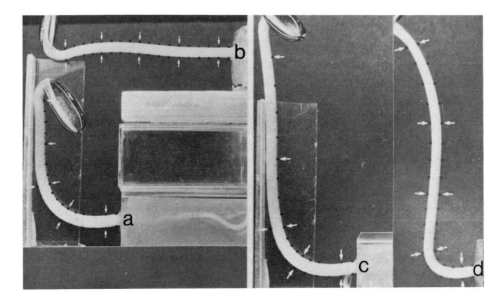

Fig. 3 A comparison of growth over 24 h of a horizontal sunflower seeding with a seedling flexed to a right-angle. a and c; flexed seedling at the beginning and end of the experiment; b and d; horizontal seedling at similar times. Note the absence of growth in the basal zones of the flexed seedling.

similar response was noted in the coleoptile of the grass Setaria veridis by Francis Darwin (1899). In the light of this evidence, we maintain that the apical regions of the hypocotyl do play a regulatory role in some aspects of tropic reorientation, though not as the unique site of stimulus perception. Some form of environmentally-induced instruction does originate from the apex to produce a response in the basal regions of the hypocotyl.

4 Summary of Tropic Events

It is evident that tropic curvature involves early and later events which may be summarised as follows. The initial responses, occurring within minutes, consist of growth inhibition on the concave side of the organ and growth stimulation on the convex side. These responses, especially growth inhibition, may be imposed simultaneously along the length of the growing zone of the organ. The apex does not seem to be necessary for the induction of these early events and the stimulus for the initial responses may be perceived by the responding regions themselves, with no involvement of longitudinal message transmission. Later responses, occurring within 1-3 hours, consist of a basipetal migration of growth stimulation on the convex side and the imposition of corrective autotropic growth responses, which also exhibit basipetal migration. The apical region seems to play some kind of regulatory role in these later events. Thus it is with regard to the later responses of tropic curvature that the characteristics of hormonally-mediated growth are most clearly evident. It is these responses which demonstrate that, as a consequence of an environmental stimulus, an instruction is transmitted from one region to initiate a new pattern of behaviour in another region. But to say that, is not to say that hormonal movement is not also involved in the initial growth responses of tropic curvature.

238

Fig. 4 A multi-exposure photograph of the geotropic response of a sunflower seedling anchored at its apical end. Note the continuance of curvature beyond the vertical.

EXPERIMENTS INDICATIVE OF HORMONAL INVOLVEMENT IN TROPIC RESPONSE

1 Omnilateral Auxin Application and Georesponse.

If the georesponse of horizontal hypocotyls is brought about by a redistribution of auxin as proposed by the Cholodny-Went theory, it should be possible to prevent the establishment of an auxin gradient and the concomitant differential growth rates of upper and lower surfaces, by surrounding the tissue with an auxin solution of appropriate concentration. In agreement with this prediction it can be shown that when sunflower hypocotyls are placed horizontally in a solution of 10 μM IAA, the normal georesponse does not occur (Fig. 5). Its absence is attributable, not to the prevention of growth, but to the obliteration of differential growth. The upper surface extends in parallel with the lower surface and consequently the hypocotyl remains horizontal. An identical response is obtained in a solution of NAA whereas hypocotyls immersed either in water or in a solution of GA exhibit the expected georesponse (Fig. 6). This is at least circumstantial evidence in support of the theory that an auxin gradient is involved in the georesponse. This effect of immersing a hypocotyl in 20 μM NAA was also reported by Firn and Digby (1977) but they discounted its significance. The obliteration of curvature in IAA has recently been reported with soybean hypocotyls (Salisbury et al., 1986).

239

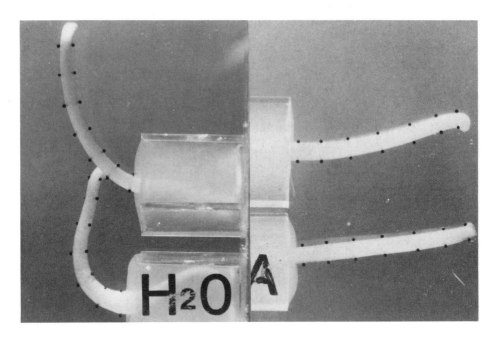

Fig. 5 A comparison of the georesponse of sunflower seedlings immersed either in water (left-hand seedlings) or in a solution of 10 μM IAA (right-hand seedlings).

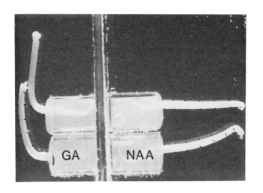

Fig. 6 A comparison of the georesponse of sunflower seedlings immersed in a solution of either 10 μM GA (left-hand seedlings) or 10 μM NAA (right-hand seedlings).

2 The Role of the Epidermis in Geocurvature

Evidence in support of the involvement of auxin in hypocotyl geocurvature can also be adduced from experiments using longitudinally bisected hypocotyls. Even in the absence of auxin treatment, these half-hypocotyls give significant pointers to the basis of geotropic growth. If the georesponse of a horizontal hypocotyl, bisected longitudinally so as to leave only the upper half of the organ intact, is compared

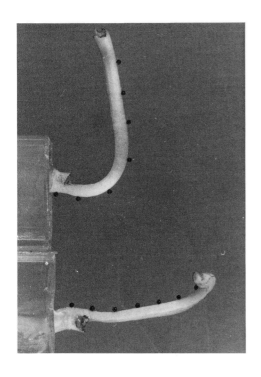

Fig. 7   A comparison of the
georesponse of sunflower seedlings
longitudinally bisected so that
only the upper, or lower, semi-
cylinder of hypocotyl remains
Resin beads adhere to the uncut
surface.   Note the better
georesponse of the seedling
retaining its lower surface.

with that of a hypocotyl bisected so as to retain only the lower half, it can be
seen that the geocurvature of the lower half is virtually complete while that of
the upper half is still rudimentary (Fig. 7). This differing response between the
two halves was first demonstrated by Copeland (1900) and later used as evidence

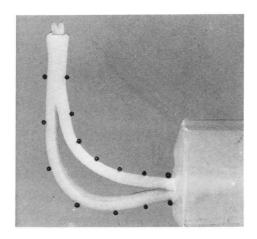

Fig.   8   The contrasting
georesponses of the upper and
lower halves of a partially-
bisected, horizontal sunflower
hypocotyl.

against the view that geocurvature of the lower half is dependent on the transmission of a substance from the upper half (Firn and Digby, 1977). It is certainly evidence that the georesponse is dictated by the orientation of the half-hypocotyl; and since curvature is more pronounced in these semi-cylinders when the convex (epidermal) surface is facing downwards rather than upwards, it points to the epidermis as having a decisive role. Partially split hypocotyls strikingly illustrate the more extensive growth which occurs in the lower half (Fig. 8).

3 Differential Auxin Sensitivity of Epidermal and Sub-epidermal Tissues.

The differences noted above are not confined to comparisons between the upper and lower halves. Growth differences can also be observed within each half, between the epidermal and cortical cells. These differences are amplified in the presence of auxin. If a vertical, partially split, hypocotyl is immersed in a solution of IAA, the epidermal cells grow more rapidly than the internal cells with the result that the halves bow outwards (Fig. 9). This differential growth is attributable to the IAA and not to an inhibitory wound effect, because split hypocotyls immersed in water or GA show no differential expansion. Clearly the IAA is here stimulating the growth of the epidermis without having the same effect on the sub-epidermal tissues. The differential expansion in the presence of IAA is no new finding. It is exactly analogous to the split pea hypocotyl auxin bioassay developed by Went in 1934. The early workers were cognizant of the fact that the bioassay operated through the "different response of the outer and inner tissues to the same hormone concentration" (Audus, 1965, p 28). It would appear, however, that the implications of this differential sensitivity, insofar as tropic curvature is concerned, were overlooked.

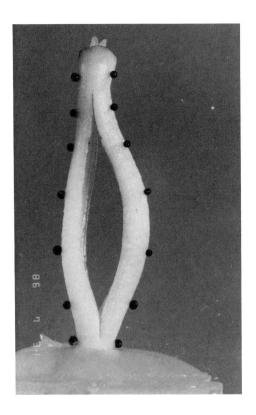

Fig. 9   Differential   growth responses   of   outer   and   inner tissues   shown   by   a   partially-bisected   sunflower   hypocotyl immersed   in   a   solution   of 10 μM IAA.

242

Fig. 10 A comparison of growth and
curvature in upper and lower halves
of longitudinally-bisected sunflower
hypocotyls immersed in a solution of
10 μM IAA for 2 h.

If half-hypocotyls are placed horizontally in a solution of IAA, the epidermal
cells expand much more rapidly than the cortical cells. This is the case
irrespective of whether the half-hypocotyl is orientated with the epidermal surface
facing upwards or downwards. The result of this differential expansion of the
epidermal tissue is that the hypocotyl commences to bend in an inward direction
relative to the epidermal surface (Fig. 10). As growth predominates at the apical
end, the hypocotyl then grows into a tight coil. In the case of the 'lower' half,
the coiling is upwards; with the 'upper' half, the coiling is downwards (Fig. 11).
In either case the direction of growth is determined not by gravity but by the
differential effect of auxin on the epidermal and sub-epidermal tissues. This
interpretation is supported by the fact that half-hypocotyls immersed in a solution
of GA show a normal georesponse (Fig. 12). It may be concluded that the epidermis
is the target tissue for the growth-promoting action of auxin and that the internal
cells do not respond in the same way.

Fig. 11 A comparison of growth
and curvature in upper and lower
halves of longitudinally-bisected
sunflower hypocotyls immersed in
a solution of 10 μM IAA for 18 h.
Note the coiling of the hypocotyl
resulting from the stimulation
of epidermal growth.

243

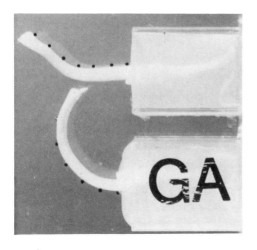

Fig. 12   A comparison of growth and curvature in upper and lower halves of longitudinally-bisected sunflower hypocotyls immersed in a solution of 10 μM GA for 18 h.

The crucial role of the epidermal cells in tropic curvature has been remarked on by several groups of workers although without fundamental agreement as to how it functions.   Questions to which opposing answers have been given include whether peeled hypocotyls are able to respond to gravity or to auxin or even to grow at all.   Many reported experiments are unsatisfactory inasmuch as no account has been taken of the 'growth' contribution resulting from the non-metabolic, non-directional expansion of cortical tissues released from the constraint imposed by the epidermis.   Firn and Digby (1977) took the view that peeled sunflower hypocotyls do grow but fail to respond to auxin (or to gravity).   Taken all in all, the evidence is good enough to lend credence to the view that peeled tissues do not react to auxin as to non-peeled hypocotyls.   The differing auxin sensitivities of epidermal and sub-epidermal tissues is fundamental to our proposed model for tropic curvature.

PROPOSED MODEL FOR TROPIC CURAVTURE

The model proposed for tropic curvature makes two assumption regarding hypocotyl growth.   The first is that the epidermis controls the extension growth of a stem of hypocotyl, a view which has received increasing support in recent years (Thimann and Schneider, 1938; Firn and Digby, 1977; Brummell and Hall, 1980).   A corollary to this proposition is that a tissue with different physiological characteristics is located adjacent to the epidermal, growth-regulating tissue.   Incidentally, it is to be noted that it is immaterial whether the epidermis regulates growth by acting as a restraining influence on some other expanding tissue, or whether it is itself the propelling force.

The second assumption is that a differential auxin sensitivity characterises the epidermal and sub-epidermal tissues.   The experiments already described point to the epidermis as being the tissue most responsive to auxin and there are numerous reports in the literature confirming its role as the target tissue (see Brummell and Hall, 1980).   Given the role of epidermal cells as the target tissue, it follows that the sub-epidermal tissue must have a different sensitivity to auxin.   Auxin concentrations that stimulate the growth of epidermal cells will have little or no effect on the sub-epidermal cells or may even inhibit their growth.   Any such difference in responsiveness may be due to any of the aspects of sensitivity discussed by Firn (1986).

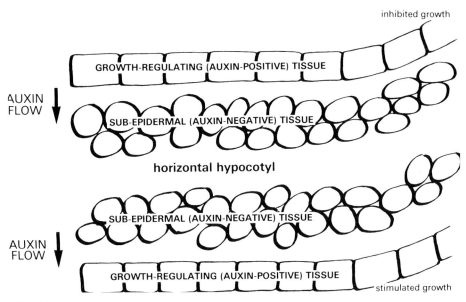

inhibited growth

GROWTH-REGULATING (AUXIN-POSITIVE) TISSUE

AUXIN
FLOW

SUB-EPIDERMAL (AUXIN-NEGATIVE) TISSUE

horizontal hypocotyl

SUB-EPIDERMAL (AUXIN-NEGATIVE) TISSUE

AUXIN
FLOW

GROWTH-REGULATING (AUXIN-POSITIVE) TISSUE

stimulated growth

Fig. 13 Diagrammatic representation of growth rate changes caused by auxin flow between differentially-sensitive tissues in a horizontal hypocotyl.

The model we now suggest for tropic curvature, proposes that the initial growth changes are a consequence of lateral auxin transport between the epidermal and adjacent, sub-epidermal tissues (Fig. 13). In a horizontal hypocotyl, auxin is transported out of the upper epidermal cells and into the sub-epidermal cells. Given the differing sensitivity of these adjacent tissues to auxin, the effect of this auxin transfer is to decrease the growth rate of both tissues, the concentration having become sub-optimal in the one and supra-optimal in the other. Growth in the upper surface is rapidly arrested. On the lower surface of the hypocotyl, auxin similarly moves downwards but, in this case, the movement is out of the sub-epidermal cells, permitting an acceleration of their growth, and into the epidermal cells, inducing a more rapid growth. Growth therefore accelerates on the lower surface and curvature commences. It has to be noted that this initial response may be quite local, the altered growth rates—on both surfaces being achieved without any need for auxin to move across the whole organ. There may not even be an auxin gradient of any magnitude.

The later stages of geocurvature involving a resumption of growth in the non-growing basal region of a hypocotyl, may be accounted for by a more traditional Cholodny-Went process in which, in response to tropic stimulation of the apex, an increased supply of auxin sweeps predominantly down the lower side of the organ. In this stage, an auxin gradient across the organ may be produced but, again, assuming the differential auxin sensitivity of adjacent tissues, it need not be of any great magnitude to produce the observed growth effects. Evidence in favour of an increased basipetal auxin flow can be seen in the continued curvature of a seedling, the apex of which is fixed horizontally (Fig. 4).

245

The model therefore explains both the initial and the later growth responses of tropic curvature in terms of hormonal movement. It brings together the more traditional elements of hormonal theory which postulate that 'information' is transmitted longitudinally by hormonal movement (the later responses) and the more recent concept of responses being due to differential sensitivity to growth regulator (the initial responses). However, the innovative elements in the model, in its application to negative geotripism, distinguishing it, for example, from the trans-organ hypothesis of Iwami and Masuda (1976), are, firstly, that differential sensitivity lies between distinct tissues (comprising epidermal and sub-epidermal cells), rather than between unspecified cells; and, secondly, that the auxin redistribution occurs between adjoining cells rather than across the entire body of the hypocotyl. This concept of close-range redistribution, if tenable, makes irrelevant not just opinions based on the magnitude or otherwise of reported auxin gradients but also questions as to whether auxin can be transported in sufficient quantity and at sufficient speed from one surface to the other. Neither, it should be said, would measurements of net changes in auxin concentration in epidermal peels alone, comprising as they do several layers of cells, necessarily reveal the predicted changes in auxin levels.

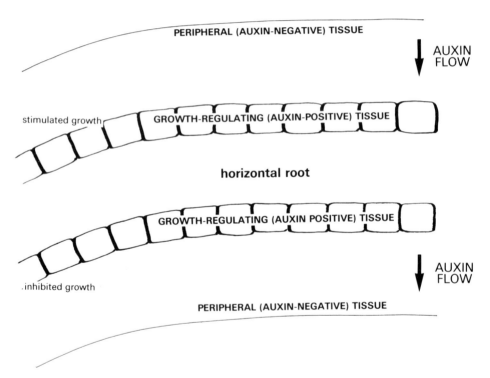

Fig. 14 Diagrammatic representation of growth rate changes caused by auxin flow between differentially-sensitive tissues in a horizontal root.

Since the fundamental feature of the model is the differing auxin sensitivities of adjacent tissues, any environmental factor giving rise to auxin redistribution between adjoining cells, could induce tropic response, and it is not difficult to there may well be complications through other effects of light on growth being overlaid on the tropic response. Furthermore, the case of phototropism is probably much more complex than that of geotropism if only because it appears to override geotropism so irresistibly (Hart and MacDonald, 1981).

With one important adjustment, the same basic model can also account for the positive geotropism of roots. The Cholodny-Went theory attempted to accommodate the inverse tropic responses of shoots and roots by postulating a difference in their relative sensitivities to auxin. In our model the differing geotropic response of the root to that of the shoot is a consequence of the differing morphology of root and shoot. Specifically this difference involves the spatial transposition in the root of the auxin-stimulated, growth-determining, tissue and its less auxin-positive counterpart. That is to say, in the root the growth regulating tissue must, according to our model, be located towards the interior, allowing it to be encircled by a more auxin-negative tissue (Fig. 14). Thus when the root is placed horizontally, the gravity-induced redistribution of auxin between 'auxin-positive' and 'auxin-negative' tissues tends to increase the auxin content of the upper, 'auxin-positive', growth-determining tissue, and, by the same token, to decrease the auxin content of the lower, growth-regulating tissue with the result that the root bends downwards.

It has, of course, still to be established that the growth-regulating tissue in a root is located internally in contrast to that in a shoot. But it is at least logical to suppose that such a vital component of root function would be protectively located. Barlow (1982) has pointed out that the choice of 'motor cells' in a root rests between the epidermal cells, the cortical cells or the endodermal cells. Interestingly enough, he concluded that cortical cells would be the most likely source of the driving force in the endodermis would be equally serviceable to the model. In this connection it is of interest that Bridges et al. (1973) found that in Zea roots, IAA was largely confined to the stele.

The model, we submit, is not without its merits. It brings together the traditional concepts of topic response and the new insights regarding tissue sensitivity. It postulates a physiological unity of action in the tropic behaviour of the whole plant, the inverse responses of root and shoot being attributable to morphological, rather than physiological, diversity. This concept of plant growth being controlled by a dynamic tension between two adjacent tissues, each having different sensitivities to a growth regulator, offers a more credible explanation of the variety and rapidity of growth rate changes in contiguous regions of a turning and twisting plant organ than is possible in terms of the crude Cholodny-Went formulation. Its presuppositions have a semblance of experimental support and its predictions are amenable to experimental test.

A century ago, insights derived from a study of tropic growth led to the discovery of plant hormones and a new understanding of the regulation of plant growth. It is not outwith the bounds of possibility that present-day investigations of the problem of tropic growth could still yield important clues to the mechanism of plant growth. In this context, one topic that should be investigated is the possibility that a dynamic tension between two adjacent tissues, one of which has a propelling role and the other of which has a restraining role, may be the basis of the power of movement in plants.

REFERENCES

Audus, L.J. (1965). "Plant Growth Substances". Leonard Hill, London.

Barlow, P.W. (1982). Cellular aspects of gravitropism, particularly in roots. In "Plant Growth Substances 1982" (P.F. Wareing ed.), pp 507-518. Academic Press, London.

Barlow, P.W. and Rathfelder, E.L. (1985). Distribution and redistributions of extension growth along vertical and horizontal gravireacting maize roots. Planta 165, 134-141.

Baskin, T.I., Iino, M., Green, P.B. and Briggs, W.R. (1985). High-resolution measurement of growth during first positive phototropism in maize. Plant, Cell and Environment 8, 595-603.

Berg, A.R., MacDonald, I.R., Hart, J.W. and Gordon, D.C. (1986). Relative elemental elongation rates in the etiolated hypocotyl of sunflower. (Helianthus annuus L.) - a comparison of straight growth and gravitropic growth. To appear in Botanical Gazette.

Bridges, I.G., Hillman, J.R. and Wilkins, M.B. (1973). Identification and localisation of auxin in primary roots of Zea mays by mass spectrometry. Planta 115, 189-192.

Brummell, D.A. and Hall, J.L. (1980). The role of the epidermis in auxin-induced and fusicoccin-incuded elongation of Pisum sativum segments. Planta 150, 371-379.

Copeland, E.B. (1900). Studies on the geotropism of stems. Botanical Gazette 29, 185-196.

Cosgrove, D.J. (1981). Rapid suppression of growth by blue light. Occurrence, time course and general characteristics. Plants Physiology 42, 745-751.

Cosgrove, D.J. (1985). Kinetic seperation of phototropism from blue light inhibition of stem growth. Photochemistry and Photobiology 42, 745-751.

Darwin, F. (1899). On geotropism and the localisation of the sensitive region. Annals of Botany 13, 567-574.

Digby, J. and Firn, R.D. (1976). A critical assessment of the Cholodny-Went theory of shoot geotropism. Current Advances in Plant Science 8, 953-960.

Digby, J. and Fiurn, R.D. (1979). An analysis of the changes in the growth rate occurring during the initial stages of geocurvature in shoots. Plant, Cell and Environment 2, 145-148.

Dolk, H.E. (1936). Geotropism and the growth substance. Recueil des travaux botaniques neerlandais 33, 509-585.

Firn, R.D. (1986). Growth substance sensitivity: the need for clearer ideas, precise terms and purposeful experiments. Physiologia Plantarum 67, 267-272.

Firn, R.D. and Digby, J. (1977). The role of peripheral cell layers in the geotropic curvature of sunflower hypocotyls: a new model of shoot geotropism. Australian Journal of Plant Physiology 4, 337-347.

Firn, R.D. and Digby, J. (1980). The establishment of tropic curvatures in plants. Annual Review of Plant Physiology 31, 131-347.

Firn, R.D., Digby, J. and Hall, A. (1981). The role of the shoot apex in geotropism. Plant, Cell and Environment 4, 125-129.

Hart, J.W., Gordon, D.C. and MacDonald, I.R. (1982). Analysis of growth during photographic curvature of cress hypotyls. Plant, Cell and Environment 5, 361-366.

Hart, J.W. and MacDonald, I.R. (1981). Phototropism and geotropism in hypocotyls of cress (Lepidium sativum L.). Plant, Cell and Environment 4, 197-201.

Hart, J.W. and MacDonald, I.R. (1984). Is there a role for the apex in shoot geotropism? Plant Physiology 74, 272-277.

Heslop-Harrison, J. (1980). Darwin and the Movement of Plants: A Retrospect. In "Plant Growth Substances 1979" (F. Skoog ed.) pp 3-14. Springer-Verlag, Berlin.

Iwami, S. and Masuda, Y. (1974). Geotropic response of cucumber hypocotyls. Plant and Cell Physiology 15, 121-129.

Iwami, S. and Masuda, Y. (1976). Distribution of labelled auxin in geotropically stimulated stems of cucumber and pea. Plant and Cell Physiology 17, 227-237.

Jaffe, M.J., Wakefield, A.H., Telewski, F., Gulley, E. and Biro, R. (1985). Computer-assisted image analysis of plant growth, thigmomorphogenesis, and gravitropism. Plant Physiology 77, 722-730.

Larsen, P. (1953). Influence of gravity on rate of elongation and on geotropic and autotropic reactions in roots. Physiologia Plantarum 6, 735-774.

MacDonald, I.R. and Hart, J.W. (1985). Apical involvement in geogrowth responses of the horizontal hypocotyl. Journal of Plant Physiology 118, 353-356.

MacDonald, I.R. and Hart, J.W. (1985). The role of the apex in normal and tropic growth of sunflower hypocotyls. Planta 163, 549-553.

MacDonald, I.R., Hart, J.W. and Gordon, D.C. (1983). Analysis of growth during geotropic curvature in seedling hypocotyls. Plant, Cell and Environment 6, 401-406.

Macleod, K., Firn, R.D. and Digby, J. (1986). The phototropic responses of Avena coleoptiles. Journal of Experimental Botany 37, 542-548.

Rich, T.C.G., Whitelam, G.C., and Smith, H. (1985). Phototropism and axis extension in light-grown mustard (Sinapis alba L.) seedlings. Photochemistry and Photobiology 42, 789-792.

Salisbury, F.B., Rorabaugh, P., White, R. and Gillespie, L. (1986). A key role for sensitivity to auxin in gravitropic stem bending. Plant Physiology 80, Suppl. p. 26.

Thimann, K.V. and Schneider, C.L. (1938). Differential growth in plant tissues. American Journal of Botany 25, 627-641.

Trewavas, A. (1981). How do plant growth substances work? Plant, Cell and Environment 4, 203-228.

Went, F.W. and Thimann, K.V. (1937). "Phytohormones". Macmillan, New York.

HORMONES AND PLANT TROPISMS - THE DEGENERATION OF A MODEL OF HORMONAL CONTROL

Richard.D.Firn and A.B.Myers

Department of Biology, University of York, Heslington, York, YO1 5DD, England.

The single most influential piece of work on plant hormones has been the study of plant tropisms. However, the 60 years of work on this subject has failed to provide an adequate hormonal explanation of any type of tropistic response. It is argued that research in this area has often been conducted without the constraint of a logical conceptual framework. Consequently, the original Cholodny-Went model has suffered from "conceptual drift" and it has evolved through several forms. During this time, the postulated role of auxin changed from being a long distance messenger to being an intracellular regulator yet this fundamental change was not formally noted. Those studying other types of hormonal control in plants might learn from the mistakes that have been made in these classical studies.

INTRODUCTION

It is tempting to use this opportunity to provide a detailed description of some tropistic responses and to explain why certain hormonal explanations of the processes are inadequate. However, such a discussion would lead us into the complexities of tropistic responses when the real purpose of this book is to critically examine the concept of hormonal control. Furthermore, many of the objections to the hormonal models of tropistic responses have been discussed elsewhere in recent years (Digby and Firn,1976; Firn and Digby,1980; Franssen et al.,1982; Digby et al.,1982; Firn and Tamimi,1986; Firn,1986). It therefore seems more useful in this chapter to focus attention on the general lessons which plant hormonologists might draw from examining how the idea of hormonal involvement in tropisms has evolved. It will be argued that many of the problems which beset the subject of plant hormones today have their roots in the studies centered around the classical Cholodny-Went (C-W) model. This model was the foundation stone of our subject and many of our approaches to studying hormonal control in plants have evolved from it. Yet these approaches have not managed to produce a satisfactory hormonal explanation of tropistic responses despite nearly 60 years of effort. It becomes apparent from considering the decades of work in this area that detailed arguments about a few aspects of hormonal involvement in tropisms have obscured the fact that the theoretical framework surrounding the C-W model has never been stable nor secure. In the first part of this article we shall examine the way in which hormonal models of tropisms evolved and in the second part we shall try to draw some generally useful conclusions from the survey.

THE EVOLUTION OF MODELS OF HORMONAL CONTROL AS APPLIED TO SHOOT TROPISMS

No doubt some readers will think this section of the article could be omitted - everyone has been taught about the C-W model and it surely needs no introduction. However, we hope to show that there is no such thing as "the" C-W model. Instead there have been a succession of models which have blended into each other. We believe that by examining the reasons for the changes which have occured over the years, one can learn much about the problems that have beset the area. Interestingly, the evolution of ideas of hormonal control, as they apply to studies of tropisms, followed very closely the attitudes prevalent in the subject generally. Hence an examination of what happened in this area could be of value to studies of plant hormonal control in general.

251

Model 1 - Auxin as a Messenger

The need to transmit information, from the tropistic sensing region in the apex to the elongation zone, was fundamental to the original model of hormonal control in plants. The apex was thought to have complete control over organ extension by supplying the elongating cells with regulatory amounts of a single controlling substance (called auxin). Although a number of workers had been investigating such a model of growth control in roots, coleoptiles and hypocotyls, a general model in relation to tropisms was formulated independently by Cholodny and by Went (Went and Thimann, 1937). It was proposed that a lateral redistribution of auxin occurred in the sensing apical cells and that this asymmetry was transmitted to the elongation zone resulting in differential growth. The beauty of the model was that it attempted to explain root and shoot gravitropism and shoot phototropism, giving a unity to the area.

Model 2 - Auxin as a Co-ordinator

The first change to the above model was soon to appear and it was a very significant one. It was known that both gravitropic and phototropic stimuli could, in fact, be perceived in cells other than the apex (Darwin, 1880). Indeed, decapitated coleoptiles and hypocotyls can show a gravitropic response. Hence processes occuring in the apex, whether involved in gravity sensing or in hormone production, are not essential for the initiation of the gravitropic response in such organs. The need for the longitudinal transmission of information, central to the thinking of Model 1, was obviously not absolute. In the revised model, auxin was still the regulatory substance but lateral auxin redistribution was thought to occur in the elongation zone, as well as near the apex. Those committed originally to Model 1 seem to have made the change to Model 2 less difficult by noting that even in cases where the stimulus was obviously not sensed exclusively in the apex, the apex was the most sensitive region for stimulus perception. This continued emphasis on the apex, even when a special general role for it had been disproved, drew attention away from the fact that the logical framework, fundamental to Model 1, was being abandoned. The need for the transfer of a message along the organ was evidently not universal, but a central role was retained for the supposed messenger substance, auxin. Auxin movement across the elongation zone in response to a tropistic stimulus could not even be seen as message transfer across the organ, because cells in the elongation zone obviously had to have information about the axis of tropistic stimulation in order to transport auxin in the right direction. The very fundamental change which had occurred when Model 1 was modified to create Model 2 is evident when one realises that, in Model 1, cells in the elongation zone were directed by auxin, yet here, in Model 2, cells in the elongation zone are actually directing the controller. It is apparent that in Model 2 a new role for auxin was needed as the hormone was no longer a simple messenger. It seems that auxin was now seen more as a means of coordinating growth across the axis. Lateral movement of auxin, from one side of the organ to the other, was an attractive way of explaining what was assumed to be co-ordinated growth rate changes causing organ curvature.

Model 3 - Auxin as a Local Messenger

Just as existing knowledge about the physiology of tropisms made Model 1 unattractive as a general model, evidence inconsistent with Model 2 was available even before it was formulated. Experiments with longitudinally bisected organs, or parts of organs, had shown that the upper and lower halves of gravistimulated organs could show graviresponses even when isolated (Copeland,1900). These experiments showed, for instance, that the growth rate stimulation at the lower side of a horizontal organ was not dependent on any substance transported into the lower half from the upper half (Firn and Digby,1977). This fact challenged the logic behind Model 2, which was based on the importance of trans-organ movement of auxin. However, a new model of auxin involvement in shoot tropisms presented itself when the importance of another old piece of knowledge was finally appreciated. Long before auxin (IAA) was discovered, ample evidence existed that, in shoots, the elongation rate of the organ was largely controlled by the mechanical properties of the epidermal and sub-epidermal cells (the "peripheral cell layers") (Firn and Digby,1977). It was logical to propose that the elongation rate of some part of an organ might be controlled, not by the total auxin content of that part of the organ, but by the auxin content of the adjacent peripheral cell layers. In the case of shoot gravitropism, it was proposed that movement of auxin into these cells at the lower surface, and out of these cells at the upper surface, could give rise to organ curvature. In the original proposal of this kind (Iwami and Masuda, 1976), the apex was proposed as the source of the auxin for movement into the lower side, but this involvement of the apex was an unnecessary remnant from Model 1. The reasons outlined above for the rejection of Models 1 and 2 require that Model 3 be concerned only with local auxin movement. Model 3 proposes that tropistic sensing does not occur in the peripheral cell layers but in some more internal cells (near the starch sheath?). These internal sensing cells somehow move auxin into, or out of, the peripheral cell layers, auxin returning to a messenger role albeit a more localised one. While Model 1 was logical if the apex had to control the organ and Model 2 offered a logical way of coordinating growth across an organ, the logical attractions of Model 3 are less obvious. Why not combine the sites of tropistic sensing and growth control and link them directly (Firn and Digby, 1977)? The attractions of Model 3 are seen to be largely ones of continuity with previous models, and in particular Model 3 allows one to retain a role for auxin, even when the original logical reasons for involving auxin have been left behind.

Model 4 - Auxin as a Second Messenger or Internal Regulator

In models 1-3, the idea of auxin controlling the rate of cell elongation has remained paramount, but the way in which auxin movement contributes to the co-ordination of organ elongation has changed. This uncertainty over the role of auxin movement was eventually to result in models appearing in which auxin movement played no major part. This retreat from the idea that plant hormones were long distance messengers was marked by considerable debate as to whether the term 'hormone' was applicable to plant physiology (see Audus, 1953). However, it was soon widely accepted that hormones need not move in order to change the concentration of the regulator in the responsive cells. Hormone production within the responsive cells was accepted as a possibility. More recently, hormone movement between compartments within responsive cells has been proposed. In the case of auxin and gravitropism, both these types of proposal have been made. In grass-node gravitropism, for instance, it has been proposed (and evidence has been presented) that gravistimulation promotes IAA synthesis, and the cells increase their elongation rate as a consequence (Wright et al.,1978). In the case of gravity effects on IAA distribution within cells (Mertens and Weiler,1983), no supporting evidence has yet been produced. The unanswered question here is whether either type of mechanism is particularly appealing as a generalised control mechanism. Given that a number of possible control points must exist in the biochemical pathways leading to cell enlargement, why employ IAA as an intermediary? If some environmental signal can be sensed in a cell, and that signal is then used to control some biosynthetic pathway, why control the biosynthesis of some intermediary rather than the ultimately controlled process? The only logical reason that occurs to us is that an amplification stage could be obtained by using an intermediary; but does auxin have the properties of a second messenger?

Model 5 - Tropistically Induced Changes in Cell Sensitivity to Auxin

All the models discussed above have one feature in common - all assume that there is a strict relationship between hormone concentration in a cell (or compartment of the cell where the hormone acts) and the rate of elongation of that cell. This dose dependence was of course a necessary part of the logic which was used to discover the hormone in the first place. However, even shortly after the discovery of auxin, the possibility that the sensitivity of cells to the regulator might change was considered (Went and Thimann,1937). The reason why the concept of sensitivity was considered seems to have been largely negative, in that the concept seems to have been introduced to help explain some discrepancies. For instance, sensitivity changes seemed a possible way of explaining why some cells contained considerable amounts of auxin yet did not grow rapidly, or why other cells managed to grow rapidly yet contained little auxin. The concept of sensitivity changes has an attraction as a logical explanation of certain developmental changes. As a cell differentiates, for instance, it is not an unreasonable idea that it might irreversibly gain or lose sensitivity to a hormone. However, it seems very likely that such changes are fairly dramatic and absolute rather than relative. When the concept of sensitivity changes is applied to tropisms (Brauner, 1966), it is less easy to produce a logical framework to sustain the idea. In the case of tropisms, the concept of sensitivity changes being important only arose after it became evident that the expected auxin concentration changes were not found in tropistically stimulated organs. By invoking sensitivity changes to auxin, nearly all the assumptions and logic behind the previous models were abandoned, and the only idea carried forward to the new model was that auxin must be involved in tropistic responses (the idea of auxin involvement having of course come from the original logical arguments now being discarded!). However, ignoring the somewhat dubious logic that leads to the model, the model should be examined on its own merits. The first problem is a conceptual one. Models 1,2 and 3 all provided some explanation of growth control or possible coordination at the organ or tissue level, but Model 5, like Model 4, is essentially a model for cell regulation. In Model 5, an organ would simply be envisaged as a collection of individual cells, each controlling its own growth by adjusting its sensitivity to auxin. Overall coordination of growth within the organ is not addressed by Model 5. The second problem is that sensitivity modulation seems an indirect way of controlling a process. As in the case of Model 4, if a cell can sense a tropistic stimulus and then modulate its sensitivity to auxin, why does it not simply modulate its growth rate? Another level of control has been introduced for no very good reason.

Model 6 - Substituting Another Hormone for Auxin

Models 1-5 have been evolved from the original basic assumption that a single regulator (auxin) must be used to control similar or equivalent physiological responses. Once that basic assumption is placed to one side, further elaborations of the concept of hormonal control become possible. If the physiological process being studied involves cell elongation, and if it is believed that a plant hormone must be involved as the ultimate controller, it can now be argued that any hormone capable of influencing cell elongation might be that controller. Furthermore, because tropistic responses can involve the stimulation or inhibition of cell elongation (Sachs, 1888), there is ample scope to involve inhibitors or promoters in various ways. Just such a process of hormone substitution has occurred in studies of tropistic responses. Versions of the previous models have been roughly outlined in which another hormone was substituted for auxin. Old, outmoded ideas were sometimes renovated with the help of a new hormone. For example, attention was focused again on the apex in a model involving gibberellins (Phillips, 1972). Likewise, the lateral trans-organ movement of gibberellins was studied in some detail (Wilkins and Nash, 1974; Phillips and Hartung, 1976). A version of Model 4 was also studied in relation to gibberellins (Pharis et al., 1981). However, the evidence for the involvement of gibberellins was very slender (Firn, 1983) and could be positively disproved in some cases (Firn et al., 1977). What was usually ignored when such hormone substitutions were attempted was the fact that the substituted hormone usually had very different basic characteristics from that of IAA. The biosynthesis, site of synthesis, route and mode of transport and the mode of action of all the other hormones obviously differ completely from that of IAA. Despite these differences, the framework of the Cholodny-Went model was somehow stretched to accommodate each possible new regulator. There can surely be no better example of the way in which the Cholodny-Went model and its derivatives have gripped the mind of those working on hormonal control in plants. It seems that, even when possible alternative regulators were considered for a role, they were considered only in the same terms as IAA, and no attempt was made to formulate new, more logical models tailored to the new potential regulator.

Advocates of hormone substitution never proposed abandoning all the previous models.

Instead they seem to have accepted the idea that there was no unifying model of tropisms, and that depending on the circumstances more than one of the above models might be applicable. Instead of a unifying model, a unifying concept was retained, in that hormone gradients, or gradients of hormone sensitivity, were thought to be important.

Model 7 - Multiple Regulator Control

In Model 6, it was proposed that different hormones might control a similar type of tropistic response in different species, or in different organs of the same species. It was implied that one regulator had absolute control in any one particular situation. Model 7 is an extension of Model 6 and differs from it by postulating that more than one regulator might contribute to the control system even in the same organ. Various versions of multi-regulator control have been proposed and a recent one is outlined by Pickard (1985a):-

"If mediation of geotropism is hormonal, it must be complex - for no tissue is controlled by a single hormone, and different hormones are rate limiting for growth in different tissues and at different times...."
The motivation for such proposals need close examination. Very often, it would seem, such complex control systems were suggested because the evidence in favour of any one regulator alone controlling the process was inadequate. The choice was to reject the involvement of each regulator in turn for lack of evidence, or to propose a new, more complex model involving more than one regulator in some poorly specified manner. The latter course of action obviously had its appeal to those committed to hormonal control. Further elaborations of the multi-regulator model have recently been advanced, these extended models introducing a new element of complexity. It has been proposed that hormones might not have a monopoly as regulators and that simple ions might play a role in controlling organ extension. It has been shown that protons and calcium can influence cell elongation and evidence has been presented that protons (Ganot & Reinhold,1970) and/or calcium gradients (see Pickard,1985b) are established across gravistimulated organs. This has led Pickard (1985a) to propose the most elaborate multi-regulator model of gravitropism to date:-

"It now appears that (1) lateral redistribution of IAA is a sine qua non of geotropism, (2) asymmetries in GA metabolism and perhaps redistribution are tightly linked with IAA redistribution, and (3) at least as importantly, IAA assymmetry educes a corresponding asymmetry of protons and an opposing redistribution of an inorganic regulator of growth, the calcium ion. Exactly how a given tissue responds to these asymmetries will depend on its physiological condition, but in general, IAA redistribution and the tightly coupled proton asymmetry will tend to slow growth on the upper and enhance it on the lower side, the GA asymmetries will tend to act similarly, and the Ca^+ redistribution will tend to inhibit growth on the lower side. It is unlikely that a growing shoot will ever be simultaneously nonresponsive to each of these asymmetries, so that upward geotropic curvature will reliably result from a combination of them."

This proposal is described by Pickard (1985a) as "a contemporary generalisation of the Went-Cholodny theory". Obviously the unity of the original model has been completely abandoned and this generalised model is an amalgam of Models 1-6, with some extra non-hormonal elements added. The flexible nature of the model, and the inclusion of apparently optional elements, makes this model very difficult to disprove and its value as a predictor of events seems very limited. Some serious theoretical objections to this generalised model will be discussed later.

Interestingly, a recent model of root gravitropism is also a multi-regulator model. Moore & Evans (1986), trying to fill the gap left by the demise of the abscisic acid/root cap model of gravitropism (Moore & Smith,1984), have proposed that the electrochemical gradient, which develops across gravistimulated roots, (Behrens et al.,1985) results in a calcium gradient being established across the root tip. They suggest that the calcium gradient acts so as to create a gradient of sensitivity to

IAA across the root, hence root gravitropism is a consequence of the concerted action of calcium and IAA. The authors admit that the model is largely speculative and there are some weaknesses in the evidence in its support (why do phytotropins inhibit root gravitropism?). Once again, however, it is interesting that this recent model combines elements of two earlier models (5 & 7) and that, even when a non-hormonal regulator (Ca^{2+}) is given a prime role, it is still fitted into the old framework.

Dedicated Followers of Fashion? (Kinks, 1966)

In the previous section we have given our interpretation of the way in which models of hormonal control evolved. The main influences guiding this evolution seem to have been fashion and a determination to find a role for hormones in tropistic responses.

A group without a very clear sense of direction is always prone to distraction by fashions. When studies of hormones and tropisms were in their infancy, such studies were the fashion and they carried thinking forward. However, once auxin lost its monopoly, and more especially when plant hormonology lost some of its confidence, studies of the role of plant hormones and tropisms became less directed and more inclined to distraction. As each new hormone was discovered, the possibility that it was involved in some way in tropistic responses was considered. Because many tropistic responses are the combined result of growth stimulation and growth inhibition, there was plenty of scope to implicate any promoter or inhibitor. Indeed, over the years, very few fashionable ideas have not turned up at some stage in the tropism literature. With the benefit of hindsight, it is apparent that, all too often, fashionable ideas have been adopted without any real consideration of the basic physiology of the response under study. However, the reason why the whims of fashion were so influential was because the C-W model had become parted from firm conceptual restraints, and was consequently prone to others seeking to give it a new sense of direction. This led to those working in the area trying to find a role for a hormone. Physiological studies were conducted, not to see if some form of hormonal control was needed to explain some observed response, but to see how and where a hormone exerted its control.

In the final section below we shall consider this point in more detail because the lessons which can be learned apply to many areas of hormonal physiology, not simply tropisms.

SOME GENERAL LESSONS WHICH CAN BE LEARNED FROM THE EVOLUTION OF THESE MODELS

1. Unifying Models Should Not be Abandoned Simply for Convenience but Only for Excellent Reasons.

Originally, hormonal control was seen as a unifying idea in plant physiology. However, some hormonologists have been ready to sacrifice the concept of common, evolutionarily conserved, control mechanisms underlying basically similar physiological processes. Faced with a choice between abandoning this concept or admitting that a particular hormone cannot have a general role in controlling some particular process, they have chosen the former. Yet, as far as we can ascertain, no logical case has ever been made as to why plants should use their hormones like an artist uses primary colours - sometimes one, sometimes another and sometimes a mixture. A case could be made for different members of one group of regulators being used in different situations (various gibberellins would be a sensible choice), but it is hard to imagine why entirely different molecules should be used for the same purpose. This fundamental theoretical objection is joined &y the more practical one that such a belief in the diversity of hormonal control mechanisms for a single process encourages those working on the same basic problem to ignore evidence inconsistent with their own view simply because it comes from a different species or organ. Once the guidance of a unifying mechanism is lost, the research area becomes fragmented, evidence is used more selectively and consequently the opportunity for disproof declines. Under such circumstances, models can proliferate because there is no longer any logical case for restricting the number. In other words, the abandonment of the idea of common control mechanisms has so many disadvantages that it should only be considered if an overwhelming case can be made out for such action.

2. Our Knowledge of Physiology Should Guide our Approach to Hormones, Not Vice Versa

It is significant that all the early hormonal models of tropisms were challenged immediately by existing physiological knowledge yet the models were not readily dismissed. It is also interesting that the response of the hormonologists to these early problems was not to look more closely at the physiology before producing new models. Instead they concentrated on speculative ways of keeping elements of the original, inadequate model, and paid little attention to physiological studies. The momentum of the C-W model and the appeal of the idea of hormonal control was creating theory but without the theory being rooted in experimental evidence. The failure to recognise the need for physiological studies led to fewer such studies being conducted, consequently our knowledge of the physiology of tropisms has advanced little during the last 50 years. But basic physiological information was just what was needed to define the precise role for any possible hormonal involvement in tropisms. If proper attention had been paid to finding the sites of tropistic perception and establishing where, when and how the growth rate of cells was changed after tropistic stimulation, a precise model of hormonal control could possibly have been constructed. Although models 1-7 were of course based on some physiological knowledge, very often the models simply ignored the complex spatial and temporal growth rate changes known to cause organ curvature (see Firn and Digby 1980). This tendency to ignore physiological data, or to treat it as less important than the results of chemical or radiochemical analyses, is a serious fault in hormone research. Sadly, it is a problem still evident. For instance, a recent comprehensive review of gravitropism not only omitted an adequate discussion of the spatial and temporal growth rate changes which cause tropistic curvatures but argued that such knowledge was somehow unimportant (Pickard, 1985a). Yet these changes are precisely the changes which the hormonal models seek to explain! Being certain that hormones controlled all physiological processes, some plant hormonologists obviously felt that a knowledge of the hormonal events told them all they needed to know about the physiology. Anyone who doubts the validity of this observation need only note how information about plant hormones replaced much basic information about whole plant physiology in many textbooks and reviews published in the last 40 years.

All hormonal models, not just those addressing themselves to tropisms, need to be rooted in knowledge about the actual physiological changes which they purport to explain. Only when a clear general physiological framework has been established can hormonal theories be coherently erected and tested.

3. The Use and Abuse of Models

Models are essential to good experimental research since they can provide a rational framework to guide the scientist. The usefulness of models is two-fold. Firstly, a good model will force one to relate as much of the current knowledge as possible into a coherent form, and that structure can then be extended into testable predictions. Secondly, the process of testing these predictions provides the framework for experiments, which, if they result in refinement or rejection of the model, should increase the understanding of the subject under investigation. Feedback from experiments into new models will mean the field progresses. This process is drawn schematically in Fig.1.

This scheme should apply to any field of science, but it seems to have significantly broken down in some important areas of plant hormonal research. The symptoms of this breakdown have been evident for many years, indeed it is nearly 30 years since the first cure was proposed (Jacobs, 1959). By examining the problems as they relate to hormonal involvement in tropisms, it should be possible to identify the ways in which research has deviated from the ideal framework as shown in Fig.1.

257

The major breakdown in the scheme centres around the reluctance of hormonologists to reject inadequate models. In the case of plant tropisms, there has been a belief in the ultimate correctness of 'the' C-W theory - the hypothesis that hormones are causal agents in tropistic responses was being treated as a fact. This dogmatic belief short-circuited the logic flow of Fig.1 so that hormonal involvement was not being critically tested. As a consequence, new models grew out of old models, and not out of results or knowledge.

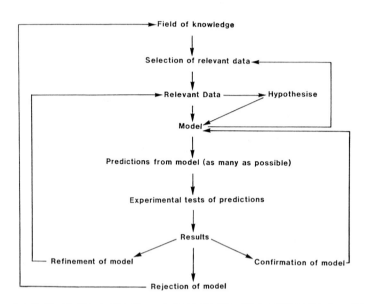

Fig. 1   A scheme of the logic flow characteristic of a scientific investigation

The scheme shown in Fig.1 was also avoided partly by some researchers concentrating on very specific aspects of the overall problem. Firstly the rejection of the idea of common, evolutionarily conserved, mechanisms (as discussed in section 1), gave workers the freedom to avoid inconvenient data. Such selection was justified on the grounds that data need not apply if it came from work using another species (or variety?) grown under different conditions. Yet Fig.1 shows that a model is dependent upon what is deemed to be 'relevant data', just as what is 'relevant data' is dependent upon the nature of the model. If this 'local' argument is used, then it follows that the questions being addressed are equally local. The opportunity to address the larger question about the nature of tropistic responses in general was being lost. Secondly, as discussed in section 2 there has been a tendency not to validate general physiological experimental data. This resulted in the field of knowledge expanding rather slowly. Indeed, the effective field of knowledge about plant tropisms possibly declined as old knowledge slipped from the reviews and languished in half forgotten journals - most current journals grew to prominence with the rise of hormonology. None of the models 1-7 were successful in stimulating productive experimental work based on predictions, hence relatively few important new results were reported over the years (the ideas under investigation in 1930 were still under investigation in 1970). The more recent work on tropisms rarely did more than validate earlier work, such validation being a somewhat sterile process, because progress only results from models being refined or rejected. The lack of new experimental data, and the gradual fading of old data, resulted in an overemphasis on certain pieces of information as "relevant data" - for example the magnitude of the auxin gradient across a tropistically oat coleoptile.

258

Even so, the large body of data which accumulated forced workers to create ever larger, more diffuse and generalised models (ultimately leading to the creation of 'models' 5, 6 and 7), in order to hold onto the hormonal concept. Sometimes these models were backed up by arguments which were no-longer rooted in logical necessity (see comments on models 3, 4 and 5). These vague, generalised models brought with them three important problems. Firstly, rigorous testing of such a model can no longer take place because a vague model can only produce vague predictions. Secondly, feedback from models into the selection of what is relevant knowledge breaks down, so that experiments can become mistakenly guided by predictions which have actually been tested and rejected (e.g. experimental emphasis on events in the apex long after model 1 was evidently inadequate). And thirdly, by not distinguishing clearly between models, there is the risk that data consistent with one model may be deemed to be giving (unjustifed) support to what is in fact a separate model.

The overall result of this poor use of models has been an area of research without a sensible logical framework. The area has been afflicted by "conceptual drift" and discussions have become confused. Although these conclusions have been drawn from considering work on tropisms, there is ample evidence that similar problems exist in some other areas of hormonal control. How many precise models of hormonal control exist in others areas of plant physiology? It seems that work on tropisms set a bad example by tolerating vague models for so long.

OVERALL CONCLUSION

Some years ago John Digby and Richard Firn started their first article criticising the Cholodny-Went model with the following quotation:-

"By doubting we come to questioning and by questioning we perceive the truth"

Abelard, the 12th century scholar who expressed these views, argued that to have a faith one must understand the essentials of that faith and a proper understanding only comes from a sceptical analysis of those essentials. Such a view was diametrically opposed by those such as Anselm who argued that one must have the faith first and only then will evidence for the faith be convincing. It seems to us that many of those investigating the hormonal control of tropisms have been followers of Anselm rather than Abelard. Yet great reliance on faith and a firm disapproval of sceptics has obviously not helped the study of the Cholodny-Went model(s). If the Cholodny-Went model had been but a footnote in the history of plant physiology this might have mattered little, but the model has been regarded as as classical piece of work (widely taught in schools in the UK for instance). It is evident, however, that many of the faults which have beset too many studies of plant hormones (poor experimental design, poor quantitation, faulty logic and a selective use of evidence) can be found in studies guided by the classical Cholodny-Went model. If a less than rigorous approach is tolerated in work regarded as "classical", it is hardly surprising that it is accepted too readily elsewhere. It is time to identify the weaknesses in some studies of hormonal physiology in plants, simply to allow the strengths to show through.

ACKNOWLEDGEMENTS

We would like to thank John Digby for his helpful discussions. Mrs J.Myers is thanked for instructing us on the use of the comma.

REFERENCES

Audus,L.J. (1953) In "Plant Growth Substances". p 553 Leonard Hill, London
Behrens,H.M., Gradmann,D. and Sievers,A. (1985). Membrane-potential responses following gravistimulation in roots of Lepidium sativum L.. Planta 163, 453-462.

Brauner,L. (1966). Versuche zur Analyse der geotropischen Perzeption V. Mitteilung. Uber den Einfluss des Schwerefeldes auf die auxinempfindlichkeit von Helianthus-Hypokotylen. Planta 69, 299-318.

Copeland,E.B. (1900). Studies on the geotropism of stems. Botanical Gazette 29, 185-196.

Darwin,C. (1880). "The Power of Movement of Plants". Murray, London.

Digby,J. and Firn,R.D. (1976). A critical assessment of the Cholodny-Went theory of shoot geotropism. Current Advances in Plant Science 8, 953-959.

Digby,J., Firn,R.D. and Carrington,C.M.S. (1982). Studies on the differential growth causing tropic curvatures in plants. In "Plant Growth Substances 1982" (P.F.Wareing, ed.), pp 385-393. Academic Press, London.

Firn,R.D. (1983). The involvement of gibberellins in geotropism and phototropism. In "The Biochemistry and Physiology of Gibberellins" (A.Crozier, ed.), Volume 2, pp 375-394. Praeger, New York.

Firn,R.D. (1986). Phototropism. In "Photomorphogenesis in Plants" (R.E.Kendrick and G.H.M.Kronenberg, ed.), Kluwer, Dordrecht.

Firn,R.D. and Digby,J. (1977). The role of the peripheral cell layers in the geotropic curvature of sunflower hypocotyls: a new model of geotropic curvature. Australian Journal Of Plant Physiology 4, 337-347.

Firn,R.D. and Digby,J. (1980). The establishment of tropic curvatures in plants. Annual Review of Plant Physiology 31, 131-148.

Firn,R.D. and Tamimi,S. (1986). Auxin transport and shoot tropisms. In "Plant Growth Substances 1985" (M.Bopp, ed.), pp 236-240. Springer-Verlag, Berlin Heidelberg.

Firn,R.D., Digby,J. and Pinsent,C. (1977). Evidence against the involvement of gibberellins in the differential growth which causes geotropic curvature. Zeitschrift fur Pflanzenphysiologie 82, 179-185.

Franssen,J.M., Firn,R.D. and Digby,J. (1982). The role of the apex in the phototropic curvature of Avena coleoptiles: positive curvature under conditions of continuous illumination. Planta 155, 282-286.

Ganot,D. and Reinhold,L. (1970). The acid growth effect and geotropism. Planta 95, 62-71.

Iwami,S. and Masuda,Y. (1976). Distribution of labelled auxin in geotropically stimulated stems of cucumber and pea. Plant and Cell Physiology 17, 227-237.

Jacobs,W.P. (1959). What substances normally controls a given biological process? I. Formulation of some rules. Developmental Biology 1, 527-533.

Kinks, The (1966) "Dedicated Follower of Fashion" (Composer Ray Davies), On Pye 7N 17064.

Mertens,R. and Weiler,E.W. (1983). Kinetic studies on the redistribution of endogenous growth regulators in gravireacting plant organs. Planta 158, 339-348.

Moore,R. and Evans,M.L. (1986). How roots perceive and respond to gravity. American Journal of Botany 73, 574-587.

Moore,R. and Smith,J.D. (1984). Growth, graviresponsiveness, and the abscisic-acid content of Zea mays seedlings treated with Fluridone. Planta 162, 342-344.

Pharis,R.P., Legge,R.L., Noma,M., Kaufman,P.B., Ghosheh,N.S., La Croix,J.D. and Heller,K. (1981). Changes in the endogenous gibberellins and metabolism of ^{3}H-GA4 after geostimulation in shoots of the oat plant (Avena sativa). Plant Physiology 67, 892-897.

Phillips,I.D.J. (1972). Endogenous gibberellin transport and biosynthesis in relation to geotropic induction in excised sunflower shoot tips. Planta 105, 234-244.

Phillips,I.D.J. and Hartung,W. (1976). Longitudinal and lateral transport of 3-H^3 gibberellin A1 and IAA in upright and geotropically responding green internode segments from Helianthus annuus. New Phytologist 76, 1-9.

Pickard,B.G. (1985a). The role of hormones, protons and calcium in geotropism. In "Hormonal Regulation of Development III. Role of Environmental Factors." Encyclopedia of Plant Physiology Volume 11 (R.P.Pharis and D.M.Reid, eds.), pp 193-281. Springer, Berlin

Pickard,B.G. (1985b). Early events in geotropism of seedling shoots. Annual Review of Plant Physiology 36, 55-75.

Sachs,J. (1888). Bespiele geotropischer Krummungen aufrecht Wachsender Sprossachsen. Arbeiten des Botanischen Instituts in Wurzburg 3, 553-560.

Went,F.W. and Thimann,K.V. (1937). "Phytohormones". MacMillan, New York.

Wilkins,M.B. and Nash,L.J. (1974). Movement of radioactivity from ^{3}H-GA3 in geotropically stimulated coleoptiles of Zea mays. Planta 115, 245-251.

Wright,M., Mousedale,D.M.A. and Osborne,D.J. (1978). Evidence for a gravity-regulated level of the endogenous auxin controlling cell elongation and ethylene production during geotropic bending in grass nodes. Biochemie und Physiologie der Pflanzen 172, 581-596.

SECTION IV

REVIEW AND FORWARD LOOK

PHYSIOLOGICAL CONSIDERATIONS IN DEVELOPMENTAL STUDIES: HORMONES AND TARGET CELLS

Daphne J. Osborne.

Department of Plant Sciences, University of Oxford, Oxford OX1 3RA, England

> How does a plant cell know how to perform in the community of
> its fellows? What kinds of signals are exchanged between them
> such that an organised and recognisable member of the species
> can result? Is every cell a target cell and are hormones
> critical to their successful development?

INTRODUCTION

During the course of this meeting we have seen much experimental detail and heard
many different viewpoints on the role of hormones as organizers, directors, or
purveyors of information on the growth and differentiation of plants. We have
observed where there could be new opportunities for manipulating plants by chemical
or hormonal means to make them more attractive to man both agriculturally and
horticulturally.

Physiologists may speculate upon the most profitable lines of future research for
improving our understanding of plant growth and development and can make assessments
as to how far we are justified in awarding a central role to hormones in the
direction of differentiation events. Whereas forecasting a line of research that
will bring high scientific reward is generally an uncertain gamble, the generation of
new ideas and the re-thinking of accepted dogma must enrich the overall potential for
achieving this goal.

On the physiological consideration of development a central concept will be extended,
namely that every living cell in a plant possesses a specific target status with
respect to the numerous environmental, hormonal or chemical signals to which it is
exposed. This means that if a cell has competence to recognise a signal and respond
to that signal in a specific way, it is a target cell for that signal. If it is
competent to recognise but fails to respond, it is then a repressed target cell. If
the cell does not possess the competence to recognise the signal it cannot respond to
that signal; the cell cannot then be a target cell for that specific signal
recognition and response.

Target cells can be grouped into two general classes:

1) Those that are committed cells - we can recognise these most easily since they
perform highly predictable functions. In normal development they lack the
flexibility to differentiate to another committed state.

2) Cells that are in the process of progression through directional developmental
programmes so that recognition and response to a signal changes as the target status
changes. After recognition of a specific response to one signal the cells become
permissive to the recognition and response to a new signal in the programme.

It is axiomatic that each target state reflects a biochemically recognisable
condition of that cell state, the target state being designated in precise molecular
terms and detectable by the physiologist in a complement of proteins or
immunologically antigenic determinants that express the operating conditions of the
genome.

EVIDENCE FOR COMMITTED TARGET CELL TYPES

It is very apparent that each of the cell types listed in Table 1 is highly recognisable without seeking a biochemical marker because each can be identified by its very specialised performance. In the case of cotyledon cells, aleurone cells, abscission cells and stelar cells there is evidence of a terminal and committed state from which we have no indication of further differentiation to another class of cell.

Table 1 Examples of cell types containing cell or tissue specific protein (or enzyme) markers.

SEED PROTEINS

        Barley aleurone cells   - Jacobsen and Beach (1985).
        (Gibberellin-induced -amylase)
        Soybean cotyledon cells   - Goldberg et al. (1981).
        (Specific globulins)

ABSCISSION CELL PROTEINS

        Phaseolus zone cells   - Koehler et al. (1981).
        (ethylene-induced -1:4-glucan-hydrolase)
        Phaseolus and Sambucus zone cells   - Osborne et al. (1985).
        (cell specific proteins)

STELAR PROTEINS (ESTERASES)

        Xylem - root and shoot   - Gahan (1981).
        Somatic carrot embryo   - Caligo et al. (1985).
        Xylogenesis

FLOWERING PROTEINS

        Photoperiodic induction   - Pierard et al. (1980).
        response in Sinapis alba following
        irreversible commitment

Aleurone cells and abscission cells can retain this committed state for long periods - for years in the case of the aleurone cells in dormant imbibed seeds - and for the duration of the life-span of the organ in abscission zones of leaves and many other shedding plant parts. With such cells one can identify switching processes that are regulated by hormones. Aleurone cells, for example, produce α-amylase as long as the gene expression promoter gibberellin (GA) is present. If GA is removed, or the gene expression repressor abscisic acid (ABA) is added, then the production of α-amylase ceases. An aleurone cell is a target cell for the activator of its α-amylase genes, i.e., for the hormone gibberellin (D. Baulcombe, these proceedings).

In the two rows of cells that comprise the abscission zone of the bean Phaseolus vulgaris, a specific isozyme of β-1:4-glucanhydrolase is produced when the gene expression promoter ethylene is present in appropriate concentration (Koehler et al., 1981). If ethylene is removed or the gene expression repressor auxin (IAA) is added, the production of the glucanhydrolase ceases. In parallel with these hormone-regulated enzyme changes, the ultrastructural profiles of the dictyosome membranes in the zone cells dilate and vesiculate in response to ethylene and contract and cease production of vesicles if ethylene is removed or auxin is added (Osborne et al., 1985). Both enzyme production and vesiculation can be "turned on" again by a second exposure to ethylene. An abscission zone cell is hence a target cell for the activator of its β-glucanhydrolase genes, i.e., for the hormone ethylene.

How much abscission zone cells may differ between vegetative and flowering tissues we have yet to discover, but research on this aspect of abscission is of special interest in the mechanical harvesting of - for example - evergreen trees like olives and oranges. Bernier's group (Pierard et al., 1980) have identified a specificity in protein complement between vegetative buds and reproductive buds of Sinapis alba following photoinduction - they report the appearance of two new proteins and the disappearance of another. It is not unreasonable therefore to consider differences in the protein complements of abscission zones from vegetative and flowering parts. All dicotyledonous zone cells may be target cells for ethylene, but differences in their response and performance to the hormone could result from differences in other gene expressions consistent with an origin of the zone from either reproductive or vegetative tissues. There is evidence that leaves and fruits can be distinctive in their abscission performance as for example, in the peach (Rascio et al., 1987).

DIFFERENTIATION OF TARGET CELLS

A cell must pass through a progression of gene expressions from the time it is formed at cell division until it takes its place in a mature tissue. The numbers of cells that are specifically committed, like those of aleurone, abscission zone or stelar cells, are relatively few. Most cells will be arrested in essentially uncommitted states but with a defined competence for further differentiation. The degree of flexibility (or differentiation options) remaining to a particular cell in a tissue will vary depending upon the history of options that has been achieved previously.

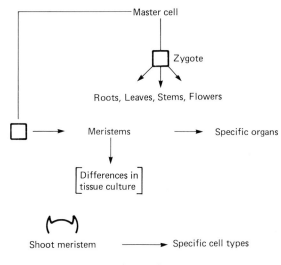

We can consider the zygote as the most flexible cell type of all since from it are derived the many different meristems that provide the cell lines for continued plant growth (Fig. 1). We know that these meristems when transferred to in vitro culture can give rise to calluses that are distinctive for the parent meristem (Wareing and Al-Chalabi, 1985). To this extent, each meristem type is already a determined state.

One can perhaps think of a plant cell as a captive of its neighbours. From them it receives local cues and through them it obtains also long distance information which will include hormones, nutrients and metabolites. Imposed on all the cells are the environmental signals of light, and temperature.

One can conceive of a cell passing through a progression of target states, and as each new signal recognition and response is achieved and each new state of competence is superseded by another, the options remaining for further differentiation and development become progressively restricted. Such a series of modifications in gene expression before the final differentiation of the committed abscission zone cell is depicted in Fig. 2.

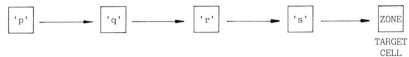

TARGET
CELL

Fig. 2

In the bean, Phaseolus vulgaris we can identify the committed abscission zone cell biochemically, (a) by the presence of zone specific peptides (after rigorous competition of the extracted proteins with antibodies from neighbour non-target tissues, Osborne et al., 1985), (b) by the zone specific distribution of an antigenic component of zone cells visualized by immuno-fluorescence and immuno-gold recognition (Osborne and McManus, unpublished), (c) by the fact that zone cells - and only zone cells - will enlarge and separate in response to ethylene (Wright and Osborne, 1974) and, of course by (d) the ethylene-induced production of a zone specific isozyme of β-1:4-glucanhydrolase (Koehler et al., 1981).

To date we do not know how to recognise any of the earlier progenitor states of zone cells. So unlike the situation in stelar tissues (Table 1) studied by Gahan (1981) and by Caligo et al. (1985) where a progenitor status has been pinpointed by the presence of esterase activity, we have no handle yet to try to arrest the formation of abscission zone cells at a precommitment stage. At present, if we wish to prevent abscission we must either block the zone cell's recognition of ethylene (e.g., by Ag ion, Beyer, 1979) or maintain the cells in a repressed condition by maintaining high levels of auxin.

Bearing in mind the importance of shedding processes in so many cropping practices it seems to me that one future research goal should be the control of zone cell differentiation. If we accept that a zone target cell is the expression of a specific array of genes then it should be possible to eliminate or block the expression of one or more genes that are critical to the differentiation programme.

HOW MIGHT AN ABSCISSION ZONE CELL DIFFERENTIATION PROGRAMME DEVELOP?

Let us consider a cell responding to a series of signals during progressive differentiation to zone cell target status. For example, cell type 'p', after it receives and responds to Signal A can differentiate to cell type 'q', and so on.

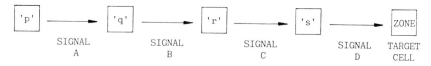

| SIGNAL A | SIGNAL B | SIGNAL C | SIGNAL D | TARGET CELL |

Fig. 3

Each cell type has a cell specific (or in a collection of cells a tissue specific) phenotypic expression which we should - if we looked - recognise biochemically by a cell specific protein complement. The cell specific protein complement or, more precisely, the cell specific expression of the genome, gives the cell its target status. In the case of cell type 'q' it signifies the potential competence to recognise Signal B and progress to cell type 'r'. On this model, cell type 'p' cannot recognise Signal B and cannot, therefore, differentiate directly to cell type 'r'. It is assumed that cell type 'p' can also recognise other signals say X, Y or Z and progress along a different set of developmental signal recognitions and responses – but it cannot then progress through the phase transitions of the cell types that eventually become ZONE.

HORMONES AND DIFFERENTIATION SIGNALS

Is there evidence that hormones play a part in the differentiation of abscission zone cells? The answer is yes. Pierik (1980) showed that secondary abscission zones could be induced by auxin and cytokinin in the pedicels of young pear fruits. The precise location of the initiation was determined by the concentration of IAA applied to the cut end of the stalk. Warren Wilson et al. (1985) have demonstrated how auxin can control the position of induced secondary abscission sites in their stem explants of Impatiens sultani. In the bean, certain cells of the petiole can be modified hormonally to exhibit the competence typical of the normally differentiated abscission zone cell (Osborne and McManus, 1986). The conversion to the committed state is brought about when the dome of target cells on the surface of a freshly abscinded explant is treated with 1 μl drops of a solution of IAA and then maintained continuously in a low concentration of ethylene. In the absence of cell division, a new zone cell competence is expressed in certain of the cortical cells of

Table 2 Positional induction of abscission zone cells by IAA and ethylene in the petioles of P. vulgaris explants (Osborne and McManus)

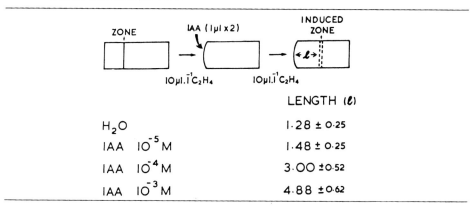

	LENGTH (ℓ)
H_2O	1.28 ± 0.25
IAA 10^{-5} M	1.48 ± 0.25
IAA 10^{-4} M	3.00 ± 0.52
IAA 10^{-3} M	4.88 ± 0.62

the petiole within 5-6 days. A narrowly defined band of secondary abscission zone cells forms at a precise position along the petiole. The distance of the new zone from the original abscinded zone is determined by the concentration of IAA that is applied (Table 2).

Only the cells of the cortical parenchyma of the petiole are converted to cells with the competence of zone cells, and only the new zone cells exhibit the ethylene-induced cell enlargement, enzyme production and cell separation responses normally restricted to zone target cells.

It is tempting to speculate that the diffusion gradient of auxin determines, with ethylene, the positional differentiation of zone cells. But most importantly, the conversion of a petiole cell to one of zone cell status occurs only in the cortical parenchyma, not in the pith. We can therefore, include this information in the proposed sequence of transitions of cell types to the committed zone cell (Fig. 4). Cortical cells of the petiole still possess options for further differentiation and may be an intermediate target type in the progression to zone target status. So we do now have one potential handle on zone cell formation even if we have no direct handle on how to suppress such differentiation.

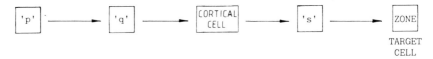

Fig. 4

DIFFERENTIATION SIGNALS: CELL RECOGNITION AND RESPONSE

During differentiation in an actively dividing meristem, signals may be encountered at any stage in the cell cycle. If a signal can be perceived and responded to only at a critical stage in the cell cycle then the "time slot" for recognition leading to response may be short. The activation of the mitotic cycle in the shoot meristem of Sinapis alba, following photoinduction or cytokinin treatment (this meeting, Lejeune, Kinet and Bernier, Abstract 42), may therefore be interpreted as an "enabling" situation that maximises the number of cells that will be in the right stage of the cell cycle to respond to a flowering signal. Critical temporal recognitions of hormone signals are clearly involved in Vanden Driessche's (1984) experiments with Acetabularia in which auxin accelerates cap formation in the early part of the dark phase and where ethylene control is differentially effective with time of day.

Such short term temporal "recognition slots" imply that, although the chemical signal, say Signal A, may be present in a tissue in "response-controlling" concentrations over a long period, recognition and response could be rapid events, with the cell changing its developmental target status from say cell type 'p' to cell type 's' without any change in the measurable level of Signal A in the cell. We know from the experiments of Zurfluh and Guilfoyle (1980) that auxin can elicit the production of elongation-specific polypeptides in soybean and suppress the production of others within 1 h. Auxin-induced changes in in vitro translatable mRNA populations from both elongating soybean and pea epicotyls occur even sooner, within 15 or 20 min respectively (Zurfluh and Guilfoyle, 1982; Theologis and Ray, 1982).

The performance of a specific cell type may also be modified with age. The basis of age-related change, particularly with respect to hormonal responses, is presently little understood. Jackson and Lyndon (this meeting Abstract 34) have demonstrated how, in tobacco pith cultures, habituation for cytokinin synthesis is greater in those cultures derived from apical parts of stems rather than from the basal parts. This raises the question of whether the target status and the gene expression of these two differently aged but apparently similar cell types is, in fact, quite the same.

Attempts to equate differentiation events with hormone levels have evoked great criticism in the past because of mis-match in relating hormone concentration and response. Future research should therefore look more rigorously to the target status of the cell with respect to its hormones, in the context of temporal parameters such as cell cycling, cell size and cell age.

HORMONES AND BINDING PROTEINS

One should make comment here about the possible nature of the proteins that mark the differentiated zone target cell. Some may like to think that these could include hormone-binding proteins - or even specific receptors for ethylene or auxin; but it is not necessary to make such a speculation. It could be for example, that all plant cells contain a similar auxin binding site located at the plasma membrane - or even similar ethylene and gibberellin binding sites - and that these binding sites function as carrier proteins being always permissive to the entry of the hormone to the cell (Rubery, this volume). These carrier proteins would function differently from the receptor proteins present on the surface of animal cells where the extent of binding is critical to the response. The effective hormone receptors in plants may be cytoplasmic and many could be present at low concentrations only, resulting in a plurality of potential responses - the target response being related to the receptor currently in abundancy. The concept of hormones thus driving a cascade of differentiation events in which new gene expressions and hence new receptors are progressively deployed is perhaps worth speculation. It might help to explain the difficulty so far encountered in unequivocally relating high affinity binding to a specific physiological event (Venis, this volume). There is actually no need to invoke very many receptors to accommodate the recognition of the many signals. Cell type 'p' for example, may recognise and respond to the same signal in its passage to 'q' as cell type 's' in its differentiation passage to ZONE.

FLUIDITY AND FLEXIBILITY OF THE GENOME

A few comments seem appropriate on the subject of genome fluidity or the dynamics of DNA reorganisation and genome flexibility in respect to hormones, target cells and gene expression. A change in the position of a gene along its chromosome or its transposition to a specific site upon another chromosome could be the prerequisite for the permissive expression of that gene in the differentiation of certain heritable cell lineages. The committing of genes in this way to the authority of new regulators is common to other eukaryotes and may be basic to the condition of cell commitment at terminal differentiation. The ease with which such gene re-arrangements can be reversed on changing the cell's environment may be the measure of the so-called totipotency of plant cells. The fact that so many cell types can regenerate new plants which exhibit the original parent phenotype tells us that the sequence information must, in general, be conserved. What we do not know however is the role, if any, of hormones in the control of such re-arrangements. Nor do we know if the type of cell as exemplified by the committed abscission zone cell, or aleurone cell is an example of a genome that has been re-arranged or alternatively if it is an example of a re-arranged state in which some segment of DNA has been permanently lost. If the latter is the case then the cell no longer possesses the basic genetic information required of totipotency. In those tissues from the Gramineae and the Palmaceae from which whole-plant regeneration is difficult and the percentage success on a per cell basis is low, we must question whether the problem resides in a too-well repressed genome or in information loss.

Not only may DNA fragments re-arrange within the chromosomes of the nucleus, extra chromosomal DNA from chloroplasts and mitochondria may also migrate between the DNA-containing organelles. The mitochondria commonly exhibit the greatest variation in size and organisation of their genomes, but large changes can also take place in the nucleus. In inter-specific crosses of Nicotiana tabacum and N. otophora, hybrids can be produced with chromosomes up to 15 times the normal length in corolla, root tip and pollen mother cells (Gerstel and Burns, 1976).

What is not clear is whether cells at a particular stage of the cell cycle are more prone to genomic change, such as amplifications, deletions, chromosomal loss or rearrangements - or whether the state of cell differentiation and commitment (i.e. target cell status) determines these adjustments. But it does raise the question, do hormones play a regulatory role in such events or are hormone responses determined by them?

There is certainly evidence that hormones are involved. For example, in the potential shedding locus in the female flower buds of the squirting cucumber Ecballium elaterium, ethylene induction of abscission occurs only after a critical phase of development is reached and when the bud and ovary are longer than 6 mm. Wong and Osborne (1978) showed that at this specific stage pockets of cells sited just below the ovary would enlarge and separate, but only those cells with an endoreduplicated DNA content of the nucleus - 8C rather than 2C or 4C - would exhibit this response to ethylene. The 8C DNA content of the nucleus was a cytological "marker" of a target condition of the cells in their separation response to ethylene.

Preliminary experiments (Wong and Osborne unpublished) indicated the possibility that ethylene might also be involved in the timing of DNA amplification to the 8C condition, for this stage coincided with a period of rapid bud growth and an elevated production of ethylene. Furthermore, added ethylene enhanced the incorporation of ^{3}H-thymidine into nuclear DNA and increased the number of cells with 8C nuclei at the potential abscission zone. Investigations designed to explore hormonal involvements in genomic rearrangements - or the hormonal responses of cells that exhibit genomic rearrangements is likely to be a fruitful field of study. I believe that research into these questions is not only critical to an understanding of plant differentiation but also to future hopes for successful plant propagation.

STATOCYTES AS TARGET CELLS

Lastly, I should like to make reference to another target cell type - the one that is implicated in so many gravitropic responses - namely the statocyte. I shall mention statocytes in relation to:

a) the transport of auxin (discussed by Rubery in this volume)
b) the production of auxin (Wright et al., 1978)
c) the possibility of an involvement in assimilate partitioning (reviewed by Patrick in this volume).

Michael Wright carried out an elegant series of experiments on the statocyte-containing region of the gravitropically-responding tissue of the leaf-sheath base at the nodes of flowering shoots of grasses. He showed that: (a) a segment of the graviperceptive node would, when placed horizontally, produce an enhanced level of IAA in the tissues of the lower side, (b) segments of this leaf sheath base, when turned from the vertical position with respect to gravity through 180° to the inverted orientation, would totally reverse the polarity of IAA transport within 20 min and resume the normal transport polarity again within a further 20 min of returning the node back to the vertical position (Wright, 1982), (c) these gravity-regulated events took place only when statocytes were fully differentiated and contained a minimal complement of developed statoliths (Wright, 1982).

The nodes of grasses contain a very high proportion of cells as statocytes. Each statolith in the statocyte is a modified chloroplast that functions as a sedimenting particle in the gravity field. As Wright (1986) showed, the young rapidly extending nodes do not possess statocytes with sedimenting statoliths nor do they respond to gravity in any of the ways described for the mature grass node. Furthermore, they do not produce IAA on the lower sides when placed horizontally, nor do they exhibit a reversal of polarity of auxin transport. It is clear that, at some critical stage in development of the flowering shoot, the statocyte progenitor cells cease to export sugars and instead their chloroplasts accumulate starch. Once the chloroplasts have become sufficiently dense to sediment in the 1 x g field, the node is graviperceptive/graviresponsive and the attendant gravity associated changes in IAA production and polarity of IAA transport occur.

We have no idea of the nature of the gene switch that determines this critical change in the chloroplasts but from then on the statocytes play a central role in the control of auxin production, auxin transport and, I venture to speculate, in hormone directed assimilate transport though the nodal tissue, perhaps along the pathway between source (the leaf) and sink (the ear). This is an area of research that in my view warrants active exploitation in the future.

I might conclude therefore, that although there is good evidence that hormones can precisely regulate the growth reponses of certain cells (GA$_1$ is such an example in the internodes of specific pea mutants, (Macmillan, this volume and Ingram et al., 1986), it is also abundantly clear that hormones can do this only if the cell has the genetically determined competence to receive and respond to that particular hormonal signal. Not all parts of the plant express the same genes and not all parts of the plant perform in the same way. Let me make a plea that generalisations are not made for any plant, either mutant or wild type, on the basis of the studies of one target tissue only!

REFERENCES

Beyer, E.M. (1979). Effect of silver ion, carbon dioxide and oxygen on ethylene action and metabolism. Plant Physiology 63, 169-173.

Caligo, M.A., Nuti-Ronchi, V., and Nozzolini, M. (1985). Proline and serine affect polarity and development of carrot somatic embryos. Cell Differentiation 17, 193-198.

Gahan, P.B. (1981). An early cytochemical marker of commitment to stelar differentiation in meristems from dicotyledonous plants. Annals of Botany 48, 769-775.

Gerstel, D.V. and Burns, J.A. (1976). Enlarged euchromatic chromosomes ("Mega chromosomes") in hybrids between Nicotiana tabacum and N. plumbaginifolia. Genetica 46, 139-153.

Goldberg, R.B., Hoscheck, G., Tam, S.H., Ditta, G.S. and Breidenbach, R.W. (1981). Abundance, diversity and regulation of mRNA sequence sets in soybean embryogenesis. Developmental Biology 83, 201-217.

Ingram, T.J., Reid, J.B. and MacMillan, J. (1986). The quantitative relationship between gibberellin A$_1$ and internode growth in Pisum sativum L. Planta 168, 414-420.

Jacobsen, J.V. and Beach, L.R. (1985). Control of transcription of α-amylase and rRNA genes in barley aleurone protoplasts by gibberellin and abscisic acid. Nature 316, 275-277.

Koehler, D.E., Lewis, L.N., Shannon, L.M. and Durbin, M.L. (1981). Purification of a cellulase from kidney bean abscission zones. Phytochemistry 20, 409-412.

Osborne, D.J. and McManus, M.T. (1986). Flexibility and commitment in plant cells during development. Current Topics in Developmental Biology 20, 383-396.

Osborne, D.J., McManus, M.T. and Webb, J. (1985). Target cells for ethylene action. In "Ethylene and Plant Development" (J.A. Roberts and G.A. Tucker eds.), pp 197-212 Butterworths.

Pierard, D., Jacqmard, A., Bernier, G. and Salmon, J. (1980). Appearance and disappearance of proteins in the shoot apical meristem of Sinapis alba in transition to flowering. Planta 150, 397-405.

Pierik, R.L.M. (1980). Hormonal regulation of secondary abscission in pear pedicels in vitro. Physiologia Plantarum 48, 5-8.

Rascio, N., Ramina, A., Masia, A. and Carlotti, C. (1987). Leaf abscission in peach (Prunus persica L. Batsch): Ultrastructural and biochemical aspects. Planta (in press).

Theologis, A. and Ray, P.M. (1982). Early auxin-regulated polyadenylated mRNA sequences in pea stem tissue. Proceedings of the National Academy of Sciences USA 79, 418-421.

Vanden Driessche, T. (1984). Temporal morphology and cap formation in Acetabularia II. Effects of morphactin and auxin. Chronobiology International 1, 113-120.

Wareing, P.F. and Al-Chalabi, T. (1985). Determination in plant cells. Biologia Plantarum 27, 241-248.

Warren Wilson, P.M., Warren Wilson, J. and Addicott, F.T. (1985). Induced abscission sites in internodal explants of Impatiens sultani: a new system for studying positional control. Annals of Botany 57, 511-530.

Wong, C.H. and Osborne, D.J. (1978). The ethylene induced enlargement of target cells in flower buds of Ecballium elaterium (L) A. Rich and their identification by the content of endoreduplicated nuclear DNA. Planta 139, 103-111.

Wright, M. (1982). The polarity of movement of endogenously produced IAA in relation to a gravity perception mechanism. Journal of Experimental Botany 33, 929-934.

Wright, M. (1986). The aquisition of gravisensitivity during the development of nodes of Avena fatua. Journal of Plant Growth Regulation 5, 37-47.

Wright, M., Mousdale, D.M.A. and Osborne, D.J. (1978). Evidence for a gravity-regulated level of endogenous auxin controlling cell elongation and ethylene production during geotropic bending in grass nodes. Biochemie und Physiologie der Pflanzen 172, 581-596.

Wright, M. and Osborne, D.J. (1974). Abscission in Phaseolus vulgaris. The positional differentiation and ethylene induced expansion growth of specialized cells. Planta 120, 163-170.

Zurfluh, L.L. and Guilfoyle, T.J. (1980). Auxin-induced changes in the patterns of protein synthesis in soybean hypocotyl. Proceedings of the National Academy of Sciences USA 77, 357-361.

Zurfluh, L.L. and Guilfoyle, T.J. (1982). Auxin-induced changes in the population of translatable messenger RNA in elongating sections of soybean hypocotyl. Plant Physiology 69, 332-337.

BIOCHEMICAL CONSIDERATIONS IN DEVELOPMENTAL STUDIES

J.L. Stoddart

Welsh Plant Breeding Station, Aberystwyth, Dyfed, SY23 3EB, Wales

Areas of current uncertainty relating to primary mechanisms of
hormone action in plant tissues are discussed. Emphasis is
placed upon the roles of cell walls and various classes of
endomembranes as direct, or indirect, modifiers of hormone
action. Regulation of enzyme secretion processes is discussed
and an attempt is made to recognise homologies between such
events and those involved in modifications of cell extension.
Roles for growth regulators in the maintenance of cell
integrity are considered.

INTRODUCTION

It is implicit in the title of this Symposium, and in the content of many of the
preceding contributions, that plant growth regulating substances are viewed as
specific, targeted agents for the modulation of metabolic or developmental processes.
The use of the term 'hormone', because of a history of zoological and
medico-physiological usage, prejudices consideration in this direction and underlies
the concept of the receptor protein. In most cases, good evidence exists for the
occurrence of a specific interaction between the regulatory molecule (hormone) and a
subcellular entity, and a relation between a physiological response to the presence
of the regulator. It is, however, an equally valid generalisation to state that the
intervening events between the putative initiating interaction and the ultimate
physiological effect is largely unknown and remains the challenge to be overcome in
establishing the hormonal status for endogenous plant growth regulators.

Throughout this process it is important to distinguish between a regulated chain of
biochemical action and the results of more general effects on subcellular structure.
The latter lead to pleiotropic effects and culminate in secondary, tertiary or even
higher-order consequences.

It is also possible that a given regulator may have multiple points of action, either
ultrastructurally or with respect to time. There are indications that this may be
the case with, for example, ethylene and gibberellins. In such circumstances there
may be a relationship between the organisation or expression state of the genome, and
the sensitivity, or nature of response to a given regulatory molecule.

This chapter covers selected aspects of the relationship between both applied and
endogenous growth regulators and developmental events, and attempts to assess the
specificity, or otherwise, of the observed interactions. Areas of uncertainty or
ambiguity are indicated and discussed.

EXTENSION GROWTH

Biomass is directly related to growth rate. Plant stature, determined by the
integration of growth rate with respect to time, and conditioned by a variable
duration factor, can indirectly affect a range of characteristics contributing to the
input/output relationships of a given crop. Growth regulators are known to have a
range of effects on cell division and elongation, which in turn influence growth rate
or stature. Although we can utilise such effects empirically, variations in response
and the contemporary drive to reduce chemical inputs point to the need to gain a
detailed understanding of underlying growth control mechanisms. Growth regulating

chemicals, even though they may not occur endogenously, provide some of the most convenient perturbing probes available for such studies.

Present knowledge indicates that growth regulator responses can rest upon complex biochemical chains of action and that, far from requiring massive shifts, it may be necessary to change key components by only a small margin ultimately to arrive at a big difference. The compound interest rule applies equally to plant growth and to financial operations.

Having said this, it also becomes clear that changes in efficiency at a number of points can result in equivalent outcomes and that a desired objective is achievable by several routes. A number of alternative, but not mutually exclusive, sites for growth regulator intervention can be envisaged, and most have been discussed in the symposium. This paper addresses some of the biochemical uncertainties which have been identified.

RECEPTOR PROTEINS

Venis (1985) has drawn attention to the distinction between hormone receptors and hormone binding sites: the latter indicate specific affinity, the former suggest a directed response consequent upon the association.

Binding sites have been detected for all the known plant growth regulators (Venis, 1985). Most show affinity characteristics which are consistent with the sensitivity range of the associated biological response. Both soluble and particulate interactions have been described and the candidate 'receptor' status is best supported for auxin, where detailed studies have been conducted with maize and zucchini membranes (Ray, 1977; Jacobs and Hertel, 1978). In maize, three classes of binding sites are distinguished by NAA K_d values and putatively localised in different cell membrane sites (Dohrmann et al., 1978). All classes are present in similar abundance. Soluble auxin-binding sites have not been characterised.

Cytokinin binding to ribosomes, mediated by extractable protein components, has been described extensively (Erion and Fox, 1977; Fox and Erion, 1978) using wheat-germ preparations. Cytokinin-binding protein (CBP) is considered to be a trimer of identical 54 kD subunits with one binding site per subunit and a high affinity for active cytokinin structures. Anomalously, however, the most active naturally-occurring structure, zeatin, binds with only low affinity. The biological relevance of CBP is still open to question.

Particulate ethylene-binding sites have been isolated from bean (Phaseolus vulgaris) endosperm tissue (Bengochea et al., 1980) and localised, tentatively, in protein-body membranes and in endoplasmic reticulum. The binding moiety can be solubilised by detergent from high-speed centrifugation pellets, without apparent detriment to binding kinetics (Thomas et al., 1984). Generally, affinities for ethylene analogues and antagonists are in excellent agreement with predictions (Smith and Hall, 1984), but the presence of large concentrations of such sites in non-responsive tissues remains an enigma.

Binding data for abscisic acid (ABA) are limited and exclusively related to membraneous fractions. Hocking et al. (1978) described, in preparations from Phaseolus leaves, greatest affinity of saturable binding of ^{3}H-ABA in sucrose density-gradient fractions corresponding to endoplasmic reticulum. Two classes of binding sites were described but no data on structural specificity was presented. More recently Hornberg and Weiler (1984) have used immunological and photoaffinity techniques to demonstrate the existence of saturable ABA receptors located on the plasmalemma in stomatal guard cells of Vicia faba. Guard-cell protoplasts were selective for the (+)ABA enantiomer and binding properties were abolished by short treatments with proteolytic enzymes. Three peptides with M_r values of 20, 19 and 14 kD were photoaffinity labelled and the relative distribution of label was shown to be pH sensitive. Stomatal closure and binding behaviour were closely correlated using various ABA analogues with differing biological activities.

Gibberellins have also been shown to bind to sub-cellular components in a number of species, including Pisum, Zea, and Cucumis (Venis, 1985). Early studies (Stoddart et al., 1974; Konjevic et al., 1976) indicated association with soluble components and selectivity for biologically-active structures. The major difficulty lay in the apparent non-exchangeability of the binding. Latterly, a series of studies by Keith et al. (1980, 1981) using soluble preparations from cucumber hypocotyls have demonstrated saturable, high affinity, exchangeable binding of labelled GA_4 to 'soluble' components. Binding site concentrations were, however, very low and in similar abundance in responsive and non-responsive regions of the hypocotyl.

Generally there is no difficulty in showing that plant hormones can associate with subcellular components in a manner consistent with the presence of steroid-type primary receptors. Many of these interactions show appropriate levels of sensitivity and selectivity but, except in the case of guard-cell ABA receptors, the challenge of linking their behaviour with the appropriate biological response remains. Furthermore, it has been suggested (Stoddart, 1982) that the binding properties of many of these moieties match those of metabolising enzymes and, indeed, some of the binding preparations studied are capable of structurally transforming the supplied ligands. The possibility that enzymes of the biosynthetic sequence, rather than primary receptors, are being studied must be ruled out. Fortunately, a number of groups (Smith and MacMillan, 1986) are engaged in purifying specific enzymes of plant hormone biosynthetic pathways. Success in such endeavours will allow necessary direct kinetic comparisons between the behaviour of relatively crude binding preparations and purified catalytic proteins.

It seems a fair opinion that, although substantial headway has been made during the past five years, we will best serve progress by maintaining a healthy scepticism about the receptor concept, as it applies to plant hormones.

PHYSICAL INTERACTIONS BETWEEN PLANT HORMONES AND CELL MEMBRANES

Some hormones, particularly GAs and ABA, are lipophilic at some pHs and hydrophilic at others. Furthermore, hydrophilic and hydrophobic domains can exist on the same molecule in the cellular environment. Behaviour of such molecules at cytosol/membrane, cell wall/plasmalemma, or vacuole/tonoplast-membrane interfaces could, therefore, exert significant effects on the physical properties of the interface and on the progress of associated biochemical events. Wood and Paleg (1972) showed that GAs could affect the permeability of artificial membrane systems (liposomes) to sugars based upon lecithin/sterol mixtures. Sugar loss increased with GA_3 concentration and the interaction between temperature and membrane fluidity was perturbed in a parallel fashion (Wood and Paleg, 1974). A more exhaustive study of changes in membrane properties in response to GAs has been conducted by Pauls et al. (1982) using spin-labelling and differential scanning calorimetry. Mixtures of GA_4 and GA_7 were shown to lower phase-transition temperatures and co-operativity in phospholipid membranes in proportion to concentration. In contrast to the earlier studies, the biologically-inactive GA_8 was found to be ineffective but, in conformity, the effective concentration range (around 10^{-3}M) was at least an order of magnitude higher than that known to be optimal for intact plant or organ growth responses. However, when pH was reduced to 3.5, the optimum fell to more consistent concentration values. Superficially, such conditions may appear to be unphysiological in a cytoplasmic context, but the same workers point out that ion-pumping activities in the vicinity of membrane surfaces generate an acidic environment of this order. Endogenous levels of GAs could, therefore, be capable of modifying membrane physical properties in a manner consistent with observed changes in associated metabolic or transport processes.

Early studies on the possible localisation of hormones in membranes have tended to seek some form of preferential accumulation, which would be the case if a selective receptor function was operational. Ginzburg and Kende (1968), for example, found

277

only 0.4% of applied radioactive GA could be recovered in isolated membrane fractions from Pisum. However, if we are considering a purely physical effect, it is only necessary for a membrane to be in equilibrium with the ambient concentration and to change in sympathy with the surrounding soluble phase. No preferential accumulation is required and failure to see a build-up of applied hormones in membranes is then entirely consistent. Bearing in mind the pre-eminent role played by membrane barriers in most aspects of cellular function, it is fair to question the degree to which multiple effects of lipophilic hormone molecules can be explained by modifications to the fluidity of lipid bilayer structures. It is even possible that fluidity could be modified by hormone binding to extrinsic membrane proteins (which then translate the ligand to the inter-lamellar zone) or by association with intrinsic proteins after initial physico-chemical penetration events.

Membrane/hormone interactions have the potential to explain large areas of currently puzzling 'hormonology'. They deserve wider study and may also provide explanations for observed changes in sensitivity.

CELL WALLS AND HORMONE ACTION

The control of cell growth rate and the duration of this process are basically related to two parameters; the generation of turgor pressure and the extensibility of the cell wall. This area has been reviewed by various workers (e.g. Labavitch, 1981), and a number of hypotheses have been erected for the primary intervention of auxins in controlling cell wall cross-linkages, and thereby extensibility (Zeroni & Hall, 1980). Early studies of GA responses in Avena stem segments (Adams et al. 1975) showed that the hormone had little effect on elasticity but enhanced the plastic component of extensibility. This effect was arrested by removal of GA and inhibited by cycloheximide. Confirmation of cell wall responses to GA has been provided for the lettuce hypocotyl system (Stuart and Jones, 1977), showing that extensibility was markedly altered without measurable proton extrusion, as occurs with auxin-induced extension. We are, therefore, contemplating a chain of action for GAs, and possibly auxins, which is believed to commence with a specific soluble or membrane-bound receptor interaction and to culminate in modification of cell wall rheology. If this is the case, there must either be a chain of intervening metabolic events, or else more direct mechanistic interactions must be contemplated. For example, rapid growth responses to auxin may be mediated via proton extrusion from the cell wall (Cleland, 1973), possibly as an immediate consequence of the presence of the growth regulator in the extracellular matrix. The relationship between these responses and the membrane-based binding sites discussed previously is unclear and the rapid time course of growth/proton extrusion events suggests that mediation via concurrent protein synthesis is unlikely. Cell wall incorporation of GA by lettuce hypocotyls has been reported (Stoddart, 1979a,b) and, although the kinetics and specificity of the process match closely to the growth response, the precise biological significance of this observation remains to be determined. A further effect of GAs on cell wall events in the lettuce hypocotyl has been described by Moll and Jones (1981), who followed Ca^{++} movements in a flow-through system. Using additions of calcium salts, chelators or GA, they demonstrated that the growth regulator provoked a marked redistribution of Ca^{++} between cell wall and cytoplasm. Additions of $CaCl_2$ were able to negate GA stimulated growth, whilst calcium chelators promoted elongation. Given that calcium is thought to rigidify pectic gels by forming co-ordination spheres with adjacent carboxyl functions (Rees, 1977), such displacements must be regarded as having potential significance in regulating wall rheology. The quantitative aspects need to be examined in order to determine whether the relocations are large enough to effect significant changes in wall matrix properties. Displacement from wall to cytoplasm, and vice versa, suggests a change in the calcium transporting properties of the plasmalemma, which may itself relate to the primary action site of GA or, alternatively, Ca^{++} flux across the plasmalemma could be governed by the mobile calcium levels on either side. Freeing of bound calcium by direct action within the wall could then affect uptake by perturbing the equilibrium.

The temporal dimension of cell wall behaviour is a further area where our understanding is fragmentary. It is evident from general observation that the extension growth phase of most plant organs is of limited duration and that the ability to respond to growth regulator additions is restricted to a defined time window. The termination of responsiveness can to be related to the formation of permanent cross-linkages between wall components; for example, protein-linkages between extensin chains via isodityrosine (IDT) bridges (Fry, 1986) or permanent bonds between phenylpropanoid depositions on primary fibrils. IDT links are mediated by peroxidative enzyme reactions and 'insoluble' or cell wall peroxidase levels are sensitive to growth regulator levels (again, mainly auxins and GAs). Thus, we have the elements of a hormone-dependent timing mechanism to determine the duration of responsiveness in a given tissue. Similarly, massive secondary metabolite deposition or lignification is thought to be regulated both by hormone levels and photomorphogenic switching of early steps in the shikimic acid pathway.

Wall synthesis continues during cell extension and, in Avena, (Montague and Ikuma 1975) have shown an enhanced incorporation of ^{14}C-glucose into cell walls in the presence of GA. However, the chemical composition was unaffected. In lettuce, wall labelling also paralleled GA enhanced growth (Jones, 1982) and the proportion of extractable neutral sugars was increased by GA treatment (Metraux, 1982), suggesting a relative increase in the hemicellulose fraction.

Given that the cell wall is clearly identified in many studies as the ultimate site of hormone action during extension growth, it is an evident priority area for increased study. We need more precise information on the ways in which extensibility and yield threshold are governed, as well as a better conception of the influences of growth regulators on physical structure and microtubular involvement in cell wall biosynthesis.

TURGOR REGULATION AND WATER MOVEMENT

Lockhart (1965) provided a mathematical description of steady state growth $(\dot{V}_s)$ which has been restated recently by Cosgrove (1981) and Jones (1982). It takes the form:

$$\dot{V}_s = \frac{L \cdot \emptyset}{L + \emptyset} \left(\sigma.\Delta \pi - Y \right)$$

where L is hydraulic conductance, $\emptyset$ is wall extensibility, Y is the yield threshold of the cell wall, σ is the solute reflection coefficient and $\Delta\pi$ is the osmotic potential difference between the internal and external media. In theory, any of the parameters can limit growth rate or the time course over which this is achieved but, in studies on Nitella (Green et al., 1971), growth was shown to be controlled by wall properties and the time-course of adjustment to a new steady state was determined by hydraulic conductivity. Thus, it is evident that, in addition to considering the role of hormones in modifying cell wall physical characteristics, we must also investigate the 'push' which gives expression to altered rheology. Both maintenance of turgor pressure, and the associated water movements are membrane-conditioned phenomena. We still need to know how intercellular movements of water are governed in order to consider how plant hormones may intervene at this level.

Initial data derived from pressure probe studies on leaf meristems of Lolium temulentum show clearly that turgor pressure is unrelated to growth rate between $20^\circ C$ and $2^\circ C$ (on a cooling profile) but that the elastic modulus of the cell wall and the hydraulic conductivity (L) of the tissue decline (A. D. Tomos, personal communication). This suggests strongly that the factors governing water movement

will repay further study, if only to determine whether the change in the L
parameter is consequentially related to variations in wall properties, or whether
it is governed by a separate sub-cellular mechanism. The apparently differential
responses to, say, auxins and gibberellins also require clarification.

REGULATION OF SYNTHETIC AND SECRETION PROCESSES

Most of the known plant hormones can be associated with growth rate changes or
shifts in developmental emphasis and the biophysical relationships involved have
been discussed in the previous section. In addition, there are well characterised
hormonal effects on enzyme synthesis and secretion. The most intensively described
example is the barley aleurone response to GAs. This system is, apparently,
qualitatively different to GA responses in elongating tissues. Generally, it is
described in terms of massive increases in hydrolase synthesis and secretion during
a period of 24 to 72 hours (depending upon species) after addition of the hormone.
About 60% of the secreted protein is as iso-forms of α-amylase, falling into two
immunologically-distinct groups (A = low, B = high pI) (Jacobsen et al., 1982).
Interestingly, the hypotheses covering GA action in this tissue have undergone a
cyclic evolution during the past 20 years. The early studies of Chrispeels and
Varner (1967) reached the conclusion, based upon inhibitor data, that
transcriptional control was being exerted and that hormone action led to the
increased synthesis of enzyme-specific RNA molecules. Over the succeeding decade,
there was a move away from this position towards one favouring an enabling action
of GA on elements of the translation and/or secretion apparatus. For example, GA
was thought to be involved as a controlling factor in membrane phospholipid
synthesis (Johnson and Kende, 1971) and the rapid proliferation of rough
endoplasmic reticulum (RER) in treated cells was postulated as being related to
hormone presence (Jones, 1969). In fact, it was a more detailed examination of RER
distribution, revealing a concentration around the nuclear membrane, coupled with
immunolocalisation of newly synthesised α-amylase in the peri-nuclear region
(Jones and Chen, 1976), which initiated the cycle back to the present point where
the possibility of transcriptional control occupies a central position. The advent
of molecular biological techniques, most notably c-DNA probes for α-amylases, has
permitted the unequivocal demonstration that amylase m-RNAs increase in abundance
following GA treatment. Detailed immunological studies of the α-amylase 'family',
including the use of chromosome addition lines (Jacobsen et al., 1982), have
revealed that transcriptional control of enzyme synthesis must occur at multiple
sites situated on different chromosomes. Furthermore, the additional complication
of a requirement for Ca^{++} to permit the synthesis of the high pI sub-group (B) of
isoenzymes hints at control processes of a more complex nature. It is evident,
however, that m-RNAs for group B isoenzymes continue to accumulate in the absence
of Ca^{++} and the nominal role for GA in facilitating transcription is not
compromised.

The evidence for regulation of transcription of α-amylase genes by GA is becoming
very strong but, at present, it stops short of any demonstration of direct
causality. There is a lack of correspondence between the rise of m-RNA and protein
synthesis levels, the latter continuing to rise after stabilisation of message
levels. It is also uncertain whether translatable m-RNA is enhanced as a result of
unmasking of pre-existing forms or by modifying components of the message turnover
process. c-DNA hybridisation indicates an increase in amylase m-RNA abundance,
thus pointing to increased synthesis; but a reduction in degradation is an equal
possibility. That this process has some selectivity is supported by the finding
that the GA_3-induced increase in α-amylase mRNA is more persistent than that of
other hormone-stimulated mRNA species (Baulcombe and Buffard, 1983).

The mechanism for stimulation of transcription is undefined and may still be
indirect. In spite of attempts with many tissues (including aleurones) there has
been no convincing demonstration of direct binding of GAs to DNA or histones, or of
association of a GA/receptor complex with chromatin or non-histone protein. Either
event would be detectable by a preferential localisation of radioactive hormone

within nuclei, as is evident, for example, in the case of the steroid hormone response in chick oviducts or in uterine tissues (Roy and Clark, 1980). A more viable alternative would be GA-stimulated synthesis of a regulatory protein capable of binding to upstream control regions associated with α-amylase structural genes. This mechanism would fit well to observed behaviour and could also account for the fact that isolated nuclei, when supplied with GA, do not produce α-amylase gene transcripts.

Early observations by Chrispeels and Varner (1967b) indicated that GA was continuously required to maintain enzyme secretion. Removal in mid-course prevented further rise and restitution of the hormone restored enzyme secretion. Logically, for a 'gene-switching response' the expectation would be a progressive independence of hormone presence after the initial critical phase where receptor sites were being occupied, or when a regulator protein was being synthesised. An obvious explanation for continued dependence would be a high dissociation rate of hormone from active site, but there seems little evident need for such sensitive control in the context of endosperm mobilisation. An effective osmotic feedback mechanism already exists. Alternatively, we may be looking at a lack of synchrony in the responses of the total population of aleurone cells, with the continued need for GA being a reflection of the dispersed induction times in the tissue as a whole.

Other aspects of the cereal aleurone response remain puzzling. For example, genera (Hordeum, Triticum, Avena) vary widely in their sensitivities to GA and in the exposure time required to elicit a response. Barley aleurones secrete maximally after 24 hours, whilst Avena fatua requires 48 to 72 hours to reach the same stage (Zwar and Hooley, 1986) and protoplasts from the latter species need several days to exhibit a full response (Hooley, 1982). The obvious inference that protoplasts must regenerate a cell wall as a prerequisite for response appears to be disproved by Calcofluor studies (Hooley, 1982) and we are, therefore, left without an easy explanation.

Carrying this point further, it is notable that many aleurone tissues produce measurable levels of α-amylase in the absence of added GAs and, indeed, wheat aleurones can synthesise appreciable quantities without added hormone (Eastwood et al., 1969). Does this support Atzorn and Weiler's (1983) contention that aleurone cells have a capacity to synthesise GA and that classical control via translocation of embryo-synthesised factors may not be the case?

To complete the catalogue of functional uncertainties it is worth mentioning that the dominant dwarfing gene Rht3 in wheat, confers GA insensitivity in aleurone tissue (Gale and Marshall, 1973). In spite of this, germination proceeds successfully and there are no apparent metabolic or competitive disadvantages arising from this genetic state.

HOMOLOGIES BETWEEN GA RESPONSES IN EXTENDING AND SECRETING TISSUES

A reductionist approach would seek a homology between effects of a given hormone in different tissues. Thus, GA effects in the barley aleurone and, say, the excised lettuce hypocotyl would be viewed as expressions of a common mode of action. Can such a reconciliation be made? The preceding section presents convincing evidence for action via transcriptional control leading to the synthesis and secretion of specific enzyme proteins. In the case of the aleurone layer there is a strong predisposition towards the synthesis of a single enzyme group, and the presence of an inducing factor (i.e. GA) simply stimulates the tissue to 'do its thing'. The response has the timescale of protein synthesis.

In elongating tissues responses can be relatively rapid and, generally, can be associated with changes in cell wall rheology, measured either in terms of yield threshold or as duration of the extendable phase. Changes in wall extensibility are interpreted consequences of enzyme-controlled linkage turnover (Dugger and

Bartnicki-Garcia, 1984) and it can be envisaged that GA control of the synthesis and/or secretion of wall-loosening agents could provide an appropriate mechanism with clear relationships to the barley aleurone response. By this means we can arrive at an homology in which GA stimulates the production of a transcription initiating factor, leading to expression in the form of metabolically active proteins (enzymes?). The nature of the product will depend upon the portion of the genome available for transcription. Aleurone cells have genes for endosperm mobilising enzymes in an unmasked state whereas, in post-division-phase meristematic cells, it is reasonable to suggest that genes governing the secretion of wall-loosening enzymes might be preferentially available for expression. Alternatively, GA could sustain the repression of genes determining the formation of permanent cell wall cross-linkages which preclude further cell expansion. In such circumstances developmental control passes to factors dictating DNA accessibility and the hormone (GA) functions as a general enabling influence. Aspects of programming and temporal control then assume central importance.

REGULATORS AND THE MAINTENANCE OF STRUCTURAL INTEGRITY

Both endogenous hormones and synthetic growth retardants modify rates of structural assembly or disassembly in plant tissues. Chloroplast demolition, usually more globally described as leaf senescence, is the most extensively-studied manifestation of this property and progress has been reviewed frequently (e.g., Thomas and Stoddart, 1980). Cytokinins are widely associated with the maintenance of sink activity and a correlated delay of senescence, but similar effects have been reported for other growth regulators in particular circumstances. For example, GAs retard leaf senescence in Rumex (Osborne, 1967) and CCC has a similar influence in a number of ornamentals. The specificity of intervention has always been questionable and, as our detailed knowledge of chloroplast structure and function increases, the likelihood of direct regulatory influences of hormones on the senescence process have receded. It is established that chloroplast disassembly is multigenically regulated (Thomas and Stoddart, 1975) and that the sequential action of a series of enzymes is essential for the complete degradation of thylakoid lamellae and the hydrolysis of stromal proteins. The synthesis/ activation of these components cascades from a triggering process which is, apparently, sensitive to metabolite fluxes across the chloroplast envelope. For example, exposure to CO_2-free air or darkness are equally effective initiators of senescence (Lloyd, 1980).

Once the syndrome has been initiated, cytokinins do not exhibit specific effects on the progress of leaf senescence, although the capacity for translation and (in some species) transcription is still present. There is good evidence to postulate that the hormone acts to postpone triggering by maintaining cytoplasmic metabolic activity above levels critical for senescence initiation (Thomas and Stoddart, 1980). The work of Fox and Erion (1978) suggests that the mechanism could involve polysome integrity or, alternatively, may reflect an enhanced stability of m-RNA consequent upon changes in turnover processes. In either case the crucial action is the maintenance of normal metabolic activity rather than the expression of a stimulating hormone action. The phrase 'hormone-directed-transport' associated with senescence-retarding activities of cytokinins does not, therefore, accurately reflect the probable action. Sustaining metabolism against a normally declining trend should, more accurately, be described as 'metabolism-directed-transport'. Effects on senescence of other hormones, or unrelated chemicals such as retardants or protein biosynthesis inhibitors, are reconcilable with this interpretation. It does not, of course, preclude a specific hormone action in the pre-senescence phase but it does illustrate the difficulties in relating putative primary interactions to ultimate visible effects.

CONCLUDING REMARKS

It is a prime characteristic of research that it generates questions faster than answers and this propensity is illustrated well in the field of growth regulator research. The generality of plant responses to many hormones has led to difficulties in identifying primary response pathways and, even where tightly targeted systems such as the barley aleurone have been investigated, the level of interaction remains unresolved. Adoption of the range of powerful techniques spawned by the onward rush of molecular biology has begun to bring some order to the biochemical confusion associated with many aspects of plant hormonology. Soon, it should be possible to determine whether specific hormones act as regulators of gene expression in various systems, what effects they have on message availability, and which translation products are preferentially directed. The ability to adopt such an 'inside-out' approach, as opposed to chasing inwards from a series of diffuse final responses, could well have a dramatic effect on the rate of progress towards an understanding of plant hormone action.

REFERENCES

Adams, P.A., Montague, M.J., Tepfer, M., Rayle, D.L., Ikuma, H. and Kaufman, P.B. (1975) Effect of gibberellin on the plasticity and elasticity of Avena stem segments. Plant Physiology 56, 757-760.

Atzorn, R. and Weiler, E.W. (1983). The role of endogenous gibberellins in the formation of α-amylase by aleurone layers of germinating barley caryopses. Planta 159, 289-299.

Baulcombe, D.C. and Buffard, D. (1983). Gibberellic-acid-regulated expression of α-amylase and six other genes in wheat aleurone layers. Planta 157, 493- 501.

Bengochea, T., Dodds, J.H., Evans, D.E., Jerie, P.H., Niepel, B., Shari, A.R. and Hall, M.A. (1980). Studies on ethylene binding by cell-free preparations from cotyledons of Phaseolus vulgaris L.: separation and characterisation. Planta 148, 397-406.

Chrispeels, M.J. and Varner, J.E. (1967a). Gibberellic acid-enhanced synthesis and release of α-amylase and ribonuclease by isolated barley aleurone layers. Plant Phsyiology 42, 398-406.

Chrispeels, M.J. and Varner, J.E. (1967b). Hormonal control of enzyme synthesis: on the mode of action of gibberellic acid and abscisin in aleurone layers of barley. Plant Physiology 42, 1008-1016.

Cleland, R. (1973) Auxin-induced hydrogen ion excretion from Avena coleoptiles. Proceedings of the National Academy of Sciences, USA 70, 3092- 3093.

Cosgrove, D.J. (1981). Analysis of the dynamic and steady-state responses of growth rate and turgor pressure to changes in cell parameters. Plant Physiology 68, 1439-1446.

Dohrmann, U., Hertel, R. and Kowalik, H. (1978). Properties of auxin binding sites in different subcellular fractions from maize coleoptiles. Planta 140, 97-106.

Dugger, W.M. and Bartnicki-Garcia, S. (1984). Structure, Function and Biosynthesis of Plant Cell Walls. American Society of Plant Physiologists, Symposium no. 7, pp 1-501.

Eastwood, D., Tavener, R.J.A and Laidman, D.L. (1969). Sequential action of cytokinin and gibberellic acid in wheat aleurone tissues. Nature 221, 1267.

Erion, J.L. and Fox, J.E. (1977). Purification and properties of a cytokinin binding protein isolated from wheat germ ribosomes. Plant Physiology Supplement 59, 83.

Fox, J.E. and Erion, J.L. (1978). A cytokinin binding protein from higher plant ribosomes. Biochemical Biophysical Research Communications **64**, 694-700.

Fry, S.C. (1986). Cross-linking of matrix polymers in the growing cell walls of angiosperms. Annual Review of Plant Physiology **37**, 165-186.

Gale, M.D. and Marshall, G.A. (1973). Insensitivity to gibberellin in dwarf wheats. Annals of Botany **38**, 729-735.

Ginzburg, C. and Kende, H. (1968). Studies on the intracellular localisation of radioactive gibberellin. In "Biochemistry and Physiology of Plant Growth Substances" (F. Wightman and G. Setterfield eds.), pp 333-340. Runge Press, Ottawa.

Green, P.B., Erickson, R.O. and Buggy, J. (1971). Metabolic and physical control of cell elongation rate. In vivo studies in Nitella. Plant Physiology **47**, 423-430.

Hocking, T.J., Clapham, J. and Cattell, K.J. (1978). Abscisic acid binding to subcellular fractions from leaves of Vicia faba. Planta **138**, 303-304.

Hooley, R. (1982). Protoplasts isolated from aleurone layers of wild oat (Avena fatua L.) exhibit the classic response to gibberellic acid. Planta **154**, 29-40.

Hornberg, C. and Weiler, E.W. (1984). High affinity binding sites for abscisic acid on the plasmalemma of Vicia faba guard cells. Nature **310**, 321-324.

Jacobs, M. and Hertel, R. (1978). Auxin binding to subcellular fractions from Cucurbita hypocotyls: in vitro evidence for an auxin transport carrier. PLanta **142**, 1-10.

Jacobsen, J.V., Chandler, P.M., Higgins, T.J.V. and Zwar, J.A. (1982). Control of protein synthesis in barley aleurone layers by gibberellin. In "Plant Growth Substances 1982" (P.F.Wareing ed.), pp 111-120 Academic Press, London.

Johnson, K.D. and Kende, H. (1971). Hormonal control of lecithin synthesis in barley aleurone cells: regulation of the CDP-choline pathway by gibberellin. Proceedings of the National Academy of Sciences USA **68**, 2674-2677.

Jones, R.L. (1969). Gibberellic acid and the fine structure of barley aleurone cells. II. Changes during the synthesis and secretion of α-amylase. Planta **88**, 73-86.

Jones, R.L. (1982). Gibberellin control of cell elongation. In "Plant Growth Substances 1982" (P.F. Wareing ed.), pp 121-130. Academic Press, London.

Jones, R.L. and Chen, R.F. (1976) Immunohistological localisation of α-amylase in barley aleurone cells. Journal of Cell Science **20**, 183-198.

Keith, B. and Srivastava, L.M. (1980). In vitro binding of gibberellin A_1 in dwarf pea epicotyls. Plant Physiology **66**, 962-967.

Keith, B., Foster, N.A., Bonettemaker, M. and Srivastava, L.M. (1981). In vitro gibberellin A_4 binding to extracts of cucumber hypocotyls. Plant Physiology **68**, 344-348.

Konjevic, R., Grubisic, D., Markovic, R. and Petrovic, J. (1976). Gibberellic acid binding proteins from pea stems. Planta **131**, 125-128.

Labavitch, J.M. (1981). Cell wall turnover in plant development. Annual Review of Plant Physiology **32**, 385-406.

Lloyd, E.J. (1980). The effects of leaf age and senescence on the distribution of carbon in Lolium temulentum. Journal of Experimental Botany **31**, 1067-1079.

Lockhart, J.A. (1965). An analysis of irreversible plant cell elongation. Journal of Theoretical Biology **8**, 264-275.

Metraux, J.P. (1982). Changes in cell wall polysaccharide composition in developing Nitella internodes - analysis of walls of single cells. Planta **155**, 459-466.

Moll, C. and Jones, R.L. (1981). Calcium and gibberellin-induced elongation of lettuce hypocotyl sections. Plant Physiology **152**, 450-456.

Montague, M.J. and Ikuma, H. (1975). Regulation of cell wall synthesis in Avena stem segments by gibberellic acid. Plant Physiology **55**, 1043-1047.

Osborne, D.J. (1967). Hormonal regulation of leaf senescence. Symposia of the Society for Experimental Biology **21**, 305-322.

Pauls, K.P., Chambers, J.A., Dumbroff, E.B. and Thompson, J.E. (1982). Perturbation of phospholipid membranes by gibberellins. New Phytologist **91**, 1-17.

Ray, P.M. (1977). Auxin binding sites of maize coleoptiles are localised on membranes of the endoplasmic reticulum. Plant Physiology **59**, 594-599.

Rees, D.A. (1977). "Polysaccharide Shapes". Outline Studies in Biology, pp 51- 52. Chapman and Hall, London.

Roy, A.K. and Clark, J.H. (1980). "Gene Regulation by Steroid Hormones" pp 1- 309 Springer-Verlag, New York.

Smith, A.R. and Hall, M.A. (1984). Mechanisms of ethylene action. Plant Growth Regulation **2**, 151-165.

Smith, V.A. and MacMillan, J. (1986). The partial purification and characterisation of gibberellin 2 β -hydroxylases from seeds of Pisum sativum. Planta **167**, 9-18.

Stoddart, J.L. (1979a). Interaction of $[^3H]$-gibberellin A_1 with a subcellular fraction from lettuce (Lactuca sativa L.) hypocotyls. I. Kinetics of labelling. Planta **146**, 353-361.

Stoddart, J.L. (1979b). Interaction of $[^3H]$-gibberellin A_1 with a subcellular fraction from lettuce (Lactuca sativa L.) hypocotyls. II. Stability and properties of the association. Planta **146**, 363-368.

Stoddart, J.L. (1982). Gibberellin perception and its primary consequences. In "Plant Growth Substances" (P.F. Wareing ed.), pp 131-140. Academic Press, London.

Stoddart, J.L., Briedenbach, W., Nadeau, R. and Rappaport, L. (1974). Selective binding of $[^3H]$ gibberellin A_1 by protein fractions from dwarf pea epicotyls. Proceedings of the National Academy of Science, USA **71**, 3255-3259.

Stuart, D.A. and Jones, R.L. (1977). The roles of extensibility and turgor in gibberellin- and dark-stimulated growth. Plant Physiology **59**, 61-68.

Thomas, C.J.R., Smith, A.R. and Hall, M.A. (1984). The effect of solubilisation on the character of an ethylene binding site from Phaseolus vulgaris L. cotyledons. Planta **160**, 474-479.

Thomas, H. and Stoddart, J.L. (1975). Separation of chlorophyll degradation from other senescence processes in leaves of a mutant genotype of meadow fescue (Festuca pratensis). Plant Physiology **56**, 438-441.

Thomas, H. and Stoddart, J.L (1980). Leaf senescence. Annual Review of Plant Physiology **31**, 83-111.

Venis, M. (1985). "Hormone Binding Sites in Plants" pp 1-90 Longman, Plant Science, New York.

Wood, A. and Paleg, L.G. (1972). The influence of gibberellic acid on the permeability of model membrane systems. Plant Physiology **50**, 103-108.

Wood, A. and Paleg, L.G. (1974). Alteration of liposomal membrane fluidity by gibberellic acid. Australian Journal of Plant Physiology **1**, 31-40.

Zeroni, M. and Hall, M.A. (1980). Molecular effects of hormone treatment on tissue. In "Hormonal Regulation of Development I. Molecular Aspects of Plant Hormones". Encyclopaedia of Plant Physiology, New Series Vol. 9 (J. MacMillan ed.), pp 511-586, Vol. 9. Springer-Verlag, Berlin.

Zwar, J.A. and Hooley, R (1986). Hormonal regulation of α-amylase gene transcription in wild oat (Avena fatua L.) aleurone protoplasts. Plant Physiology **80**, 459-463.

MOLECULAR APPROACHES FOR THE MANIPULATION OF DEVELOPMENTAL PROCESSES IN PLANTS

T.C. Hall and T.L. Thomas

Biology Department, Texas A & M University, College Station, Texas 77843-3258, U.S.A

INTRODUCTION

The past decade has witnessed revolutionary advances in understanding life processes at the molecular level. These advances are primarily attributed to the development of recombinant DNA procedures that have permitted the isolation, characterisation and modification of genes, and the refinement of immunochemical procedures which permit very sensitive detection of proteins that are essential in confirming the expression of specific gene products. In this article we review current progress resulting from the application of molecular techniques to developmental problems, and provide several specific examples of such progress. We also speculate on prospects that challenge researchers in plant biology.

CHARACTERISATION OF PLANT GENOMES

A rather obvious difference between plants and most other organisms is the presence of chloroplasts and the evolution of oxygen as a result of photosynthesis. Although the fractionation of plant organelles led to remarkably accurate descriptions of chloroplasts and mitochondria, both in terms of structure and function, acceptance that the chloroplast and the mitochondrion contain their own genetic information has been dependent on the characterisation of their genomes through recombinant DNA approaches. Clearly, the nucleus contains the major quantity of heritable material in the plant cell, but organelle development is intrinsic to plant functions and is now amenable to study in far greater detail. Because the three genomes present in plant cells have different characteristics, they will be considered separately.

The Nuclear Genome

Work in a nmumber of laboratories, using DNA reassociation kinetics as a major tool, showed that nuclear genomes contained several major classes of DNA. These DNA sequence classes were represented in the genome at one extreme by highly repeated sequences present in hundreds, sometimes thousands, of copies per nucleus; other sequences, including many genes, were present in very few copies, sometimes only one copy, per haploid genome. From work of this type, it was soon realised that in most plants and animals, one class of highly repetitive elements were the genes encoding ribosomal RNAs.

Ribosomal genes

A major contribution to understanding the origin of biological macromolecules was the recognition that proteins are synthesised from mRNA templates on ribosomes, complex structures of ribosomal RNAs (rRNAs) and proteins. Sequences of rRNAs are conserved from bacteria to plants to man. Tissues that are active in protein synthesis contain many ribosomes, and it is evident that many copies of ribosomal RNA and mRNAs encoding ribosomal proteins must be synthesised in such tissues prior to the onset of protein synthesis.

Developmental studies have shown that several strategies are used in making adequate numbers of ribosomes available (Davidson, 1986). The most fundamental strategy is the availability of many copies of ribosomal genes in nuclear DNA and the tandem arrangement of these ribosomal DNA (rDNA) sequences. This organisation allows rapid transcription of the ribosomal genes at appropriate developmental stages. Other strategies often involve the accumulation of rRNAs and ribosomal proteins such as occur during animal oogenesis.

Despite the overall conservation of rDNA sequences from organism to organism, variation occurs, even within the nuclear genome of any given organism. Clearly, the existence of multiple copies of any gene permits variation of sequence through mutation; if the mutation yields a non-functional ribosomal component it is not lethal since a functional product from wild-type genes will also be present in the cell. As a result, there are undoubtedly copies of non-functional ribosomal genes within plant cells, but determination of which sequences are functional is difficult. The presence of lethal mutations in protein coding regions can be deduced by disruption of the open reading frame, but such mutations in rDNA sequences are especially hard to identify. Although some of the variation in ribosomal sequences results from detrimental mutations, it is certain that many functional variants of ribosomal sequences exist. However, it is still not known if specific classes of ribosomes, i.e. ribosomes with certain mRNA or ribosomal proteins, are selected for translation of specific mRNAs. One speculative model is that transcriptional activation of certain ribosomal genes may be associated with developmentally regulated expression of specific gene products.

Other repeated DNA sequences
In plants, there has been little characterisation of highly repeated DNA sequences other than ribosomal genes. Attempts to construct wheat-rye hybrids to yield Triticale appear to be hampered by the extent of repeat sequences that contribute to the heterochromatin seen in cytological studies. Flavell (1982) has postulated that large quantities of such sequences slow cell division. Consequently, the presence of a chromosome. or part of a chromosome that undergoes replication at a rate intrinsically different from that of other chromosomes in the nucleus will disrupt normal cell division. This has additional practical implications in attempts to form hybrid plants as a result of protoplast fusion. Clearly, we have much to learn about the various molecular events that contribute to the timing of events in the cell cycle, and an exciting future surely awaits those unravelling these mysteries.

Genes encoding messenger RNAs
Although the discovery of the DNA double-helix by Watson and Crick was the foundation stone of molecular biology, the elucidation of the existence and function of mRNA provided the formal structure, or central dogma, for molecular biology investigations. The decade following the discovery of mRNA function was dedicated to understanding bacterial and bacteriophage functions; the insight gained by phage genetics was intrinsic to the identification of individual genes within bacteria and their viruses. Subsequently, DNA sequencing procedures were developed, and the role of mRNA in mediating the transfer of the genetic information encoded in DNA to the primary amino acid sequences of proteins was unequivocally established. With this background, studies on eukaryotic organisms were initiated. Subsequent work (Galan et al., 1974; Kamalay and Goldberg, 1980), established that mRNAs were typically present in low abundance. These studies also permitted the estimation of the complexity of various animal genomes and the complexities of the mRNA populations expressed from these genomes; it became apparent that, whereas the protein coding portion of bacterial genomes comprised a few thousand genes, animal and plant genomes encoded fifty to one hundred thousand genes. Plant genomes were found to the especially variable in size, with the genome of Arabidopsis being substantially smaller than that of man, 7×10^7 bp, (Leutwiler et al., 1984) and some, such as that of the pumpkin, several orders of magnitude greater (Bennett and Smith, 1976).

Due to the relatively large size of eukaryotic genomes, even after bacterial plasmid cloning procedures were established, the possibility of isolating any given protein coding sequence from a higher eukaryote appeared remote. However, the use of bacteriophage vectors, especially the Charon series of phage ψ developed by Blattner et al. (1977), radically changed the situation because literally millions of DNA fragments (obtained by restriction endonuclease digestion of genomic DNA) could be cloned and amplified in bacterial hosts using these bacteriophage vectors. This collection or "library" of DNA sequences could be maintained almost indefinitely and could be used repeatedly for the isolation of genomic DNA sequences encoding specific mRNAs. Hybridization procedures, based on the RNA re-association concepts developed in the late 1960s and early 1970s, now make the isolation of almost any gene sequence routine once a suitable nucleic acid probe sequence is available (Benton and Davies, 1977).

The key to identification of specific eukaryotic genomic sequences encoding mRNA sequences was the ability to prepare specific hybridisation probes. These were, and typically still are, cDNA sequences synthesised by reverse transcription of mRNAs. Early on, the problem was to identify sources of relatively pure mRNA. Pioneering studies used globin mRNAs. Erythrocytes make globin almost exclusively, and as a consequence globin mRNAs are by far the most abundant messenger species in these cells. In plants, the seed proteins are abundantly synthesised in developing embryonic tissues (typically, in the cotyledons of dicots and endosperm of monocots), and one of the first plant genomic DNA sequences cloned was that for phaseolin the major storage protein of the French bean, Phaseolus vulgaris (Sun et al., 1981). The cloning of less prevalent mRNAs as cDNA sequences has required the development of more sophisticated screening and cloning procedures such as antibody screening in expression vectors (Young and Davis, 1983).

The development of rapid DNA sequencing techniques permitted total characterisation of cloned DNA sequences and led to several unexpected revelations. The most remarkable was the discovery of nucleotide sequences that interrupt the protein coding sequence in genomic DNA, but which are not present in mature mRNA. These sequences, termed introns or intervening sequences, are present in newly transcribed mRNA (heterogeneous nuclear, hnRNA) but are removed before the mRNA is exported from the nucleus; such processing events undoubtedly have a role in developmental regulation and are referred to later.

Hybridisation and sequencing experiments also revealed that genes encoding abundant proteins (such as the seed proteins) are often represented in the genome by multiple copies and comprise a gene family. The concept of gene families has become important in deciphering developmental events. Different gene family members may be expressed in different tissues, cell types or at different developmental times. This strategy may allow the organism to express a slightly different gene product in each situation, or perhaps more importantly may place different gene family members in different regulatory networks.

The Chloroplast Genome

Mesophyll cells of plant leaves contain many chloroplasts; these can be isolated intact and relatively free from other organelles, including the nucleus. Genetic evidence and early molecular analyses showed that chloroplasts had their own genome. Chloroplast genomes are circular and approximately 150 Kb in length; complete sequences are now available for chloroplasts from Nicotiana (Shinozaki et al., 1986) and the liverwort, Marchantia polymorpha (Ohyama et al., 1986). This and other work showed that chloroplasts contain functional ribosomes and synthesise a portion of the protein within this organelle. Many features of the chloroplast genome mimic those of bacterial genomes, including the presence of prokaryotic promoters and ribosome binding sites. Although it appeared at first that introns were absent from chloroplast genes, several chloroplast coding sequences have now been shown to contain introns (Shinozaki et al., 1986; Ohyama et al., 1986).

A finding of major importance to developmental biology from the chloroplast studies was that several chloroplast enzymes consist of subunits encoded by chloroplast nuclear genomes. For example, ribulosebisphosphate carboxylase, the enzyme involved in CO_2 fixation by chloroplasts, consists of eight large subunits and eight small subunits; approximate subunit molecular weights are 56000 and 14000 daltons respectively (Wildman, 1982). A number of studies, including that of Berry-Lowe et al. (1982), showed the small subunit of ribulosebisphosphate carboxylase is encoded by a small family of nuclear genes, whereas the large subunit of this enzyme is encoded by the chloroplast. Work further showed that a hydrophobic N-terminal sequence of approximately 20 amino acids was cleaved from the small subunit precursor as it passed through the chloroplast membrane. Subsequently, similar "signal" sequences have been found on virtually all polypeptides that pass through membranes. Indeed, as will be mentioned later, the presence of such a sequence appears to be primarily responsible for directing the passage of proteins through specific membranes.

The Mitochondrial Genome

The mitochrondrion has long been recognised as the cell's powerhouse. However, as with the chloroplast, it is only with the advent of recombinant procedures that its possession of a discrete genome has been recognised. In parallel with the chloroplast, it is now evident that although some mitochondrial proteins are synthesised within the organelle, several proteins are encoded by the nuclear genome, translated in the cytoplasm and transported into the mitochondrion or inserted into its membrane. Particularly fascinating is the discovery that the genetic code used by the mitochondrion differs slightly from that previously considered to be ubiquitous; the most notable difference is that the codon UGA, normally a translation stop codon, is read in mitochondria as a tryptophan (Anderson et al., 1981).

The mitochondrial genome of plants is typically much larger than that of animals, and it varies substantially in size among plant species (Levings, 1983). Londsdale et al. (1984) have convincingly argued that many of the circular mitochondrial DNAs of plant cells are permutations of a "master" mitochondrial genome; the reason for this organisation of plant mitochondrial DNA remains to be elucidated, as does its role in plant metabolism. Another intriguing finding is the overall similarity of gene sequences within the chloroplast and the mitochondrion; indeed, it is now thought that the chloroplast contains all the mitochondrial genes, even though they may not all be expressed within the chloroplast (Stern and Palmer, 1984). Another particularly important attribute of the mitochondrial genome is its apparent involvement in cytoplasmic male sterility (cms). For example, Dewey et al. (1986) suggest that the mitochondria of male sterile lines of corn contain specific transcripts that appear to be associated with cms.

Before leaving the subject of the structure and function of organelle genomes it should be noted that plant cellular development clearly involves coordinated interaction between the nuclear and organellar genomes. At present, however, we have little or no information as to how such coordination occurs. One approach to this question might be the investigation of plastid development in plants containing variegated leaves and the investigation of mutants that block specific events of plastid ontogeny.

INFORMATIONAL TRANSFERS DURING PLANT DEVELOPMENT

Apparently many informational transfers must occur during plant ontogeny so that the genetic information encoded in the genome is expressed in the appropriate morphogenetic time and space. Another way of describing this same problem is that informational flow from the nucleus to the cytoplasm is a major driving force for differentiation and development. Unfortunately, few of these informational transfers are presently well characterised in plants; consequently, examples from animal systems have to be cited although previous experience suggests that similar mechanisms occur ubiquitously in animals and plants.

Ontogenetic DNA Modification

Relatively little is known about modification of DNA during plant development, although it almost certainly occurs. Probably the best described modification of plant DNA is methylation. Eukaryotic DNA is typically much more highly methylated than is prokaryotic DNA. Plant DNA is much more highly methylated than is animal DNA; in wheat, for example, 80% of all possible sites are methylated (Gruenbaum et al., 1981). Much of our current knowledge about methylation of DNA depends on the fact that certain endonucleases will cleave a given DNA sequence when it is methylated, whereas others will not (Msp I/Hpa II). It has been suggested that highly methylated DNA is transcriptionally inactive (Doerfler, 1983). Although this generalisation needs much qualification, correlation between methylation of T-DNA in transformed plant tissues and lowered activity of included genes such as nopaline synthetase (nos) has been observed by several groups (Fraley et al., 1986). Such observations, as well as those indicating reversion of the methylation phenotype with 5-azacytidine (van Slogteren et al., 1984), are highly suggestive that methylation may have a role in controlling development, and undoubtedly this represents a fertile area for future research.

The association of both histone and non-histone proteins with nuclear DNA to form chromatin has been extensively studied, but major questions remain as to how these proteins interact with DNA, with each other, and with other chromatin proteins to regulate gene expression. Chromatin studies have shown that DNA is typically coiled around octamers of histones, the nucleosomes (McGhee and Felsenfeld, 1980). Despite elegant studies in this area, the relationship between nucleosome structure and gene expression remains elusive. It is also well established that several enzymes are capable of altering the supercoiled status of DNA; such gyrases and topoisomerases are typically associated with DNA metabolism, but they may well function to render certain chromatin domains transcriptionally active or inactive. Genetic engineering depends on the ability to insert functional DNA sequences into the existing genome; this process occurs within the chromatin context and therefore chromatin structure must be considered. In plants, it seems apparent that the location of insertion within a host genome affects the relative expression levels of some recombinant constructions (Fraley et al., 1986), but if, or how, this relates to chromatin architecture is not known.

An active area of current research is the analysis of proteins that bind to specific DNA sequences (trans-acting factors) and the sequences to which they bind. Such studies have been stimulated by the discovery of enhancers: DNA sequences that greatly increase transcriptional activity of genes associated with these enhancer elements. Although "core" sequences have been identified in enhancer elements associated with a small number of animal genes (Gillies et al., 1983), there is as yet no "consensus" enhancer sequence. The Watson-Crick double-helix is now recognised as only one conformation of DNA. Rich et al. (1984) have shown that other conformations, such as that present in "Z-DNA", are not only possible but more likely for certain nucleotide sequences, especially within the chromatin milieu. These Z-DNA regions frequently are associated with increased transcriptional activity and may well overlap with the sequence domains operationally defined as enhancers. The study of protein-DNA interactions will undoubtedly increase our insight as to the effect of these trans-acting factors on DNA topology, but more importantly such analyses may provide information on their role in regulation of gene expression during development.

Developmental Regulation of Transcription

Although it was once thought that developmentally regulated promoters would not be suitable for gene transfer experiments, it is now clear that they in fact are particularly advantageous for such experiments. Indeed, one of the many amazing findings derived from gene transfer studies is the detailed information contained within the untranslated, often untranscribed, regions flanking eukaryotic genes. In plants, early findings included the tissue-specific expression of β-phaseolin (Sengupta-Gopalan et al., 1985) and light-regulation of carboxylase small subunit (Morelli et al., 1985). More recent results, again using gene transfer methods, have now identified specific DNA regions located 5' of the transcribed regions of soybean β-conglycinin (Chen et al., 1986) and pea rbcS genes (Timko et al., 1985).

These cis regulatory elements function as developmentally regulated enhancer complexes presumably through their interaction with ontogenetically controlled proteins or trans-acting factors. One of the most exciting areas of molecular biology is the analysis of protein DNA interactions involved in the developmental control of gene expression. These studies may lead to the cloning of genes directly involved in ontogenetic control of gene expression and thus could provide the means of designing gene constructs with specific gene regulatory characteristics.

RNA Processing

The presence of introns in coding sequences of genomic DNA was discussed above. At first it seemed likely that the ability correctly to excise these sequences would be highly organ and species specific. However, gene transfer experiments have shown that, although specificity exists, it is not highly restrictive; for example, the five introns present in the bean phaseolin coding sequence are efficiently and correctly excised in tobacco seed (Sengupta-Gopalan et al., 1985). Bean and tobacco are evolutionarily distant and it is clear that, in this case at least, species specificity does not exist. In contrast, yeast is unable to excise phaseolin introns; when genomic constructions are introduced, heterogenous transcripts are observed. However, transformation of yeast with a "processed" phaseolin genomic sequence, one containing the intronless cDNA sequence within the normal genomic 5' and 3' flanking sequences, yielded transcripts of defined length which were effectively translated to yield full-length phaseolin polypeptides (Cramer et al., 1985). Thus, the processes of intron excision does not appear to have phylogenetic boundaries.

Some types of introns can excise autocatalytically (Cech, 1986), but it is clear that most, if not all, introns of genes transcribed by RNA polymerase II require specific enzymes and other factors, including small ribonucleoprotein particles (SnRPs), for their excision (Ruskin and Green, 1985). The ontogenetic expression of the factors involved in the splicing of Pol II transcripts has not been explored. However, the observation in animal systems of alternative splicing of precursor RNAs resulting in mRNAs that encode related but distinct polypeptides (Rosenfeld et al., 1984; Laski et al., 1986) indicate that complex regulatory events must occur at the level of pre-mRNA splicing, although the mechanism of these regulatory events is unknown. Thus far, alternative splicing of plant pre-mRNAs has not been demonstrated.

Eukaryotic mRNAs also typically undergo 5' and 3' processing during maturation; these modifications do not affect the informational content of the resulting mRNAs but probably do affect their stability. The 5' termini of many mRNAs have a m^{7}GpppG "cap" structure (Shatkin, 1976) that contributes to the efficiency of translation for some mRNAs. For other mRNAs the "cap" appears to be of minor importance; for example, brome mosaic virus (BMV) RNA4, an mRNA without a "cap", encodes the viral coat protein and is efficiently translated in vitro by the wheat germ system (Shin and Kaesberg, 1973). However, BMV RNA transcripts synthesised in vitro must be capped to be infective (Ahlquist et al., 1984); these data suggest that the cap structure confers stability on BMV mRNAs in the host cell. It is likely, but unproven, that other stabilising mechanisms acting at the 5' end of the message exist, and they undoubtedly play a role in the kinetic characteristics of specific mRNAs.

With the exception of histone mRNA and a few others, eukaryotic mRNAs bear a lengthy (20-200 base) poly(A) sequence added post-transcriptionally to the 3' terminus. A consensus of AATAAA sequence is found some 20 nucleotides upstream of the site of poly(A) addition; this sequence apparently serves to locate the cleavage site on the precursor RNA transcript which is subsequently polyadenylated. Evidence suggests that the 3' poly(A) sequence also participates in mRNA stability, although other functions for the poly(A) tracts cannot be excluded. From data of gene transfer experiments (Fraley et al., 1986), it appears that transcripts derived from the same gene with different 3' termini are heterogeneous in length and their extent of polyadenylation varies; however, overall transcript levels do not appear to be affected.

292

Protein Processing

Post-translational modification and protein transport is one of the most ignored informational transfers in terms of its role in development. Many proteins contain hydrophobic sequences of 20-30 amino acids at their amino termini that are involved in their passage through membranes. These transit sequences are cleaved during membrane passage, and polypeptides in the mature protein are consequently smaller than those initially translated from the mRNA transcript. Much is now known about such sequences, and their processing, and it is becoming clear that, at least in certain instances, these sequences are specifically involved in the insertion of the polypeptide into particular membranes, contributing to the final destination of the protein. Examples include sequences that target rbcS and other proteins into the chloroplast (Fraley et al., 1986; Karlin-Neumann and Tobin, 1986). Considerably less is known about the sequences involved in targeting proteins to plant mitochondria. Application of protein targeting methodologies include directing atrazine resistant psb A gene products, or the enzyme which degrades the herbicide glyphosate, to the chloroplast and targeting-improved seed storage proteins to their appropriate subcellular compartments.

Several seed proteins are known to contain internal protease-sensitive sites that are cleaved during protein maturation. The widely distributed legumins of dicots contain acidic and basic regions, separated by a proteolytic cleavage site. Although the exact mechanisms of legumin processing are not yet known, it is likely that disulphide bonds between the acidic and basic subunits position them during cleavage. Modification of genes to eliminate, or to introduce additional, cleavage sites is likely to change the ontogenetic expression of these proteins. Furthermore, these changes may affect the stability of the storage proteins and could result in higher (or lower) digestibility of the protein. Viral proteins often depend upon proteolytic cleavage for maturation. Although some viruses themselves encode proteases, it is likely that host proteases are involved in at least some of the necessary maturation steps. Conceivably, modification of host proteases could reduce the ability of such a virus to infect its host.

Glycosylation of plant proteins is another widespread example of protein processing. In some cases, it appears that glycosylation may influence the stability of the protein. Phaseolin, the major storage protein of the French bean, is normally glycosylated. Removal of the sugar residues greatly increases its susceptibility to degradation (Sharon, 1984). Like most characterised glycosylations of plant proteins, the sugar residues are N-linked to the phaseolin polypeptide at asparagine residues; the sequences, asn-x-ser or asn-x-thr (Sharon, 1984), are the usual sites of N-glycosylation, although it appears that such sites are not always glycosylated. Alteration of such sequences in seed proteins to eliminate glycosylation is seen as a way of making them more digestible, although it may also reduce their stability or targeting within the seed.

ROLE OF GROWTH REGULATOR GENES IN DEVELOPMENT

It is now unequivocably established that the phenotypic expression of galls or "hairy" roots in plant tissues infected with Agrobacterium tumefaciens containing Ti or Ri plasmids results from the expression of plasmid-encoded genes whose products synthesise cytokinins and auxins (Morris, 1986). This expression accounts for the hormone-independent growth of tissues transformed with wild-type Ti plasmids. Deletion of these phytohormone genes was essential before Ti plasmid transformation systems could be used to produce phenotypically-normal plants. It appears that the biosynthetic pathways of growth regulators in crown-gall cells differ from the corresponding pathways of untransformed plant tissues. Consequently, the regulation of phytohormone expression encoded by Ti plasmids probably differs from the expression of the homologous phytohormone encoded by plant genes. Nevertheless, interesting experiments are underway to introduce cloned Ti plasmid cytokinin and auxin genes into plants to determine their effects on growth and developmental characteristics.

An important question yet to be addressed, is how many plant genes encode enzymes involved in the auxin biosynthetic pathway? Similarly, in the case of cytokinin, where a single enzyme step appears to be involved in the synthesis of iPMP from 5'AMP (Letham and Palni, 1983), is there a single gene, or are there many genes involved? These questions are fundamental to understanding the action of these growth regulators. For example, it could be postulated that a plant contains five cytokinin genes. However, the expression of each gene may be developmentally regulated, e.g. one may be flanked by an enhancer region activated by a trans-acting factor present only in leaves, while another is activated only in flowers, and another expressed only in embryos.

If phytohormones are the penultimate products of families of differentially-expressed and regulated genes, then many of the confusing observations in the literature may be explained. Within a plant the absolute and relative auxin and cytokinin levels could vary considerably from tissue to tissue. The addition of equal amounts of either auxin or cytokinin could result in differing hormone ratios in the two tissues. Similar explanations may apply to the different reaction of monocot and dicot plants to auxin application, which forms the basis of the broadleaf herbicide industry and the observation that Agrobacterium does not induce galls on monocots. Furthermore, it is conceivable that auxins or cytokinins themselves are involved directly in the developmental control of gene expression in much the same way as steroid hormones are involved in animal gene expression. If so, it is not unreasonable that various genes may be activated differentially by changes in hormone levels in different tissues.

FUTURE DIRECTIONS

Major insights in understanding plant ontogeny are to be gained from the study of Ti plasmid-encoded phytohormone genes and their expression in transgenic plants. However, it is clear that the cloning of genes encoding plant enzymes involved in auxin and cytokinin biosynthesis is an urgent need in the field of growth regulators as is the identification and cloning of genes involved in the synthesis of abscisic acid and gibberellins. These genes could then be reintroduced into plants followed by the expression of the introduced genes under heterologous control. Such experiments would disrupt the normal hormone ratios and the effects could be monitored phenotypically during embryogenesis and growth. These genes also could be used for decreasing tissue-specific expression of auxin or cytokinin biosynthesis by their expression as anti-sense RNAs in transgenic plants. We believe that such experiments represent high priority targets for growth regulator studies, and we predict that results from such experiments will revolutionise our understanding of the mode of action of these important compounds, and perhaps ultimately they will tell us how these relatively simple compounds control plant development.

ACKNOWLEDGEMENTS

The authors thank Drs T. McKnight , R. DeRose and M. Guiltinan of the Biology Department for their critical comments on this manuscript.

REFERENCES

Ahlquist, P., French, R., Janda, M. and Loesch-Fries, L.S. (1984). Multicomponent RNA plant virus infection derived from cloned viral cDNA. Proceedings of the National Academy of Sciences USA, 81, 7066-7070.

Anderson, S., Bankier, A.T., Barrell, B.G., de Bruijn, M.H.L., Coulson, A.R. Drouin, J., Eperon, I.C., Nierlich, D.P., Roe, B.A., Sanger, F., Shreier, P.H., Smith, A.J.H., Staden, R. and Young, I.G. (1981). Sequence and organization of the human mitochondrial genome. Nature 290, 457-465.

Bennett, M.D. and Smith, J.B. (1976). Nuclear DNA amounts in angiosperms. Philosophical Transactions of the Royal Society London B 274, 227-274.

Benton, W.D. and Davis, R.W. (1977). Screening ψ gt recombinant clones by hybridization to single plaques in situ. Science **196**, 180-184.

Berry-Lowe, S.L., McKnight, T.D., Shah, D. and Meagher, R.B. (1982). The nucleotide sequence, expression and evolution of one member of a multigene family encoding the small subunit of ribulose-1,5-bisphosphate carboxylase in soybean. Journal of Molecular and Applied Genetics **1**, 483-498.

Blattner, F.R., Williams, B.G. Blechl, A.E., Denniston-Thompson, K., Faber, H.E., Furlong, L.A., Grunwald, D.J., Kiefer, D.O., Moore, D.D., Sheldon, E.L. and Smithies, O. (1977). Charon phages: safer derivatives of bacteriophage lambda for DNA cloning. Science **196**, 161-166.

Cech, T.R. (1986). The generality of self-splicing RNA: relationship to nuclear RNA splicing. Cell **44**, 207-210.

Chen, Z-L., Schuler, M.A. and Beachy, R.N. (1986). Functional analysis of regulatory elements in a plant embryo-specific gene. Proceedings of the National Academy of Science USA **83**, 8560-8564.

Cramer, J.H., Lea, K. and Slightom, J.A. (1985). Expression of phaseolin cDNA genes in yeast under control of natural plant DNA sequences. Proceedings of the National Academy of Sciences USA **82**, 334-338.

Davidson, E.H. (1986). Gene Activity in Early Development. Academic Press, New York.

Dewey, R.E., Levings, C.S., III and Timothy, D.H. (1986). Novel recombinations in the maize mitochondrial genome produce a unique transcriptional unit in the Texas male-sterile cytoplasm. Cell **44**, 439-449.

Doerfler, W. (1983). DNA methylation and gene activity. Annual Review of Biochemistry **52**, 93-124.

Flavell, R. (1982). Sequence amplification, deletion and rearrangement: major sources of variation during species divergence. In "Genome Evolution", (G.A. Dover and R.B. Flavell, eds), pp. 301-323, Academic Press, New York.

Fraley, R.T., Rogers, S.G. and Horsch, R.B. (1986). Genetic transformation in higher plants. CRC Critical Reviews in Plant Sciences **4**, 1-46.

Galau, G.A., Britten, R.J. and Davidson, E.H. (1974). A measurement of the sequence complexity of polysomal messenger RNA in sea urchin embryos. Cell **2**, 9-21.

Gillies, S.D., Morrison, S.L., Oi, V.T. and Tonegawa, S. (1983). Tissue-specific enhancer element in the major intron of the immunoglobulin heavy-chain gene. In "Current Communications in Molecular Biology", (Y. Gluzman and T. Shenk, eds), pp. 121-128, Cold Spring Harbor Laboratory.

Gruenbaum, Y., Naveh-Many, T., Cedar, H. and Razin, A. (1981). Sequence specificity of methylation in higher plant DNA. Nature **292**, 860-862.

Kamalay, J.C. and Goldberg, R.B. (1980). Regulation of gene expression in tobacco. Cell **19**, 935-946.

Karlin-Neumann, G.A. and Tobin, E.M., (1986). Transit peptides of nuclear-encoded chloroplast proteins share a common amino acid framework. Journal of the European Molecular Biology Organization **5**, 9-13.

Laski, F.A., Rio, D.C. and Rubin, G.M. (1986). Tissue specificity of Drosophila P element transposition is regulated at the level of mRNA splicing. Cell **44**, 7-19.

Letham, D.S., Palni, L.M.S. (1983). The biosynthesis and metabolism of cytokinins. Annual Review of Plant Physiology **34**, 163-197.

Leutwiler, L.S., Hough-Evans, B.R. and Meyerowitz, E.M. (1984). The DNA of Arabidopsis thaliana. Molecular and General Genetics **194**, 15-23.

Levings, C.S., III. (1983). The plant mitochondrial genome and its mutants. Cell **32**, 659-661.

Lonsdale, D.M., Hodge, T.P. and Fauron, C.M. (1984). The physical map and organization of the mitochondrial genome from the fertile cytoplasm of maize. Nucleic Acids Research **12**, 9249-9261.

McGhee, J.D. and Felsenfeld, G. (1980). Nucleosome structure. Annual Review of Biochemistry **59**, 1115-1156.

Morelli, G., Nagy, F., Fraley, R.T., Rogers, S.G. and Chua, N-H. (1985). A short conserved sequence is involved in the light inducibility of a gene encoding ribulose 1-5-bisphosphate carboxylase small subunit in pea. Nature **315**, 200-204.

Morris, R.O. (1986). Genes specifying auxin and cytokinin biosynthesis in phytopathogens. Annual Review of Plant Physiology **37**, 509-538.

Ohyama, K., Fukuwaza, H., Kohchi, T., Shirai, H., Sano, T., Sano, S., Umesono,, K., Shiki, Y., Takeuchi, M., Chang, Z., Aota, S-i., Inokuchi, H. and Ozeki, H. (1986). Chloroplast gene organization deduced from complete sequence of liverwort Marchantia polymorpha chloroplast DNA. Nature **322**, 572-574.

Rich, A., Nordheim, A. and Wang, A.H.J. (1984). The chemistry and biology of left-handed Z-DNA. Annual Review of Biochemistry **53**, 791-846.

Rosenfeld, M.G., Amara, S.G. and Evans, R.M. (1984). Alternative RNA processing: determining neuronal phenotype. Science **225**, 1315-1320.

Ruskin, B. and Green, M.R. (1985). Specific and stable intron-factor interactions are established early during in vitro pre-mRNA splicing. Cell **43**, 131-142.

Sengupta-Gopalan, C., Reichert, N.A., Barker, R.F., Hall, T.C. and Kemp, J.D. (1985). Developmentally regulated expression of the bean β -phaseolin gene in tobacco seed. Proceedings of the National Academy of Sciences USA **82**, 3320-3324.

Sharon, N. (1984). Glycoproteins. Trends in Biochemical Sciences, **9**, 198-202.

Shatkin, A.J. (1976). Capping of eukaryotic mRNAs. Cell **9**, 645-654.

Shih, D.S. and Kaesberg, P. (1973). Translation of Brome mosaic virus ribonucleic acid in a cell free system derived from wheat embryos. Proceedings of the National Academy of Sciences USA **70**, 1789-1803.

Shinozaki, K., Ohme, M., Tanaka, M., Waksugi, T., Hayashida, N., Matsubayashi, T., Zaita, N., Chunwongse, J., Obokata, J., Yamaguchi-Shinozaki, K., Ohto, C., Torazawa, K., Meng, B.Y., Sugita, M., Deno, H., Kamogashira, T., Yamada, K., Kusuda, J., Takaiwa, F., Kato, A. Tohdoh, N., Shimada, H. and Sugiura, M. (1986). The complete sequence of the tobacco chloroplast genome: its organization and expression. Journal of the European Molecular Biology Organization **5**, 2043-2049.

Stern, D.B. and Palmer, J.D. (1984). Extensive and widespread homologies between mitochondrial DNA and chloroplast DNA in plants. Proceedings of the National Academy of Sciences USA **81**, 1946-1950.

Sun, S.M., Slightom, J.L. and Hall, T.C. (1981). Intervening sequences in a plant gene-comparison of the partial sequence of cDNA and genomic DNA of French bean phaseolin. Nature **289**, 37-41.

Timko, M.P., Kausch, A.P., Castresana, C., Fassler, J., Herrera-Estrella, L., van Montagu, M., Schell, J. and Cashmore, A.R. (1985). Light regulation of plant gene expression by an enhancer-like element. Nature **318**, 579-582.

van Slogteren, G.M.S., Hooykaas, P.J.J. and Schilperoort, R.A. (1984). Silent T-DNA genes in plant line transformed by Agrobacterium tumefaciens are activated by grafting and by 5-azacytidine treatment. Plant Molecular Biology **3**, 333-336.

Wildman, S.G. (1982). Further aspects of fraction-1 protein evolution. In "On the Origins of Chloroplasts", (J.A. Schiff ed.), pp. 229-242. Elsevier, North Holland.

Young, R.A. and Davis, R.W. (1983). Efficient isolation of genes using antibody probes. Proceedings of the National Academy of Sciences USA **80**, 1194-1198.

TITLES OF POSTER PAPERS PRESENTED AT THE SYMPOSIUM

1. Genotypic differences in the response of <u>Triticum turgidum</u> to chlormequat
   S. ABBO, M.J. PINTHUS and E. MILLET
   (The Herbrew University, Faculty of Agriculture, Rehovot, Israel).

2. Use of plant growth regulators as seed dressings to improve winter hardiness in cereals
   H.M. ANDERSON
   (Long Ashton Research Station, University of Bristol).

3. Effect of CO^{++}, AVG, GA_3 and kinetin on some 2,4-D induced morphological effects and ethylene production in marrow seedlings
   B. AYISIRE and N.J. PINFIELD
   (Dept. of Botany, University of Bristol).

4. Variation in the ABA content during germination of chick-pea (<u>Cicer arietinum</u> L.) seeds
   M.J. BABIANO and G. NICHOLAS
   (University of Salamanca, Salamanca, SPAIN).

5. An analysis of differential growth in relation to root gravitropism
   P.W. BARLOW, J. ADAM and P. BRAIN.
   (Long Ashton Research Station, University of Bristol).

6. The effect of nutrient conditions on the internal organization of tomato roots
   P.W. BARLOW and D.N. BUTCHER
   (Long Ashton Research Station, University of Bristol).

7. <u>In vivo</u> and <u>in vitro</u> effects of auxin, abscisic acid and calcium on protein kinases from apple fruit membranes
   N.H. BATTEY and M.A. VENIS
   (Institute of Horticultural Research, (EMRS), East Malling).

8. Studies on seed development in <u>Acer</u>
   S.A. BAZAID and N.J. PINFIELD
   (Dept. of Botany, University of Bristol).

9. Gibberellin recognition - an integrated chemical approach
   M.H. BEALE
   (Chemistry School, University of Bristol).

10. Growth and tuberisation of potatoes <u>in vitro</u>: effect of hormones on mini-tuber dormancy
    A. BELCHER and A. J.ABBOTT
    (Long Ashton Research Station, University of Bristol).

11. Uptake and metabolism of 6-benzylaminopurine and zeatin in cultured shoots of <u>Gerbera jamesonii</u>
    D. BLAKESLEY[1], J.R. LENTON[2] and R. HORGAN[3]
    (1. Twyford Plant Laboratories, Baltonsborough, Glastonbury
    2. Long Ashton Research Station, University of Bristol
    3. Dept. of Botany and Microbiology, U.C.W., Aberystwyth).

12. Investigation of a gibberellin-sensitive dwarf mutant of barley
    G.M. BOOTHER
    (Chemistry School, University of Bristol).

13. The inhibition of growth and sterol biosynthesis in cereal plants by EBI fungicides and growth regulators
    R.S. BURDEN and D.T. COOKE
    (Long Ashton Research Station, University of Bristol).

14. Do gibberellins regulate root growth?
    D.N. BUTCHER, J.R. LENTON, P.HEDDEN and J.A.CLARK.
    (Long Ashton Research Station, University of Bristol).

15. Plant regeneration from immature embryo callus cultures of barley
    H.S. CHAWLA and G. WENZEL
    (Institut für Resistenzgenetik, Gruenbach, West Germany).

16. Applications of plant growth regulators improve canopy structure in oilseed rape
    R.D. CHILD
    (Long Ashton Research Station, University of Bristol).

17. Response of the cereal root system to CCC
    M.R. DEVESON and P.M. CARTWRIGHT
    (Dept. of Agricultural Botany, University of Reading).

18. Effects of exogenous growth regulators on a bean disease
    R.M. DUNN, J.A. BAILEY and P. HEDDEN
    (Long Ashton Research Station, University of Bristol).

19. Monoclonal antibodies to higher plant nitrate reductase. Immunoaffinity
    purification of spinach (Spinacea oleracea L.) nitrate reductase
    R.J. FIDO, P.N. WHITFORD and B.A. NOTTON
    (Long Ashton Research Station, University of Bristol).

20. Monoclonal antibodies to higher plant nitrate reductase. Quantitation of nitrate
    reductase protein by enzyme-linked immunosorbent assay (ELISA)
    R.J. FIDO, P.N. WHITFORD and B.A. NOTTON
    (Long Ashton Research Station, University of Bristol).

21. Mode of action in hormone-autonomous Lactuca callus
    A.W. FLEGMAN and L.A. McGILLIVRAY
    (School of Biological Sciences, University of Bath).

22. The biological activity of the diterpene, candidiol
    B.M. FRAGA, P. GONZALEZ, M.G. HERNANDEZ, F.G. TELLADO, J.M. DURAN[1]
    and N. RETAMAL[1]
    (CSIC, Tenerife, Spain and [1]Universidad Politechnica, Madrid, Spain).

23. Plant growth regulators in virus-infected plants. 1. The rôle of abscisic acid
    in control of growth and symptom formation
    R.S.S. FRASER and R.J.WHENHAM
    (Institute of Horticultural Research, (NVRS), Wellesbourne).

24. Accurate analysis of cyclic AMP in plant tissue
    J.L. GADEYNE, H.A. van ONCKELEN, M. DUPON and J.A. de GREEF
    (University of Antwerp, UIA, Wilrijk, Belgium).

25. Cell replication as a rhythmic process
    D.A. GILBERT
    (Dept. of Biochemistry, University of the Witwatersrand, S. Africa)

26. Isolated stomata do not respond to osmotic stress: Implications for stomatal
    development and stomatal response to water stress and humidity
    D.A. GRANTZ[1] and A. SCHWARTZ[2]
    (1. U.S. Dept. of Agriculture, Hawaii, U.S.A.
     2. Hebrew University of Jerusalem, Rehovot, Israel).

27. Are seed hormones responsible for the biennial bearing of apples?
    J.R. GREEN and P. HEDDEN
    (Long Ashton Research Station, University of Bristol).

28. Systemic and genetic regulation of soyabean nodulation
      P.M. GRESSHOFF, J.E. OLSSON, B.J. CARROLL, D.A. DAY and A.G. DELVES
      (Dept. of Botany, ANU., Canberra, ACT, Australia).

29. Is the maternal plant a donor of auxin to growing apple fruits?
      M.J. GROCHOWSKA and U. DZIECIO
      (Skierniewice, Poland).

30. Immunological determination of endogenous zeatin and zeatin riboside in
      micropropagated apple shoots exposed to different cytokinins
      M. HALLBERG and M. WELANDER
      (Swedish University of Agricultural Sciences, Alnarp, Sweden).

31. Purification of gibberellin hydroxylases from Cucurbita maxima endosperm
      P.HEDDEN and D.A. WARD
      (Long Ashton Research Station, University of Bristol).

32. Phytochrome and seed germination
      J.R. HILTON
      (Long Ashton Research Station, University of Bristol).

33. Gibberellins and the wild oat aleurone
      R. HOOLEY[1], S.J. SMITH[1], M.H. BEALE[2] and J. MACMILLAN[2]
      (1. Long Ashton Research Station, University of Bristol
       2. Chemistry School, University of Bristol).

34. Habituation in relation to development and flowering in tobacco
      J.A. JACKSON and R.F. LYNDON
      (Dept. of Botany, University of Edinburgh).

35. Stimulation of stem extension and leaf aerenchyma in maize by poor aeration
      M.B. JACKSON and S.F. YOUNG
      (Long Ashton Research Station, University of Bristol).

36. Procera: a giant tomato with altered GA status
      M.G. JONES
      (Dept. of Biochemistry, U.C.W., Aberystwyth).

37. Fungicidal properties of PGR's in arable crops
      V.W.L. JORDAN, G.R. STINCHCOMBE and J. HUTCHEON
      (Long Ashton Research Station, University of Bristol).

38. The cellular basis of GA_3 and mutation-induced stem elongation in tomato and pea
      S.C. JUPE and I.M. SCOTT
      (Dept. of Botany and Microbiology, U.C.W., Aberystwyth).

39. The germination behaviour of GA- and ABA-deficient tomato seeds
      C.M. KARSSEN and S.P.C. GROOT
      (Agricultural University, Wageningen, The Netherlands).

40. Does sensitivity to ethylene change during fruit development?
      M. KNEE
      (Institute of Horticultural Research, (EMRS), East Malling).

41. Gibberellin action on phosphatidyl choline turnover in wheat aleurone tissue
      D.L. LAIDMAN, C.A. BREARLEY, N.A. CLARKE, D.N. VAKHARIA and M.C.
      WILKINSON
      (Dept. of Biochemistry, UCNW, Bangor).

42. Cytokinin levels in leaf and root exudates of Sinapis alba (LDP) during the floral transition
P. LEJEUNE, J.M. KINET and G. BERNIER
(University of Liege, Belgium).

43. Cytokinins and early grain growth in wheat
J.R. LENTON and N.E.J. APPLEFORD
(Long Ashton Research Station, University of Bristol).

44. The use of mutants in the study of ABA biosynthesis
R.S.T. LINFORTH and I.B. TAYLOR
(School of Agriculture, University of Nottingham, Sutton Bonington).

45. Distribution of carriers for IAA transport to maize roots
H.V. MARTIN and P-E. PILET
(Institute of Plant Biology and Physiology, University of Lausanne, Switzerland).

46. Response of plant roots to inoculation with Azospirillum brasilense and to application of indoleacetic acid
P. MARTIN and W. KOLB
(University of Hohenheim, West Germany).

47. Kaurene synthesis and α-amylase activity in de-etiolating Zea mays seedlings
R. METTRIE and J.A. de GREEF
(University of Antwerp, Belgium).

48. Hormonal regulation of morphogenesis in callus derived from mesophyll protoplasts of Brassica napus
S. R. MILLAM and T.J. HOCKING
(School of Applied Science, The Polytechnic, Wolverhampton).

49. Re-appraisal of GA-induced enzyme production in barley endosperm halves
P.B. NICHOLLS
(Waite Agricultural Research Institute, University of Adelaide, Glen Osmond, S.A., Australia).

50. Abscisic acid biosynthesis in wilty tomato mutants
A.D. PARRY, S.J.NEILL and R. HORGAN
(Dept. of Botany and Microbiology, U.C.W., Aberystwyth).

51. Quantitative assessment of sensitivity to hormones
N.W. PATERSON, J.D.B. WEYERS and R. A'BROOK
(University of Dundee, Dundee).

52. Gibberellin-mediated synergism of xylogenesis in lettuce pith cultures
D. PEARCE[1], L.R. MILLER[2], W. ROBERTS[3] and R.P. PHARIS[1]
(1. Dept. of Biology, University of Calgary, Calgary, Canada
2. Dept. of Horticulture, Ohio State University, USA
3. Dept. of Biological Sciences, University of Idaho, USA).

53. Activity of the ethylene-forming enzyme in relation to plant cell structure and organisation
A.J.R. PORTER, J.T. BORLAKOGLU and P. JOHN
(Dept. of Agricultural Botany, University of Reading).

54. Growth stages in winter wheat in the UK
J.R. PORTER
(Long Ashton Research Station, University of Bristol).

55. T-DNA GENE 1 and Pseudomonas Tryptophan-2-monooxygenase: functionally equivalent?
    E. PRINSEN[1], H. van ONCKELEN[1], P. RUDELSHEIM[1], D. INZE[2], A. FOLLIN[2],
    M. van MONTAGU[2] and J.A. de GREEF[1]
    (1. University of Antwerp, Belgium,
    2. University of Ghent, Belgium).

56. Molecular genetics of nitrogen assimilation in higher plants
    I.M. PROSSER
    (Long Ashton Research Station, University of Bristol).

57. Effect of certain substituted flavones on the growth, nucleic acid and nitrogen
    contents of Lemna paucicostata Hegelm
    PROFESSOR K.V.N. RAO and S. SEETHA RAM RAO
    (Dept. of Botany, University College of Science, Osmania University,
    Hyderabad, India).

58. Suppression of shoot formation and its effect on the endogenous phytohormonal
    levels of mutant tobacco crown gall tissues
    P. RUDELSHEIM, M.A. de SWAEF, J.A. van ONCKELEN and J.A. de GREEF
    (Dept. of Biology, UIA, Wilrijk, Belgium).

59. Arginine decarboxylase - a key enzyme in polyamine biosynthesis
    T.A. SMITH
    (Long Ashton Research Station, University of Bristol).

60. A study of the enzymes catalysing GA_{20} metabolsim in seeds of Phaseolus vulgaris
    V.A. SMITH
    (Chemistry School, University of Bristol).

61. Ethylene binding and metabolism in the Leguminosae
    R.J. STARLING, Z.D. ZHANG, D.R. ROBERTSON, I.O. SANDERS, A.R. SMITH
    and M.A. HALL
    (Dept. of Botany and Microbiology, U.C.W., Aberystwyth).

62. The source of post-pollination ethylene production: the role of ACC from pollen
    grain, pollen tube and stylar tissue
    A.D. STEAD, S.E. HILL, B.M. LUCAS and R. NICHOLS
    (Dept. of Botany, RHBNC, Egham, and Institute of Horticultural
    Research (GCRI), Littlehampton).

63. Traumatropism
    A. TAYLOR
    (Dept. of Plant Science, University of Aberdeen, Aberdeen).

64. Ethylene biosynthesis in etiolated pea seedlings
    J.E. TAYLOR, I.M. SCOTT, B.A. McGRAW and R. HORGAN
    (Dept. of Botany and Microbiology, UCW, Aberystwyth).

65. Photoperiodic and chemical effects on growth and assimilate distribution in
    carrot (Daucus carota L.)
    T.H. THOMAS
    (Long Ashton Research Station, University of Bristol and NVRS).

66. What controls gibberellin-induced dormancy release in celery seeds?
    T.H. THOMAS
    (Long Ashton Research Station, University of Bristol and NVRS).

67. Polyamine levels in primary roots of Cicer arietinum L.
    T. VALLE, C. REINOSO and G. NICOLAS
    (University of Salamanca, Salamanca, Spain).

68. Gating hormone action with circadian rhythmicity
    T. VANDEN DRIESSCHE
    (Universite Libre de Bruxelles, Belgium).

69. Free and bound gibberellins in epicotyls of chick-pea seeds: Relation with
    β-glucosidase activity
    N. VILLALOBOS, L. MARTIN and G. NICOLAS
    (University of Salamanca, Salamanca, Spain).

70. Auxin controls the position of abscission sites induced in some explants
    J. WARREN WILSON, P.M. WARREN WILSON and E.S. WALKER
    (Depts. of Botany and Developmental Biology, ANU, Canberra, ACT,
    Australia).

71. Plant growth regulators in virus-infected plants.   2. Cytokinins in control of
    resistance and symptom development
    R.J. WHENHAM and R.S.S. FRASER
    (Institute of Horticultural Research, (NVRS), Wellesbourne).

72. A radioimmunoassay for abscisic acid in aqueous extracts of maize
    P.N. WHITFORD[1], S.A. QUARRIE[2] and N.E.J. APPLEFORD[1].
    (1. Long Ashton Research Station, University of Bristol
    2. Plant Breeding Institute, Cambridge).

73. A role for leaf growth and vernalization in early summer cauliflower
    C.A. WILLIAMS and J.G. ATHERTON
    (Dept. of Agriculture and Horticulture, University of Nottingham).

74. Characterisation and purification of an ethylene-binding component from
    developing cotyledons of Phaseolus vulgaris L.
    R.A. N. WILLIAMS, A.R. SMITH and M.A. HALL
    (Dept. of Botany and Microbiology, U.C.W., Aberystwyth).

75. The partial synthesis and biological activity of ring-alkylated gibberellins
    C.L. WILLIS
    (Chemistry School, University of Bristol).

76. Endogenous gibberellins and flowering in white spruce (Picea glauca)
    S. WILSON and R.P. PHARIS
    (Dept. of Biology, University of Calgary, Canada).

SUBJECT INDEX

Enzyme, secretion, 280
Epidermis, 253
  growth factor, 11
Epigenetic changes, 124
Epinasty, 98,192
Escherichia coli, 12,65,120
Esterases, 266,269
Ethene, 169
Ethylene, 4,20,23,25,32,33,56,57,
  107-111,189-197,207,224,270,271,275
  and abscission, 30
  binding, 193,275
  biosynthesis, 108
  bio System I, 111
  bio System II, 111
  ethylene forming enzyme (EFE), 109
  receptors, 113
  and seed germination, 23,24,30
  and senescence, 30
  stress-induced, 113
  wound, 191
Ethylmethanesulphonate (EMS), 92
Etiolation, 29,30
Eucalyptus, 196
Eukaryote, 288,289,292
Evolution, 12
Extensibility, 277
Extensin, 279

trans-Farnesol, 195
Fatty acids, 5
Feed-back, 180
Flooding, 190,203-208
Floral induction, 177
Floret survival, 149-151
Florigen (Anthesin), 217,225
Flowering, 5,43,108,217-227
  inhibitors, 217,225,226
Fluridone, 97
Freezing tolerance, 98
French bean, 293
Frost resistance, 99
Fruit, 111-112
Functional change, 20
Fungi, 12,141
Fungicides, 133,137
Fusicoccin, 56,64,168

GC-MS, 75,152,153
Genes, 43,65 ,89,120-122,289
  α-amylase, 67,68,280
  auxin-regulated, 65,68
  coding, 90
  dwarfing, 145-157
  expression, 54,63-68,110,294
  gibberellin-regulated, 66
  hormone regulation, 63-68
  multigene families, 67
  products, 53,287
  Ti, 294
  tmr, 120-122

tms, 120-122
Genetic lesion, 114
Genome, 275,288
  animal, 290
  mitochondrial, 290
  nuclear, 287,290
  plant, 290
Genotypes, 79,89-100
Geocurvature, 242,245
Geostimulus, 231
Geotropism, 231,235,236,255
Geranylgeraniol, 90
Germination, 95,97,108
Gibberella fujikuroi, 31
Gibberellin, 4,26-30,43,44,46,56,67,
  73-84,107,110,133,136,145-157,178,180,
  212,217,221,223,226,231,239,240,254,
  256,266,275,277,278-281
  accumulation, 145
  action, 133
  and aerobic germination, 26
  biosynthesis, 27,77-80,133,135,137,
    140,146-154
  biosynthesis inhibitors, 146,153,155
  biotin-conjugates, 83
  and carbohydrate starvation, 26
  concentration, 146-156
  depletion, 145
  and embryo growth, 26
  2β-hydroxylation, 77
  13-hydroxylation pathway, 76
  insensitivity, 56,145-157,277,281
  and malting, 26
  molecular action, 73-84
  receptors, 81
  responsiveness, 145-157
  and scutellum, 26
  sensory adaptation, 27
  stimulated growth, 277
Gladiolus, 43
Globin, 289
Glucagon, 6,10
β-1:4-Glucanhydrolase, 266
Glucose, 279
Glycoprotein, 6,56
Glycosylation, 293
Glyphosate, 166,293
cGMP, 7
Grafting, 80
Grasses, 134
  nodes, 253,272
Gravitropism, 97,109,164,165,252-256,272
Gravity, 243
Growth, 21,275
  limiting, 21
  retardants, 153-155
Guard cells, 93,94,196,208
Gynoecia, 221

Habituated tissues, 124,126,270
Haploid, 287